Modern Science and Its Philosophy

PHILIPP FRANK

MODERN

AND ITS

SCIENCE

PHILOSOPHY

COLLIER BOOKS
NEW YORK, N.Y.

This Collier Books edition is published by arrangement with Harvard University Press

Collier Books is a division of The Crowell-Collier Publishing Company

First Collier Books Edition 1961

DEDICATED TO
HANIA
IN REMEMBRANCE OF THE PAST
AND ANTICIPATION
OF THE FUTURE

Preface

ALONG WITH THE EVOLUTION of twentieth-century science, philosophical ideas were developed which have sprouted and grown on the soil of this science. In this book I present my thoughts on this development, in the sequence in which they entered my mind during the many years of my teaching and research work in science. If we want to evaluate precisely and critically how firmly this philosophy is anchored in the ground of science, we must not ignore the extrascientific factors, but must analyze carefully the social, ethical and religious influences. Every satisfactory philosophy of science has to combine logic of science with sociology of science.

Since 1940 not only have I been teaching science, but Harvard University offered me the opportunity of teaching also the philosophy which, in my opinion, has grown up along with twentieth-century science. A large part of this book reflects the experience that I have gained by observing the interests of the students and their reactions to my teaching.

My work has been stimulated greatly by the Harvard experiment in General Education, in which I have had the privilege of participating. The Harvard University Press has been of substantial help to me in finishing this book. I am particularly obliged to Miss Eleanor R. Dobson and Mr. J. D. Elder for their fine spirit of coöperation. I hope that the Harvard Press will soon publish a volume which is written along similar lines, the lucid and straightforward book "Positivism," by R. von Mises.

PHILIPP FRANK

Contents

Contents

Modern Science and Its Philosophy

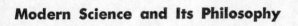

Introduction

Historical Background

1. Discussions in a Vienna Coffee House

AT THE TIME when the first chapter of this book was written (1907) I had just graduated from the University of Vienna as a doctor of philosophy in physics. But the domain of my most intensive interest was the philosophy of science. I used to associate with a group of students who assembled every Thursday night in one of the old Viennese coffee houses. We stayed until midnight and even later, discussing problems of science and philosophy. Our interest was spread widely over many fields, but we returned again and again to our central problem: How can we avoid the traditional ambiguity and obscurity of philosophy? How can we bring about the closest possible *rapprochement* between philosophy and science? By "science" we did not mean "natural science" only, but we included always social studies and the humanities. The most active and regular members of our group were, besides myself, the mathematician, Hans Hahn, and the economist, Otto Neurath.

Although all three of us were at that time actively engaged in research in our special fields, we made great efforts to absorb as much information, methodology and background from other fields as we were able to get. Our field of interest included also a great variety of political, historical, and religious problems which we discussed as scientifically as possible. Our group had at that time no particular common predilection for a certain political or religious creed. We had, however, an inclination towards empiricism on one hand and long and clear-cut chains of logical conclusions on the other. There were quite a few occasions on which these two predilections did not mix very well.

This apparent internal discrepancy provided us, however, with a certain breadth of approach by which we were able to have helpful discussions with followers of various philosophical opinions. Among the participants in our discussions were, for instance, several advocates of Catholic philosophy. Some of them were Thomists, some were rather adherents of a romantic mysticism. Discussions about the Old and New Testaments, the Jewish Talmud, St. Augustine, and the medieval schoolmen were frequent in our group. Otto Neurath even enrolled for one year in the Divinity School of the University in order to get an adequate picture of Catholic philosophy, and won an award for the best paper on moral theology. This shows the high degree of our interest in the cultural background of philosophic theories and our belief in the necessity of an open mind which would enable us to discuss our problems with people of divergent opinions.

At that time a prominent French historian and philosopher of science, Abel Rey, published a book which later was to make a great impression upon me. At the turn of the century the decline of mechanistic physics was accompanied by a belief that the scientific method itself had failed to give us the "truth about the universe"; hence nonscientific and even antiscientific tendencies gained momentum. I quote some passages in which Rey describes this situation excellently and precisely.

Fifty years ago, he says, the explanation of nature was believed to be purely mechanical.

It was postulated that physics was nothing but a complication of mechanics, a molecular mechanics . . . Today [1907] it seems that the picture offered by the physical sciences has changed completely. The general unity is replaced by an extreme diversity, not only in the details, but in the leading and fundamental ideas . . . [This accounts for] what is called the crisis of contemporary physics. Traditional physics assumed until the middle of the nineteenth century that it had only to continue its own path to become the metaphysics of matter. It ascribed to its theories an ontologic value, and these theories were all mechanistic. Traditional mechanistic physics was supposed, above and beyond the results of experience, to be the *real* cognition of the material universe. This conception was not a hypothetical description of our experience; it was a dogma.

The criticism of the traditional mechanistic physics that was formulated in the second half of the nineteenth century weakened this assertion of the ontologic reality of mechanistic physics. Upon this criticism a philosophy of physics was established that became almost traditional toward the end of the nineteenth century. Science became nothing but a symbolic pattern, a frame of reference. Moreover, since this frame of reference varied according to the school of thought, it was soon discovered that actually nothing was referred that had not previously been fashioned in such a way that it could be so referred. Science became a work of art to the lover of pure science, a product of artisanship to the utilitarian. This attitude could quite rightly be interpreted as denying the possibility that science can exist. A science that has become simply a useful technique . . . no longer has the right to call itself science without distorting the meaning of the word. To say that science cannot be anything but this means to negate science in the proper sense of the word.

The failure of the traditional mechanistic science . . . entails the proposition: "Science itself has failed.". . . We can have a collection of empirical recipes, we can even systematize them for the convenience of memorizing them, but we have no cognition of the phenomena to which this system or these recipes are applied.[1]

Our group was formed during the period which was so eloquently described by Rey. His book was discussed frequently by us in the last years of my stay in Vienna (1908-1912). The problems raised and the results obtained are reflected partly in Chapter 2 of this book. The general reaction of our group to the intellectual and cultural situation depicted by Rey can be described as follows:

We recognized the gradual decline in the belief that mechanistic science would eventually embrace all our observations. This belief had been closely connected with the belief in progress in science and in the scientific conception of the world. Therefore, this decline brought about a noticeable uneasiness. Many people lost their faith in scientific method and looked for some other method which might yield a real understanding of the world. A great many people believed, or at least wanted to believe, that the time had come to return to the medieval ideas that may be characterized as the organismic conception of the world.

In the history of science and philosophy there have always been divergent opinions about the conditions under which we may say that a scientific theory has "explained" a certain range of observations. Some authors have maintained that only an explanation by mechanical causes and by the motion of material particles can satisfy our intellectual curiosity. Others have claimed that the reduction to mechanical causes is only a superficial explanation and not a real one. Some of the opponents of the mechanistic world view have stated that

[1] A. Rey, *La Théorie de physique chez les physiciens contemporains* (Paris, 1907), pp. 16 ff.

all phenomena must be interpreted in terms of the evolution of an "organic whole" in order really to understand them. The decline of the belief in mechanistic science seemed to favor this organismic view, which has been attractive to many because of its religious and social implications. In this way there had arisen at the turn of the century what some called a crisis in science or, more accurately, in the scientific conception of the world. For more than two centuries the idea of progress in science and human life had been connected with the advance of the mechanistic explanation of natural phenomena. Now science itself seemed to abandon this mechanistic conception, and the paradoxical situation arose that one could fight the scientific conception of the world in the name of the advance of science.

2. The Failure of Mechanistic Science

The sixteen chapters of this book have been written over a period of almost forty years. They are all meant to be contributions to one task: to break through the wall which has separated science and philosophy for about one and one-half centuries. The book reflects the methods by which this wall has been besieged in the twentieth century. During the last decades of the nineteenth century, a revolution in physical science started which has itself brought about a revolution in our general scientific thought. The methods that have been tried in the fight for the unity between science and philosophy have changed along with the advance of science. Two characteristic beliefs of nineteenth-century science broke down during its last decades; these were the belief that all phenomena in nature can be reduced to the laws of mechanics, and the belief that science will eventually reveal the "truth" about the universe. In the twentieth century the revolutionary changes in science developed with ever-increasing rapidity and intensity. It is no wonder that this rapid transformation of scientific thought has been accompanied by rapidly changing methods in the scientist's approach to philosophy and in the philosopher's views on science.

The chapters of this book have played their part in this developing and changing fight for the unity of science and philosophy. Through them we can pursue a pattern that has grown from rather tentative and naively empirical beginnings to a more and more abstract technique. In order to understand this evolution precisely, it is not sufficient to follow the gradual alterations from the purely logical angle. We must also consider carefully the historical trend and background of the arguments.

Rey had the strong feeling that the place of physics in human thought had dangerously deteriorated. He says:

The physicochemical sciences are an effort made by man to explain sensed nature or what is perceived by our senses . . . The importance of this effort has been understood in all periods of history. So early a thinker as Epicurus believed that physics was the basis of the effort to liberate the human mind from its blind instinct to believe, from its prejudices and its superstitions . . . Everyone would agree that modern positivism has been nothing but an attempt to extend to all the departments of human knowledge, without exception, the general method and conception of science, that is, science constructed according to the example of physics; the spirit of positivism and the spirit of science have become synonymous in current speech.

If these sciences, which historically have played essentially an emancipatory role, were tarnished by a crisis that leaves them no other value than that of recipes which are technically useful and that deprives them of any significance in the cognition of nature, a complete upset in the art of logic and in the history of ideas must result. Physics loses all its educational value; the positive spirit which it represents is a misleading and dangerous spirit. Reason, rational method, and experimental method must be considered in good faith as having no cognitive value. All these methods are, then, procedures of action, not means of cognition. They can be developed in order to obtain certain practical results, but we must be well aware that they have no value except in their restricted domain. The cognition of the real must be sought or be given by other means. We must guard against the dangerous illusion of rationalism and scientism. It is important to know that by this method the real is ignored and that physics leads to ignorance and not to cognition of real nature . . .

If the problem of the cognition of nature and of the possibility of the physicochemical sciences remains in the same form in which it has developed from the Renaissance to the time of positivism, the rational and positive method remains the supreme educator of the human mind, in the domain that is accessible to it, of course. To give the mind a scientific attitude in the sense that has been understood by positivism and positive physics remains the necessary and sufficient condition of intellectual sanity. Physics is the school where one learns to know things.[2]

[2] Ibid., pp. 18 ff.

3. Ernst Mach's Purge of Traditional Physics

In this critical situation our minds turned towards a solution that had been advanced about twenty-five years before by our local physicist and philosopher, Ernst Mach. He maintained that "explanation" by reduction to a system of cherished conceptions is pure illusion. If all the multitude of observable phenomena are reduced to mechanical or organismic phenomena, these special types of phenomena chosen as the basis of explanation are by themselves no more understandable than the phenomena that are to be explained. Mach claimed that there is no essential difference between an "explanation" and a "description." In our everyday language the word "description" refers to a single event or phenomenon. We "describe" the fall of a specific stone at a specific time and place. If, however, we formulate Galileo's law of freely falling bodies, which tells us that all bodies fall with an equal constant acceleration, we describe the fall of a great many bodies under different circumstances. This description of a class of phenomena is called by Mach a "physical law" or an "explanation." If an explanation is nothing but a description of many cases by a short sentence, it cannot matter much whether the "explanation" is given by reduction to the laws of mechanics or to the laws of electromagnetism or even of statistics.

In this way Mach separated the conception of "scientific explanation" from "mechanical explanation." He saved the scientific world picture from going down along with the mechanistic picture. Similar ideas had been advanced by other writers in Mach's time, but none formulated them with so much lucidity and breadth of approach. No one else anchored them so firmly in the soil of science, in physics as well as in biology and psychology.

Although Mach's views were the principal background of our thoughts, they were not the most powerful stimulus to our actual work. Our group fully approved Mach's antimetaphysical tendencies, and we joined gladly in his radical empiricism as a starting point; but we felt very strongly about the primary role of mathematics and logic in the structure of science. It seemed to us that Mach had not done full justice to this aspect of science. We felt that considering the principles of science as nothing but abbreviated descriptions of sense observations did not account fully for the fact that the principles of science contain simple clear-cut mathematical relations among a small number of concepts, whereas every description of observations contains a great number of vague connections among a great number of vague concepts. We also felt that to call the principles of science "economic descriptions of observations" was not to do justice to the predominant role of reasoning in the discovery and presentation of these principles. We were even attracted by some tenets of Kant's theory of knowledge, particularly by his "Introduction to Any Future Metaphysics that may Present Itself as Science." We saw much truth in Kant's statement that the recording of observations is not a purely passive act but that a great deal of mental activity is necessary in order to formulate general statements about sense observations.

The human mind, according to Kant, can describe natural phenomena only by using a certain pattern, certain forms of thinking that are produced by the observing mind and are not provided by the observed physical object. Since these "forms" or "patterns of experience" are provided by the human mind and not by the physical facts, they cannot be changed by the advance of scientific investigations. The material delivered by sense observation can be manufactured into a scientific system only by adding forms of experience that are determined by the nature of the human mind. Our whole group understood and fully agreed that the human mind is partly responsible for the content of scientific propositions and theories. But we also felt strongly that an orthodox belief in Kant would lead us into a new type of metaphysics, not less unscientific than medieval metaphysics. For instance, Kant, and even more, many of his followers, maintained that the axioms of Euclidean geometry or Newton's laws of motion are forms of experience that are produced by the organization of the human mind. This would imply that no advance in these fundamentals of science will be possible without changing the nature of human mind. However, about 1900, scientists became accustomed to envisaging the possibility of changes in the principles that had been traditionally regarded as self-evident axioms. Non-Euclidean geometry was no longer considered a purely logical exercise, but was recognized as a serious system of geometry. This new conception, along with Mach's criticism of Newton's mechanics and with the new electromagnetic theory of matter, opened a path for some doubts whether Newton's laws of motion were actually the final word about the nature of the universe. A step in the same direction was the statistical interpretation of thermodynamics, which suggested the superposition of statistical laws on dynamical laws. As enthusiastic students of contemporary science our group rejected Kant's doctrine that the forms of experience provided by the human mind were unchangeable. We looked for some way to construe these forms as subject to an evolution that would be in accord with the evolution of science. We felt very strongly that there was a certain gap between the description of observations, necessarily vague and complex, and the principles of science, consisting, in physics particularly, of a small number of concepts (like force, mass, etc.) linked by statements of great simplicity. We admitted that the gap between the description of facts and the general principles of science was not fully bridged by Mach, but we could not agree with Kant, who built this bridge by forms or patterns of experience that could not change with the advance of science.

4. Henri Poincaré and a "New Positivism"

In our opinion, the man who bridged the gap successfully was the French mathematician and philosopher Henri Poincaré. For us, he was a kind of Kant freed of the remnants of medieval scholasticism and anointed with the oil of modern science.

Kant had claimed that there would never be another way to organize our experience than by Euclidean geometry and Newtonian mechanics. But at the turn of the century non-Euclidean geometry had been established, although its importance for physical science was not completely understood. Departures from Newtonian mechanics were already in the making. We understood that Kant's erroneous conception of geometry and mechanics must have its source in his erroneous attitude toward the relation between science and philosophy.

At this time I was very much interested in the criticism launched by Nietzsche against Kant's idealistic philosophy. Kant's primary aim was to answer the question of how the human mind can make statements about facts of the external world with absolute certainty even if these assertions are not the result of experience about this world. For Kant, the propositions of Euclidean geometry were a convincing example of assertions of this kind. By claiming that the axioms of geometry are forms of experience produced by the human mind, Kant explained man's ability to produce these assertions without external experience. Nietzsche said flippantly that Kant's explanation is merely equivalent to saying that man can do it "by virtue of a virtue." Nietzsche accused him of demonstrating by sophisticated and obscure arguments that popular prejudices are right while the scientists are wrong. We appreciated in Poincaré just what was different from Kant. We agreed with Abel Rey's characterization of Poincaré's contribution as a "new positivism" which was a definite improvement over the positivism of Comte and Mill. Rey wrote:

> The new positivism certainly has its origin in the positivism of Comte, of Taine and Mill . . . It is rejuvenated but has preserved the great directive ideas from its previous stage: the relativism and empiricism of our knowledge. But it stresses . . . the idea of experimental categories which are required by science as a central necessity . . . Positivism is renewed by building a new rationalism upon the criticism of traditional rationalism in the second half of the nineteenth century . . . What was lacking in Comte's or Mill's positivism . . . was their . . . failure to have established in a new form a theory of categories. Objective experience is not something which is outside and independent of our minds. Objective experience and mind are functions of each other, imply each other, and exist by virtue of each other. To say that the relations between physical objects derive from the nature of these objects and to say that these relations are constructed by our minds are two artificial theories . . .
>
> Our experience is a system, a relation of relations. The relation is the given.[3]

5. Mach, Poincaré and Lenin

Chapter 1 of the present book is written in the spirit of this new positivism. Poincaré claimed that the general laws of science—the law of inertia, the principle of conservation of energy, etc.—are neither statements about facts which can be checked by experiments, nor a priori statements which necessarily emanate from the organization of human mind. They are rather arbitrary conventions about how to use some words or expressions. In this chapter Poincaré's basic tenets are applied to the law of causality.

I started from Hume's formulation of this law: When a

[3] *Ibid.*, pp. 392 ff.

state *A* of a system is followed one time by a state *B*, every time that *A* recurs it is followed again by *B*. I analyzed this formulation in a way that is similar to Poincaré's analysis of the general principles of science. I put the question: How do we know when the state *A* has recurred? There is no exact method except to investigate whether it is followed by *B*. Hence the law of causality is not a statement about observable physical facts but a definition of the expression, "the state *A* has recurred."

When I first published this paper (1907) it aroused a certain amazement among scientists. Among the comments were those of two men of world-wide fame, although in different fields: Einstein and Lenin. Einstein's letter was my first personal contact with him. He approved the logic of my argument, but he objected that it demonstrates only that there is a conventional element in the law of causality and not that it is merely a convention or definition. He agreed with me that, whatever may happen in nature, one can never prove that a violation of the law of causality has taken place. One can always introduce by convention a terminology by which this law is saved. But it could happen that in this way our language and terminology might become highly complicated and cumbersome. What is *not* conventional in the law of causality is the fact that we can save this law by using a relatively *simple* terminology: we are sure that a state *A* has recurred when a small number of state variables have the same values that they had at the start. This "simplicity of nature" is the observable fact which cannot be reduced to a convention on how to use some words. These remarks had a great influence on my thought on the future course of the philosophy of science. I realized that Poincaré's conventionalism needs qualifications. One has to distinguish between what is logically possible and what is helpful in empirical science. In other words, logic needs a drop of pragmatic oil.

Lenin's comment was rather unfavorable. In his book "Materialism and Empiriocriticism" (we would call it today "Materialism and Positivism") he maintains that, "as a Kantian," I "rejoiced" to be able to give support to Kant's idealism by the "most modern philosophy of science." From my reference to the relations between Poincaré and Kant he drew the conclusion that I tried to make use of Poincaré in the service of idealistic philosophy and that, therefore, this paper had an antimaterialistic and reactionary tendency. Lenin's book did not come to my attention before the early twenties. Then, however, it stimulated me to think over more carefully the relation between Poincaré and Kant, between positivism and idealism and, particularly, to investigate the role that metaphysical interpretations of scientific theories have played in support of political and religious philosophies.

However, during the interval (1907-1917) between writing the first and second chapters of the present book, my interest was directed mainly toward any possible advance in the logic of science. I was convinced that the solution must be sought by starting from the ideas of such men as Mach and Poincaré.

At first glance these two authors seemed to contradict each other flagrantly. I soon realized that any advance in the philosophy of science would consist in setting up a theory in which the views of Mach and of Poincaré would be two special aspects of one more general view. To summarize these two theories in a single sentence, one might say: According to Mach the general principles of science are abbreviated economical descriptions of observed facts; according to Poincaré they are free creations of the human mind which do not tell anything about observed facts. The attempt to integrate the two concepts into one coherent system was the origin of what was later called logical empiricism.

6. D. Hilbert's New Foundations of Geometry

The traditional presentation of physical theories frequently consists of a system of statements in which descriptions of observations are mixed with mathematical considerations in such a way that sometimes one cannot distinguish clearly which is which. It is Poincaré's great merit to have stressed that one part of every physical theory is a set of arbitrary axioms and logical conclusions drawn from these axioms. These axioms are relations between signs, which may be words or algebraic symbols; the important point is that the conclusions that we draw from these axioms are not dependent upon the meanings of these symbols. Hence this part of a theory is purely conventional in the sense of Poincaré. It does not say anything about observable facts, but only leads to hypothetical statements of the following type: "If the axioms of this system are true, then the following propositions are also true," or still more exactly speaking: "If there is a group of relations between these symbols, there are also some other relations between the same symbols." This state of affairs is often described by saying that the system of principles and conclusions describes not a content but a structure. Hence, this system is occasionally referred to as the structural system.

The simplest example is geometry. It is the first example in the history of science of a logical system that claims to make statements about facts in the observable world as well. Geometry did not proceed according to the pattern adopted by the older positivists like Hume, Comte, or Mill. It did not collect facts and draw conclusions from these observations. Instead, it built up a system of axioms which were statements containing abstract terms like "point," "straight line," "intersection." Conclusions from these axioms can actually be drawn without knowing the meaning of these terms. In the textbooks of geometry that were written in accordance with the tradition laid down by Euclid, such terms as "straight line" or "intersection" seemed to have a "meaning" in the same sense as the words "table" or "horse" have a meaning, except that the geometric concepts were supposed to be the names of "idealized" physical objects.

After the turn of the century, however, David Hilbert started a purge of the foundations of geometry and set up a clear-cut and consistent system of axioms. He stressed that such concepts as "point" or "straight line" have no meaning besides the one defined by the axioms. The axioms are "implicit definitions" of the geometric concepts. For Hilbert, as for Poincaré, the axioms were conventions about the use of the geometric terms. In this way Hilbert made a significant contribution to the "new positivism." He restricted himself, however, to the investigation of the structural system and did not discuss, as Poincaré did, the relation of the geometric axioms to our experience or our sense observations. The propositions that are derived from the axioms cannot contain any word besides the symbols contained in the axioms. But these symbols have no meaning in the physical world. The great asset of this method is that conclusions can be drawn without being affected by the vagueness of terms that describe our actual observations, like "red," "blue," "warm," "sweet." This method of geometry became the method of the mathematical physics of the nineteenth century. Heat, electricity, and light were described by systems of principles that consisted not of observational terms but of abstract symbols. However, the symbols occurring in the axioms and propositions, of geometry as well as of mathematical physics, can be linked to observable facts in a brief and easily understandable way; for example, the straightness of a line can be checked approximately by the edge of a rigid table, or a volume or a temperature can be measured by simple physical methods.

7. The New Positivism and P. Duhem's "Thomism"

The axiomatic or structural system, including its conclusions, is merely an arbitrary convention if the purely logical viewpoint is maintained without going into the physical interpretation. It was clear to Poincaré that the structural system is logically arbitrary because it cannot be demonstrated by logical means. It is not psychologically arbitrary, however, because in practice we construct only those systems that can be interpreted in terms of physical facts and that are therefore helpful for the formulation of natural laws.

If this line of reasoning is followed, we can see, in a perfunctory way at least, how Mach's and Poincaré's ideas about the general principles of science can be integrated. The axiomatic system, the set of relations between symbols, is a product of our free imagination; it is arbitrary. But if the concepts occurring in it are interpreted or identified with some observational conceptions, our axiomatic system, of well chosen, becomes an economical description of observational facts.

Now the presentation of the law of causality as an arbitrary convention (Chapter 1) can be freed of its paradoxical appearance. The law of causality, as a part of an axiomatic system, is an arbitrary convention about the use of terms like "the recurrence of a state of a system," but if interpreted physically it becomes a statement about observable facts. In this way, the philosophy of Mach could be integrated into the "new positivism" of men like Henri Poincaré, Abel Rey, and Pierre Duhem. The connection between the new positivism and the old teaching of Hume and Comte is the requirement that all abstract terms of science—such as force, energy, mass—must be interpreted in terms of sense observations. Exactly speaking, every statement in which these abstract terms occur must be interpreted as a statement about observational facts. Mach formulated this requirement by saying that all scientific statements are statements about sense observations.

Mach's requirements have frequently been misinterpreted.

Some authors considered them a kind of subjective idealism, meaning that the world consists of sense data only. Others considered them a kind of skepticism or agnosticism, meaning that man cannot know anything about the true or real world; man and man-made science can tell us only about our sense observations, while the objective reality will be eternally unknown to human intelligence. In this interpretation science would be purely subjective, a collection of statements about subjective sense impressions. This misinterpretation had its source in traditional philosophy, according to which science and philosophy must find the hidden treasure of truth behind appearances. All the various systems of traditional philosophy seeking objective reality behind appearances were opposed to Mach's philosophy. Moreover, a great many scientists disliked the idea that the statements of science do not describe the real world but are only statements about our sense observations, without objective significance.

The property of the structural system of not telling us anything about the world of observable physical facts was particularly emphasized by the French scientist, philosopher, and historian, Pierre Duhem. His writings exerted a strong influence upon our group and, particularly, upon my own thinking. By studying Duhem thoroughly we gained a more subtle understanding of the relations among science, metaphysics, and religion than has been customary among empiricists. Duhem says, much as Mach had done,

A theory of physics is not an explanation; it is a system of mathematical propositions deduced from a small number of principles the aim of which is to represent as simply, as completely, and as exactly as possible, a group of experimental laws.[4]

This formulation is a great step on the way toward an integration of Mach and Poincaré. Duhem understood very well that no single proposition of a physical theory can be said to be verified by a specific experiment. The theory as a whole is verified by the whole body of experimental facts. As Duhem put it,

The *experimentum crucis* is impossible in physics.[5]

He says again:

[4] P. Duhem, *Théorie physique; son objet—son structure* (Paris, 1906), p. 24.
[5] *Ibid.*, p. 285.

The watchmaker to whom one gives a watch that does not run will take it all apart and will examine each of the pieces until he finds out which one is damaged. The physician to whom one presents a patient cannot dissect him to establish the diagnosis. He has to guess the seat of the illness by examining the effect on the whole body. The physicist resembles a doctor, not a watchmaker.[6]

And elsewhere:

The experimental verifications are not the basis of the theory, but its culmination.

One notes how far Duhem has proceeded on the way from Mach's conception of a physical theory to the conception which was later advocated by logical empiricism.

Duhem, however, was also, from another angle, a great influence upon the philosophy of our group. He believed, like Mach, that an "explanation" that would be distinct from "economical description" would require an excursion into metaphysics. He says,

If the object of physical theories is to explain experimental laws, physical theory is not an autonomous science; it is subordinated to metaphysics.

Although he was convinced that physics cannot provide an explanation of experimental laws, he did not mean to say that no explanation is possible.

In seeking to stress the distinction between physics and metaphysics I do not mean to disdain either of these sciences, and I think to facilitate their accord much better than if I had confounded the object and the method of the former with the object and the method of the latter . . . The knowledge that metaphysics gives us of things is more intimate, more profound than that which is furnished by physics; it therefore surpasses the latter in excellence.[7]

As a matter of fact, Duhem was an advocate of Aristotelian and Thomistic metaphysics and a faithful believer in the whole of Catholic theology. When I noted this merging of the most advanced type of "new positivism" with Thomistic metaphysics into one coherent system it impressed me strongly.

[6] P. Duhem, "Quelques réflexions au sujet de la physique expérimentale," *Revues des questions scientifiques* 36, 179 (1897).
[7] P. Duhem, "Physique et metaphysique," *Revue des questions scientifiques* 36, 55 (1897).

Duhem interpreted on the basis of this hybrid philosophy the historic conflict between the Roman Church and the Copernican system.

Although our group did not follow Duhem's metaphysical predilection, his doctrine became for us a frame of reference to which we could relate all the conflicts that have raged between science and religion and, more generally, between science and political ideologies.

8. E. Mach as a Philosopher of "Enlightenment"

Despite the aversion toward Mach that had been particularly noticeable among the German scientists and philosophers, he exerted a remarkable attraction for some groups of scientists as well as of philosophers. However, the hostile reaction against him was of great intensity. Disputes about him have been repeated again and again at gatherings of scientists, the conflict of opinions has always been intense, and the discussions have frequently had an emotional flavor.

Ernst Mach died in 1917, the year in which the Soviet government seized the power in Russia. Few among the European and American scientists realized at the time that the new ruler of Russia had published a book ten years previously in which he branded "Machism" as a reactionary philosophy. This book laid the foundation for a peculiar situation in the new Russia by making Mach a permanent target of attack. He was accused of agnosticism, subjectivism, and relativism. It was alleged that Mach had denied that science could know anything about the objective world. In this way, it seemed, the door was opened to other ways of finding the truth, particularly to the ways of traditional religion. It is interesting and amazing that Lenin denounced Machism by the same argument which has been used by advocates of physical realism among European and American scientists.

In the year of Mach's death (1917), I wrote Chapter 2 of the present book. Its purpose was the investigation of the value of Mach's philosophy of science for the future development of science and of human thought in general. Mach's philosophy is presented in such a way that those features are stressed that will survive him and remain essential parts of any future philosophy of science. This means in particular that Mach is judged from the viewpoint of the "new positivism" of men like Poincaré and Duhem. Mach's philosophy is described and characterized with respect to its place in the history of human thought at the start of the twentieth century. It is likened to the philosophy of the Enlightenment in the eighteenth century. Mach analyzed the fundamental concepts of nineteenth-century physics, such as mass and force, and made clear that all statements containing these words can be interpreted as statements about sense observations. Then concepts like these do not denote entities of a hidden real world behind the appearances, but are "auxiliary concepts" by which statements about observations can be expressed in a more convenient and practical way. As the auxiliary concepts of nineteenth-century science were mainly concepts of mechanistic physics, Mach's analysis was to a certain extent a debunking of mechanistic science as a system of statements about physical reality. Nonetheless, Mach had no special bias against the mechanistic terminology that would imbue him with a particularly antimaterialistic tendency. He tried to debunk all types of auxiliary concept in so far as they pretended to describe ontological realities or metaphysical entities. I illustrated this function of Mach's philosophy as a philosophy of enlightenment appropriate to the turn of the century by pointing out similarities between Mach and Nietzsche. The great mass of writing about Nietzsche has largely overlooked the fact that he was a philosopher of enlightenment in his acute analysis of the auxiliary concepts of contemporary idealistic philosophy.

The years after 1917 saw, as has been mentioned, the establishment of Soviet power in Russia, the end of World War I, and the founding of new democracies in Central Europe, such as the Austrian, Czechoslovakian, and Polish republics. The event that had the greatest bearing at this time on the development of the philosophy of science, however, was the new general theory of relativity advanced by Einstein after 1916. In this theory Einstein derived his laws of motion and laws of the gravitational field from very general and abstract principles, the principles of equivalence and of relativity. His principles and laws were connections between abstract symbols: the general space-time coördinates and the ten potentials of the gravitational field. This theory seemed to be an excellent example of the way in which a scientific theory is built up according to the ideas of the new positivism. The symbolic or structural system is neatly developed and is sharply separated from the observational facts that are to be embraced. Then the system must be interpreted, and the prediction of facts that are observable must be made and the predictions verified by observation. There were three specific observational facts that were predicted: the bending of light rays and the red shift of spectral lines in a gravitational field, and the advance of the perihelion of Mercury.

9. A. Einstein's New Concept of Physical Science

However, if we compare Einstein's theory with previous physical theories, we note a certain difference in structure. It is after all only a difference in degree, but it directs our attention to a considerable change in the conception of physical theory.

Whatever conclusions may be drawn from them, Einstein's fundamental laws will describe motions in terms of the general space-time coördinates. Before the results of his theory can be verified by observation, it is necessary to know how statements about these general coördinates can be expressed in terms of observational facts. In traditional Newtonian physics, spatial coördinates and time intervals could be determined by the traditional methods of measuring length and time, by using yardsticks and clocks. However, the general coördinates in Einstein's theory are quantities that define the positions and motions of moving particles with respect to systems of reference that can possess all sorts of deformations, with variable rates of deformation at every point. No rigid and defined system of reference for space and time measurement is given as a general basis for the definition of the space and time coördinates. The methods of measurement must be developed along with the conclusions from the principles of the theory. What is the bearing of these facts upon our general conception of the structure of a scientific theory?

In nineteenth-century physics the translations of statements that contain abstract symbols of the theory—mass, distance, time interval, and the like—into observational facts did not cause much trouble. It was taken for granted that the straightness of a line, the temperature of a body, or the velocity of a motion could be measured. At least, it was not suspected that there was any difficulty in assuming that such measurements are possible. In Einstein's general theory of relativity, however, the description of the operations by which these quantities could be measured becomes a serious and complex task; it becomes an essential part of the theory. These descriptions of the operations by which abstract symbols, such as the general space-time coördinates, are connected with observational facts are called today "operational definitions," according to a terminology suggested by P. W. Bridgman.[8]

As early as 1905, in his restricted theory of relativity, Einstein was well aware that the "operational definitions" are an essential part of his theory. Later he described the decisive alterations that were brought about by his new physical principles in the conception of a physical theory by stressing the fact that the connection between the symbols of the theory and the observational facts following from them is much longer, much more complex, and much more difficult to deal with than the connection assumed by nineteenth-century physics, to say nothing of the physics of the seventeenth and eighteenth centuries. The alteration brought about in the general conception of a scientific theory was a greater emphasis on the gap between the structural system and the experimental confirmation. Advancing a new theory now involved two tasks, both of which required great creative power: the invention of a structural system, and the working out of operational definitions for its symbols.

However, the great new idea in every new physical theory, according to Einstein, was the creation of the structural system. In this sense a physical theory describes "the structure of the world." This way of speaking could easily be interpreted as meaning that the symbols, which are the building stones of the structure, are also the "real building stones" of the universe and that the structure of the symbolic system is "the real structure of the world." Following Einstein's own interpretation of his conceptions, statements like "the theory describes the real structure of the world" mean that appropriate operational definitions enable us to derive from the symbolic system observational facts that check with our actual observations. Hence, the conception of physics advocated by the new positivism of Poincaré is altered by Einstein's conception in such a way that a theory remains an economical description of facts by means of a structure and operational definitions. However, the connection between the symbols and the observational fact is not so simple as was anticipated.

[8] P. W. Bridgman, *The Logic of Modern Physics* (New York: Macmillan, 1927).

10. Geometry and Experience

The old problem of the relation between reasoning and experience in geometry was satisfactorily solved by Einstein's theory. Even the advocates of a new positivism, like Poincaré and Duhem, left a feeling of uncertainty concerning the actual position of geometry between the domains of logic and experience. One might even say that they left a feeling of uneasiness. Poincaré made it clear that geometry itself as a logical system says nothing about the physical world. From the viewpoint of physics, or of empirical science in general, this logical system can be judged only as a practical tool which can be used for a description of the physical world. This procedure may be easy or difficult, simple or complicated. By using Einstein's theory, a description of motions is obtained in terms of spatial and temporal coördinates that are measured by the reading of yardsticks and clocks. However, these instruments, and therefore their readings, are affected by the same gravitational field that is responsible for the motion. An important consequence is that the distances between different points in space follow the axioms and propositions of Euclidean geometry only if the field of force is almost negligible. If we have to consider "strong" fields, the distances between points no longer fit the rules of Euclidean geometry. This means, for instance, that the sum of the angles in a rectilinear triangle is no longer exactly equal to two right angles. The departure from two right angles is the greater the larger the area of the triangle and the stronger the field of gravitation. In order to give to these statements a physical meaning we assume tacitly that "straight lines" are defined by the traditional technologic procedures by which straight edges are produced on rigid bodies, such as a bar of steel.

This means in ordinary geometrical parlance that Euclidean geometry is valid only if the field of gravitation is negligible and if the areas of triangles are small. Generally the laws that determine the relation between the measured distances will be those of non-Euclidean geometry. Poincaré and his immediate followers used to say that it is a convention whether one accepts Euclidean or non-Euclidean geometry. Actually this statement means only that we can build up structural systems of two types: Euclidean and non-Euclidean. As a structural or axiomatic system both are equally acceptable. If traditional methods of measurement are used —that is, if length and time are defined in terms of operations with rigid yardsticks and orthodox clocks—the fact must be considered that the instruments of measurement are affected by gravitational fields and therefore that the results of measurement, too, are affected. For every specific field of gravitation, the theory yields a specific influence on the yardsticks and clocks and therefore upon the results of measurement. By considering this influence "operational definitions" can be formulated. The statements of mechanics now become statements about the results of actual measurements or about actual observations. They are therefore no longer arbitrary. If they are checked, they will be found to be either true or false. In a gravitational field the yardsticks and clocks will be affected in such a way that the results of measurements follow non-Euclidean rather than Euclidean geometry.

In 1921, Einstein gave a lecture at the Academy of Sciences in Berlin with the title "Geometry and Experience," [9] in which he summarized in a conclusive way the place of reasoning and experience in geometry. According to Einstein, geometry can be either a structural system with arbitrary axioms or a physical theory. In the first case the conclusions of geometry are certain but do not tell us anything about the world of experience; in the second case the propositions of geometry can be checked by experiment and are as certain or uncertain as are any statements of physics or, for that matter, of any empirical science.

By Einstein's argument it was demonstrated with great lucidity that there is no statement in geometry that is derived by reasoning without sense observations and that at the same time tells us something about the external world. Such geometric propositions, however, had been considered the most conspicuous examples of assertions about the external world that are derived from pure reasoning. If the statements of geometry do not have this property, then the scientific basis of traditional metaphysics has disappeared. The cause of positivism against metaphysics has won a major battle.

11. Neo-Kantianism and Neo-Thomism

When Einstein had cleared up the foundations of geometry, the believers in scientific metaphysics were put on the spot;

[9] An English translation of this lecture appeared in A. Einstein, *Sidelights on Relativity* (London: Methuen, 1922).

they were deprived of their best example of the existence of metaphysical assertions in science itself.

All schools of traditional philosophy have more or less one belief in common: we can make general statements about facts of the external world with such certainty that they will never be refuted by any future advance in science. For Aristotle such statements were the principles of Greek astronomy, for Kant they were Newton's principles of mechanics. Both the Aristotelians and the Kantians of the nineteenth and twentieth centuries agreed that the validity of Euclidean geometry had been established forever. The only difference was that for one school the doctrine that was believed to prevail forever was Aristotle's physics, while the other, more modern, school permitted the pursuance of the advance of science up to Newton. Each philosophical creed petrified the state of physics that prevailed at its time.

When Einstein demonstrated the possibility or even the plausibility that Euclidean geometry might be wrong he produced a catastrophic effect upon all the schools of traditional philosophy. The metaphysical schools of the Aristotelian and the Kantian types lost their basis in science. To meet this situation two attitudes have developed within these schools. To borrow a terminology from theology, we may call them the fundamentalist and the modernist attitudes. The first group maintained bluntly and boldly that scientists were just wrong. They were specialists and not able to reason correctly because of their lack of metaphysical training.

The modernists are found in the camps of neo-Aristotelians (mostly called neo-Thomists) and of the neo-Kantians. They admitted that Euclidean geometry might be wrong. This was, according to these schools, the truth, but "not the whole truth." From the viewpoint of science proper, they have accepted fully the conception of geometry and physics advanced by the new positivism. But in the background of their teaching on geometry and physics there is a hint of a more profound wisdom which is presented in terms of Aristotelian or Kantian metaphysics. As an example of neo-Thomism we may consider the works of J. Maritain, particularly his book, "The Degrees of Knowledge." [10] An example of neo-Kantianism is the writing of Ernst Cassirer, particularly his books on

---

[10] J. Maritain, *Distinguer pour unir, ou les degrés du savoir* (Paris: Brouwer, 1935); English translation by B. Wall and M. R. Adamson (New York: Scribner, 1938).

the "Theory of Relativity" [11] and on "Determinism and Indeterminism in Modern Physics." [12] The latter one is discussed
in Chapter 9 of the present book. This metaphysical background, according to these authors, has no relevance for
science proper; it is separated by airtight walls from the
domain of scientific discourse. In this way science became
autonomous with respect to metaphysics, but the validity of
the metaphysical assertions in the background could not be
checked by any experimental test. These assertions became
more or less a tautological system of propositions, like pure
mathematics or formal logic.[13] However, this did not exclude the possibility that this metaphysical background may
provide some satisfaction to readers or listeners. As a matter
of fact, the metaphysical discourse has been usually couched
in language that has evoked a pleasant resonance in people's
minds. This kind of language has been in use to present cherished types of science, ethics, or religion. If we disregard
temporarily this background there is a large common ground
between neo-Thomism, neo-Kantianism, and the new positivism. In extreme cases this common ground may be so extensive that one can read hundreds of pages of a neo-Thomist
or a neo-Kantian without recognizing that he is not a positivist of the new type. The most outstanding example is the
French physicist and philosopher, Pierre Duhem, whom we
menioned above. His writings are among the most valuable
contributions of the new positivism. He was warmly recommended by Ernst Mach as a positivist. Many scientists were
never aware that Duhem's background was straight Aristotelian or rather Thomistic metaphysics.

12. "New Wine into New Bottles"

The neo-Thomist and neo-Kantian schools reacted to the
revolutionary changes that have arisen in science since the
turn of the century by establishing a kind of "iron curtain"
between science and philosophy. But none of these schools,
and, as a matter of fact, none of the schools of traditional
philosophy, of the idealistic or realistic type, were able to
make a valuable contribution toward integrating the new
science of the twentieth century into the general framework

[11] E. Cassirer, *Zur Einsteinschen relativitätstheoric* (Berlin: Cassirer, 1921).
[12] E. Cassirer, *Determinismus und Indeterminismus in der modernen Physik* . . .
(Göteborg: Elanders, 1937).
[13] C. W. Morris, *Signs, Language, and Behavior* (New York: Prentice-Hall,
1946), pp. 175 ff.

of human thought. From the viewpoint of intellectual history it is fair to say that the neo-Thomist and neo-Kantian schools have contributed, in a way, to the advance of scientific thought. They have helped to disintegrate the traditional systems to such a point that the remaining parts of the structure could easily merge with the new philosophy that would eventually arise on the basis of a new science.

Immediately after Einstein had published his general theory of relativity (1917), in which he advanced his new physics in full generality, writings appeared that did not attempt to integrate the new physics into traditional philosophy but to build up a new philosophy on the basis of that new science. These writings did not follow the reaction of traditional philosophy—of either the fundamentalist or the modernist types—to the new science. Theirs was a radical reaction in accordance with the words of the gospel:

No man putteth new wine into old bottles; else the new wine will burst the bottles, and be spilled, and the bottles shall perish. But new wine must be put into new bottles; and both are preserved. No man also having drunk old wine straightway desireth new: for he saith, The old is better.

The old bottles were the patterns of traditional philosophy and the new wine was twentieth-century science. A group of men went in for new bottles. They did not borrow the framework of Thomistic or Kantian metaphysics but they borrowed a pattern that had grown up in the soil of modern science, the pattern of the "new positivism." While men like Poincaré and Duhem had used this pattern for strictly domestic consumption, to clear up their own back yard, the foundations of science, the new men who emerged after 1917 ventured to build up a new philosophy that was expected to replace the traditional systems of the Aristotelian or Kantian type.

The new movement started about the time when the first world war ended (1918). New democratic republics were established in Central Europe: Austria, Czechoslovakia, Poland, and the Weimar experiment in Germany. They offered a favorable soil for the evolution of a scientific world conception. A similar situation seemed to arise in Russia after the overthrow of the Czarist regime (1917). It is interesting to note how the turn from the democratic start to the establishment of a new authoritarianism was accompanied by a turn from the philosophy of the new positivism to a philosophy which was nearer to the Aristotelian and Kantian tradition.

The first peak of the Central European movement toward a scientific world conception was reached about 1920. We can characterize it by three books: M. Schlick, "General Theory of Knowledge" (1918);[14] H. Reichenbach, "Theory of Relativity and Cognition a priori" (1920);[15] and L. Wittgenstein, *Tractatus Logico-Philosophicus* (1921).[16] The link between these books and Einstein's theory is M. Schlick's small book "Space and Time in Contemporary Physics" (1917),[17] in which the author attempts an integration of the new positivism with the ideas that have grown out of Einstein's new science.

13. M. Schlick's New Criterion of Truth

The views of the new positivism just before Schlick entered the picture are presented in Chapter 2, which was written in the same year as Schlick's "Space and Time." In this chapter a distinction is made between observational concepts—red, warm, . . .—and auxiliary concepts—force, electric charge, . . . All statements of science that contain auxiliary concepts are translatable into statements containing observational concepts only. The expression "auxiliary concept" was often interpreted as meaning that by words like "force," "electric charge," "potential," no "element of reality" is denoted. Schlick, however, stresses that the usefulness of a statement in science depends only upon whether this statement can be checked by sense observations. In other words, a scientific theory must consist of such principles that statements containing observational concepts only can be logically derived from them. It is irrelevant whether the concepts in the theory itself are "observational concepts" or "auxiliary concepts."

Schlick says:

There is no argument whatsoever to force us to state that only the intuitional elements [i.e., observational concepts], colors, tones, etc., exist in the world. We might just as well assume that ele-

[14] M. Schlick, *Allgemeine Erkenntnislehre* (Berlin: Springer, 1918; ed. 2, 1925).
[15] H. Reichenbach, *Relativitätstheorie und Erkenntnis apriori* (Berlin: Springer, 1920).
[16] L. Wittgenstein, *Tractatus Logico-Philosophicus* (London: Paul, Trenche, Trubner; New York: Harcourt, Brace, 1922); German and English on opposite pages.
[17] M. Schlick, *Raum und Zeit in der gegenwärtigen Physik*, . . . (Berlin: Springer, ed. 3, 1920); English translation by H. L. Brose (Oxford: Clarendon Press; New York: Oxford University Press, 1920).

ments or qualities which cannot be directly experienced also exist. These can likewise be termed "real," whether they be comparable with intuitional ones or not. For example, electric forces can just as well signify elements of reality as colors and tones. They are *measurable,* and there is no reason why epistemology should reject the criterion for reality which is used in physics.[18]

To say that electric forces are "measurable" means that from statements of the form, "At this point of space acts an electric force of one hundred grams," statements can be derived about the deviation of a pointer from its coincidence with a certain mark of a scale. This means, however, statements about direct sense observation. It does not matter whether the words in a statement denote observational concepts or auxiliary concepts provided that results can be derived that contain only observational (intuitional) terms.

For otherwise no measurement would be possible. Therefore, the "operational definitions"—which link auxiliary and observational concepts—are an indispensable part of every theory. This point is very important for integrating Einstein's new science into the scheme of new positivism. Now, one can, without any trouble, introduce terms like "four-dimensional space" or "curved space" into physics. These concepts are as legitimate as three-dimensional space and Euclidean geometry. We have only to make sure that our systems contain the rules by which, from the facts of the theory, only observational concepts can be derived.

From this characterization of scientific theories Schlick proceeds to an even more radical departure from traditional philosophy. He starts from the method that is generally used in science to check the "truth" of a theory. One considers, for example, the electric charge of an electron, which, according to the theory, should have a constant numerical value. Then one derives from the theory by a chain of conclusions the result that "the charge of the electron is 4.7×10^{-10} electrostatic units." Then one tries to find, on the basis of the same theory, a second chain of conclusions by which the numerical value of the charge of the electron can be derived. If this value is different from the first one, we say that our theory is "not true." If we obtain the same value as by the first method, we say that our theory may be true or "is confirmed." The "degree of confirmation" is the higher the

[18] *Ibid.,* p. 84.

more independent chains we can find that lead to the same numerical value for the charge and for other concepts of the theory.

This criterion of truth can also be formulated in a more general way. The symbols of the theory (observational or auxiliary concepts) are the state variables by means of which the course of events in the physical world—the facts of the world—can be described. Every specific state of the world is defined by specific numerical values which are assigned to these variables. Some of them, like the charge of the electron, are constants. Others, like the coördinates of an electron, are variables. As we learned by the example of the charge of the electron, we can make use of the theory to calculate these numerical values. This means that the theory indicates the facts of the world. If we obtained from two different chains of conclusions different numerical values for a symbol which, according to the theory, should be constant, then one and the same theory would indicate two incompatible facts. Such a theory would be useless.

From these remarks one will understand fairly well Schlick's criterion for the "truth" of a theory. He says:

Every theory is composed of a network of conceptions and judgments, and is *correct* or *true* if the system of judgments indicates the world of facts *uniquely*.[19]

If a theory yields two different values for the charge of the electron, the correspondence between the theory (concepts and judgments) and the facts would not be a unique correspondence.

On the other hand, no harm is done if different theories indicate one and the same world of facts. In the direction from the facts to the theory no uniqueness is required of "true" theory. Schlick says:

It is, however, possible to indicate identically the *same* set of facts by means of *various* systems of judgments; and consequently there can be various theories in which the criterion of truth [unique correspondence] is equally well satisfied . . . They are merely different systems of symbols, which are allocated to the same objective reality.[20]

[19] *Ibid.*, p. 86.
[20] *Loc. cit.*

14. M. Schlick and H. Reichenbach

From this analysis of scientific theories Schlick proceeded to the claim that every cognition, in whatever domain of knowledge, is essentially the establishment of a correspondence between the *facts of the world* and a *system of symbols*. Since between these symbols a set of relations—for example, the axioms of geometry or mechanics—is established, an arbitrary correspondence would frequently assign several worlds of facts to the same set of symbols. Then the cognition is false. According to Schlick, a cognition is "true" if the correspondence established is *unique*. A system of symbols indicates the facts of the world uniquely.

This conception of cognition and truth was a radical break with almost all systems of traditional philosophy, according to which cognition meant the finding of a truth that was hidden behind the appearances and could be discovered there by the power of reason, which the trained philosopher was supposed to possess. According to Schlick, however, cognition is the establishment of a correspondence; this means, primarily, building up a system of symbols with relations among them. Cognition becomes an activity, the construction of a system of symbols that has only to fulfill the requirement of uniqueness. If we start from this conception of cognition, most of the metaphysical problems that have puzzled generations of philosophers lose their insoluble aspect.

Consider, for example, the ancient puzzle whether the world is essentially mind or matter, the answer to which has been the shibboleth for distinguishing between idealists and materialists. Schlick would reformulate the problem: Are mental concepts or physical concepts better suited to build up a system of symbols that could indicate the world of facts uniquely? The problem loses its yes-or-no character and becomes a problem of deciding, on grounds of convenience, between two ways of describing the facts of the world.

Another author who ventured at that time to build up, on the basis of the "new positivism" and Einstein's new theories, a philosophy of science that would replace the traditional schools was Hans Reichenbach. His most significant books in this line, which to a certain extent paralleled Schlick's writings, are the "Theory of Relativity and Cognition a priori" [15] and "Axiomatics of the Relativistic Theory of Space and

Time." [21] Reichenbach went in much more for the technical discussion of physical and philosophical problems than Schlick did. He approved Schlick's conception of "true cognition," but he presented it in a way that was closer to the conception of science advanced by men like Poincaré and Duhem. Reichenbach was perhaps the first one who formulated explicitly the requirement that every theory in which nonobservational concepts appear contain relations between these abstract and observational concepts. He stressed that geometry as an empirical science must contain, besides the geometric axioms (relations among geometric concepts), the description of a method whereby the straightness of a line can be tested experimentally. As the axioms of geometry and the description of measurements form a net, we can regard the whole theory as a prescription for coördinating the abstract concepts of geometry with observational facts. In this sense, Reichenbach regarded geometry as a system of "axioms of coördination." His criterion of truth was then similar to Schlick's, namely, that the axioms of coördination should be unique.

This uniqueness could, as he stressed, be correctly decided only by observation. On this basis, Reichenbach discussed the question whether the new philosophy was compatible with the traditional Kantian system. By Einstein's new science it was demonstrated that the Euclidean axioms of coördination may be false. Einstein described definite experiments by which one can test whether the traditional axioms of coördination lead to contradictions. Kant believed that the uniqueness of Euclid's system of geometry is founded in the organization of the human mind, while Reichenbach stressed that it has to be checked by experience. In the discussion (Secs. 3 and 4) of the relation of Poincaré to Kant I made partial use of Reichenbach's views.

15. L. Wittgenstein and R. Carnap

The work done by Schlick and Reichenbach made a strong impression upon our Viennese group (Sec. 1). In our search for a scientifically founded philosophy we were glad to find collaborators who attacked the task, I would say, from a more professional angle. At that time (after 1920) Hans

21 H. Reichenbach, *Axiomatik der relativistischen Raum-Zeit-lehre* (Braunschweig: Vieweg, 1924).

Hahn was professor of mathematics at the University of Vienna, Otto Neurath started working for the City of Vienna, organizing adult education in the social sciences, and I had been since 1912 professor of theoretical physics at the University of Prague in the new Czechoslovakian Republic. Hahn had started intensive work with advanced students in the field of symbolic logic and the foundations of mathematics. In 1922, he chose as a basis of their discussions the new book by L. Wittgenstein, *Tractatus Logico-Philosophicus*.[16] These discussions were the germ of many future developments in the philosophy of science.

Wittgenstein's book followed in some respects the same line as Schlick's and Reichenbach's. Wittgenstein, who was also of Viennese origin, was a student of Bertrand Russell, the British logician and philosopher. He added a new and important component to the integration performed by Schlick. Without making much use of the technicalities of symbolic logic, Wittgenstein showed that the new philosophy could be brought into a more perfect and coherent shape with the aid of the basic ideas of Russell's logic. Wittgenstein's formulations sounded even more straightforward and provoking than Schlick's, Reichenbach's, and even Russell's. Wittgenstein claimed bluntly that the problems of traditional philosophy are merely verbal problems. Our ordinary language, which has grown up to describe the facts of everyday life, is not adapted to the task of expressing and answering problems put to traditional philosophy. If we try to use our ordinary language in this way, we get into trouble. The real problem is to find out what one actually can say clearly. The world of facts can be described in our ordinary language; therefore, says Wittgenstein, "to understand a proposition means to know what is the case if it is true."

This conception of "meaning" and "understanding" is essentially no different from Schlick's, Reichenbach's, or, as a matter of fact, Mach's, if we understand Mach as he is interpreted in Chaper 2 of the present book. Every student of philosophy will also remember C. S. Peirce's conception of "meaning," and even William James's, who said that the meaning of a sentence is its "cash value."

Wittgenstein's merit, however, was his precise logical formulation and his cutting and striking dialectic. His line was later called, quite adequately, "therapeutical positivism." Hahn became very enthusiastic, starting a close coöperation of the new men with our Viennese group. He envisaged the appointment of M. Schlick as a professor of philosophy at the University of Vienna. He met, of course, a stiff resistance among the adherents of traditional philosophy. But the interest of the scientists in the philosophical background of science had been traditionally high at the University of Vienna. Ernst Mach had owed his appointment to this predilection and Hahn succeeded in enlisting a sufficient number of scientists in a drive to carry through Schlick's appointment in 1922. In this year a close coöperation between Schlick and the old Vienna group began. This common work gained a great deal in intensity and momentum when Schlick persuaded R. Carnap to move to Vienna in 1926.

Carnap gave the new philosophy its "classical" shape. He coined many of its terms and phrases and endowed it with subtlety and simplicity. In the form created by Carnap it became a center of interest and a target of attack on a large scale.

Schlick and Reichenbach had identified "true cognition" with a system of symbols that indicated the world of facts uniquely. Carnap offered an example of such a system in his book "The Logical Structure of the World." [22] In this book the integration of Mach and Poincaré was actually performed in a coherent system of conspicuous logical simplicity. Our Viennese group saw in Carnap's work the synthesis that we had advocated for many years.

Carnap introduced as the elementary concepts of his system immediate sense impressions and the relations of similarity and diversity between them. The world is to be described by statements that may contain any symbols, provided that from them statements can be logically derived that contain nothing but assertions about similarity between sense impressions. The "meaning" of a statement in science would be the sum of all statements about similarity and diversity between sense impressions that can be derived logically from the statement in question. When I read this book it reminded me strongly of William James's pragmatic requirement, that the meaning of any statement is given by its "cash value," that is, by what it means as a direction for human behavior. I wrote immediately to Carnap, "What you advocate is pragmatism." This was as astonishing to him as it had been to me. We noticed that our group, which lived in an environment of

[22] R. Carnap, *Der logische Aufbau der Welt* (Berlin: Weltkreis-Verlag, 1928).

idealistic philosophy, had eventually reached conclusions by which we could find kindred spirits beyond the Atlantic in the United States.

From Carnap's presentation it was clear that a system from which one cannot derive results about similarities between sense impressions cannot be a "true cognition." The statements of traditional metaphysics, such as those about the existence or nonexistence of the external world, can obviously not be statements of the required type. For this reason Carnap said that "metaphysics is meaningless."

16. O. Neurath's "Index of Prohibited Words"

The men who had expanded the new positivism into a general logical basis of human thought—Schlick and Carnap —came now into personal contact with the original Viennese group, particularly with Hahn and Neurath, while my own contact was restricted to the time of the university vacations. As a result of the developing coöperation the new philosophy became more and more different from the traditional German philosophy, to which both Schlick and Carnap were bound to have some sentimental ties originating from their training at German universities.

They had demonstrated logically that no scientific metaphysics is possible because metaphysical statements do not fit into the pattern that statements must have in order to be called true or false. But the social scientist Neurath investigated the meaning of metaphysical statements as social phenomena. He insisted with a certain ruthlessness that no formulation should be allowed to slip in that would "give comfort to the enemy," even if it would be admissible from the purely logical viewpoint. The whole original Viennese group was convinced that the elimination of metaphysics not only was a question of a better logic but was of great relevance for the social and cultural life. They were also convinced that the elimination of metaphysics would deprive the groups that we call today totalitarian of their scientific and philosophic basis and would lay bare the fact that these groups are actually fighting for special interests of some kind.

In the long, thorough and intimate discussions that the Viennese group had with Schlick and Carnap, the point was made that the new philosophy must be built up in such a way that no misinterpretation in favor of metaphysics could occur. We all knew that misinterpretations were bound to happen if and when expressions like "real," "essential," "real building stone of the universe," were used in a loose way. Neurath even recommended, half jokingly, that an "index of prohibited words" should be set up. In a monograph [23] on the "Foundations of the Social Sciences" he avoided, as he explicitly states, words like "entity," "essence," "mind," "matter," "reality," "thing."

A well-known example of misinterpretation of this type is the praise or condemnation of Mach's philosophy as a brand of idealism because his doctrine was often presented as claiming that the "world consists actually only of sensations." This was interpreted again as meaning that the "world is essentially mental." This interpretation accounts for Lenin's violent attack on Mach and for the extremely hostile attitude of the official Soviet philosophy against all doctrines that traced their origin back to Mach. This holds also for the new positivism and its generalization as achieved by Schlick, Riechenbach, and Carnap.

Perhaps the most striking effect of the coöperation of Schlick and Carnap with the old Viennese group was the shift to "physicalism" and to the "unity of science." Neurath had been particularly eager to prohibit any establishment of a metaphysical doctrine by a tactic of infiltration. He suggested that sense data should be dropped as elementary concepts of the logical structure of the world and replaced by physical things. Instead of building up the system of human knowledge upon concepts like "red spot" or "feeling of warmth," one should use elementary symbols expressing concepts like "rock" or "table," and define "redness," or "warmth" as derived concepts. As the starting point in sensation had a certain tint of idealism, so the new starting point had a tint of materialism. Carnap had in his "Logical Structure of the World" spoken of "methodical materialism" as a possible language for his system. But he had come to prefer "phenomenal language," statements in terms of sense impressions. Neurath worked out a system based on physical things as elementary concepts and called by him "physicalism." Carnap refined Neurath's physicalism to a precise logical structure and even constructed a "physicalistic language" for the field of psychology.

This transition from a quasi-idealistic to a quasi-materialistic language, which took place in our group about 1930, has been misunderstood by a great many authors. They interpret it as a sudden jump into an opposite type of philosophy. As a matter of fact, the "jump" was an expression of our firm belief that the difference between an idealistic and a materialistic system is logically and scientifically of little importance and that there is actually only a difference of emphasis. The choice is determined largely by the emotional connotations or, in other words, by the language in which the pattern of our general culture is usually described.

17. O. Neurath and the "Unity of Science Movement"

The second reformulation suggested by Neurath was the characterization of the new movement as a work "towards the unification of science" or "for the construction of a unified science." This shift was for many people surprising too. Schlick and Carnap had stressed the point that there are no philosophic propositions but that there is a philosophic activity that consists in the clarification of the statements of the special sciences. This meant, briefly, that philosophy was to interpret the abstract and symbolic principles of science as statements about physical things. Frequently, particularly in Great Britain, the new philosophy has been distinguished from the traditional philosophy as "analytic philosophy" in contrast to "speculative philosophy." The work of men like Moore, Russell, or Wittgenstein has been described as analytic philosophy.

Our original Viennese group and particularly Neurath were not satisfied with ascribing to our new philosophical group mainly critical and analytical objectives. We knew well that man is longing for a philosophy of integration. If the new philosophy refuses to serve the cause of integration, a great many people, including even scientists, would rather return to traditional metaphysics than be restricted to a purely analytic attitude. As a matter of fact, the traditional goal of "philosophy," through thousands of years of human knowledge, has been integration.

Neurath pointed out that by Carnap's analysis the statements of all sciences, not only physics but also biology and sociology, had been reduced to statements about physical things or about sense impressions. The traditional opinion about the individual sciences has, however, been that the fundamental concepts of biology are essentially different from those of physics, the concepts of psychology different from those of biology and so on. Physics, biology, and psychology have to do with different kinds of "being" and can never be united on the level of science. Only by introducing metaphysical concepts can one achieve a unification. If we accept, however, Carnap's analysis of science, it follows that all statements of science are of only one type, that is, they are statements that can be expressed in the "thing language." Hence, it must be possible to introduce a unified language for all the sciences and to create a system of "unified science," in which the "special sciences" are merely products of the division of labor. The terminology of the special sciences is practical for restricted purposes, but no philosophic implication about unbridgeable gaps can be drawn from the differences in terminology.

The new philosophy now described its work as the building up of a unified science. With this goal we returned in some measure to the classical goal of philosophy as defined by Aristotle. As a matter of fact, August Comte, the father of positivism, said (1829):

I employ the word "philosophy" in the sense that was given to it by Aristotle, as denoting the general system of human conceptions.

Our group did not wish to stress the work on analysis in contrast to the creation of a synthesis. We never regarded the logic and analysis of science as a goal in itself; we believed strongly that this analysis is a necessary part of obtaining an unprejudiced outlook on life. The close connection between the positivistic attitude and the unification of science can be traced back to Ernst Mach himself. In Chapter 3 of the present book I analyze Mach's philosophy from the viewpoint of 1938, the one-hundredth anniversary of his birth, and point out to what degree the further evolution of positivism was anticipated in Mach's writings.

18. The Vienna Circle

In 1929, we had the feeling that from the coöperation that was centered in Vienna a definite new type of philosophy had emerged. As every father likes to show photographs of his baby, we were looking for means of communication. We wanted to present our brain child to the world at large, to find out its reaction, and to receive new stimulation.

We decided first to publish a monograph about our movement, next, to arrange a meeting, and eventually to get control of a philosophical journal so that we would have a way of getting the contributions of our group printed.

When we prepared the monograph we noticed that our group and our philosophy had no name. Quite a few people among us disliked the words "philosophy" and "positivism" and did not want them to appear in the title. Some disliked all "isms," foreign or domestic. Eventually we chose the name "scientific world conception." [24] Some of us, particularly Schlick, thought that every reasonable scientist would agree with our presentation of cognition. Our chosen title seemed a little dry to Neurath, and he suggested adding "The Vienna Circle," because he thought that this name would be reminiscent of the Viennese waltz, the Vienna woods, and other things on the pleasant side of life. The monograph [25] was written by Carnap, Hahn, and Neurath in close coöperation.

Two years later, A. Blumberg and H. Feigl published in the United States a paper, "Logical positivism: A new movement in European philosophy," [26] and provided the "scientific world conception" with its international trade name.

In accord with the historical and cultural inclination of the Viennese group, Neurath was eager to trace the genealogic lineage of our movement. In the monograph he recorded the following lines:

Positivism and empiricism: Hume, the philosophers of the Enlightenment, Comte, Mill, Avenarius, Mach.
Scientific method: Helmholtz, Riemann, Mach, Poincaré, Enriques, Duhem, Boltzmann, Einstein.
Symbolic logic and its application to reality: Leibniz, Peano, Frege, Schroeder, Russell, Whitehead, Wittgenstein.
Eudaemonistic ethics and positivistic sociology: Epicurus, Hume, Bentham, Mill, Comte, Feuerbach, Marx, Spencer, Mueller-Lyer, Popper-Lynkeus, Carl Menger.

A great many misunderstandings have been current about the original doctrine of the Vienna Circle, which became the germ of logical positivism. Again and again philosophers have sought to prove to the "positivists" that there is a "real world"

[24] We chose the term "world conception" (*Weltauffassung*) in order to avoid the German word *Weltanschauung*, which seemed to us loaded with metaphysical connotations.
[25] *Wissenschaftliche Weltauffassung der Wiener Kreis* (Wien: A. Wolf, 1929).
[26] A. Blumberg and H. Feigl, *Journal of Philosophy* 28, 281 (1931).

and that science explores this real world. In fact, the monograph says: "Something is real if it is a part of the system of symbols that denotes the world of facts." A number of authors have tried to refute "positivism" by showing that there are also unobservable elements in science that have to be called "real," for example, the electron. The quoted passage clearly expresses the fact that "real" is not regarded as identical with "observable." We can state the meaning of the quotation also in slightly different words: Every symbol denotes something real if this symbol is a part of a system that serves to describe observable facts uniquely.

19. The First Public Meeting

The arrangement of the meeting was not so easy. We wanted to reach a large audience. The ordinary regular philosophy meetings followed the traditional lines and would hardly have given us enough scope. By a happy coincidence I was just in 1929 arranging a meeting of the physicists and mathematicians from the German-speaking regions in Central Europe. The meeting was to be held in my place of residence, Prague, the capital of Czechoslovakia. The German Physical Society, which was the official sponsor of this meeting, did not particularly like the idea of combining this serious scientific meeting with such a foolish thing as philosophy. However, I was the chairman of the local committee in Prague and they could not refuse my serious wish to attach a meeting with the topic, "Epistemology of the Exact Sciences." This meeting was to be sponsored by the Ernst Mach Association, which was the legal organization of the Vienna Circle, and the Society for Empirical Philosophy, which was organized in Berlin and followed in general the line of H. Reichenbach. In this way we provided a nucleus of interested people and hoped that quite a few mathematicians and physicists who came to Prague for their meeting would also attend our gathering.

Some scientists wanted to minimize our program and predicted that we would have no audience from the ranks of the exact scientists. As a matter of fact, our addresses had a larger audience than papers on special scientific problems. I had prepared an elaborate paper that was intended to give the scientists a kind of preview of our ideas and to prove that the new line in philosophy is the necessary result of the new trends in physics, particularly the theory of relativity and the quantum theory. I elaborated the contrast between the "school philosophy," which sought to preserve the traditional doctrines despite the new science, and the "scientific world conception," which wants to pour the new wine into new bottles. I stressed also the similarity between the new scientific world conception and the basic ideas of American pragmatism, particularly those of William James. This lecture is Chapter 4 of the present book.

Some friends cautioned me not to speak too bluntly. The audience, which consisted mostly of German scientists, knew little of philosophy, except that they had some sentimental ties to Kantianism. This doctrine was regarded in some intellectual quarters as a kind of substitute for the traditional forms of religion. My wife said to me after the lecture: "It was weird to listen. It seemed to me as if the words fell into the audience like drops into a well so deep that one cannot hear the drops striking bottom. Everything seemed to vanish without a trace."

There is no doubt that quite a few people in the audience were shocked by my blunt statements that modern science is incompatible with the traditional systems of philosophy. Probably, most of the scientists had not been accustomed to thinking of philosophy and science as one coherent system of thought. Philosophy had been for them what the Sunday sermon is for a businessman who is only interested in profit. Philosophy had been required not to be "true" but to give emotional satisfaction.

After the meeting, however, our committee received a great many letters from scientists who expressed their great satisfaction that an attempt has been made toward a coherent world conception without contradictions between science and philosophy. We even received one letter from a professor of philosophy at a German university who wanted to go on record with his conviction that the remaking of philosophy, along the lines that we followed at our meeting, is necessary.

20. M. Schlick Announces a "Turn in Philosophy"

In the years 1930-31, there appeared the first volume of the journal *Erkenntnis* (Cognition), which became the main mouthpiece of our movement. The editors were R. Carnap and H. Reichenbach. The first issue began with the paper, "The Turn in Philosophy," by M. Schlick. I shall quote some lines in order to show that an optimistic belief in the new trend was the keynote of this journal. Schlick writes:

> I am convinced that we are in the middle of an altogether final turn in philosophy. I am justified, on good grounds, in regarding the sterile conflict of systems as settled. Our time, so I claim, possesses already the methods by which any conflict of this kind is rendered superfluous; what matters is only to apply these methods resolutely.

In the same year (1930) Schlick published a paper, "Personal Experience, Cognition, Metaphysics," [27] in which he writes:

> All cognition of the being is achieved, in principle, by the methods of the special sciences; every other kind of ontology is empty talk. Metaphysics is impossible because its goals contradict one another. If the metaphysician longs only for personal experience, his longing can be satisfied by poetry and art—or by life itself. But if he longs for a personal experience of the transcendent, he confuses life and cognition, he chases futile shadows.

For Schlick, as we know, "cognition" is the construction of a system of symbols that denotes uniquely the world of facts. It is therefore fundamentally different from personal experience.

This strong optimistic feeling is psychologically the feeling of a turn. You can ride in a car at high speed and you do not feel anything so long as the velocity remains unchanged. But if a turn or an acceleration takes place, you experience a strong reaction. Today, the movement of logical positivism is no longer so conspicuous. It had produced a turn in philosophy, which afterwards moved in a new direction and rather smoothly. I quote a passage from a philosopher who is by no means a follower of what is now called logical positivism. C. West Churchman writes: [28]

> Few can doubt the healthy impact that the positivist position has had upon modes of inquiry; it has sharply distinguished the schools of thought, and has raised a standard under which the proponents of experimental methods can fight their battles against

[27] M. Schlick, "Erleben, Erkennen, Metaphysik," *Kantstudien* 31, 146 (1926).
[28] C. W. Churchman, *Theory of Experimental Inference* (New York: Macmillan, 1948).

a reactionary movement. To return to a prepositivistic viewpoint is to return to a prescientific viewpoint, to become a reactionary as an advocate of the indisputable power of the sovereign in the eyes of one with a democratic outlook.

We find a similar position even in the most recent book of F. S. C. Northrop[29] who, in some sense, attempts a justification of metaphysics. He has been, however, in all his writing a very independent thinker who has given much thought to the foundations of science and particularly to the interdependence between the philosophy of science and the cultural background. He writes:

"In any event, the great merit of logical positivism and its main aim is satisfied, even if one leaves the scientific concepts and their meaning just as one finds them, as prescribed by the scientists in the postulates of some specific deductively formulated theory. The important desideratum at which the logical positivists were aiming, namely operational verification, can nonetheless be obtained. There are many signs that contemporary logical positivists have now come to this position.

As a matter of fact, if one traces the history of logical positivism, one will see that this has been always the position of the "scientific world conception." This becomes clear if one considers Schlick's position in "Space and Time" (Sec. 13).

To estimate how sharp the turn was for which logical positivism was responsible, we have to compare its position with the views of the school of traditional philosophy that was the nearest to it in spirit and in time. We choose for comparison H. Vaihinger's "Philosophy of 'As If' " (1911), a very ingenious and in its time very famous book, a typical example of what I called the disintegration of traditional philosophy by neo-Kantianism. Vaihinger tries to show that the concept of an atom (which he identifies with a mass point) in physics is a useful "fiction" although it is logically self-contradictory. He says:

An entity without extension that is at the same time a substantial bearer of forces—this is simply a combination of words with which no definite meaning can be connected. "Simple atoms," that must yet be something material, cannot be *causae verae,* cannot be actual things. Since, however, the physicist does require atoms

[29] F. S. C. Northrop, *The Logic of the Sciences and the Humanities* (New York: Macmillan, 1947), pp. 113, 114.

for his construction, how is this contradiction to be solved? How are we to rescue science from this dilemma?[30]

Vaihinger thinks that the method actually used in science is to

speak of atoms without really meaning to assume them . . . Unquestionably this conceptual method is the most convenient one, but this constitutes, of course, no proof of its objective-metaphysical validity.[31]

Vaihinger's view is a clear indication of the situation in philosophy immediately before the rise of logical positivism. There was a complete lack of understanding that one must distinguish between a structural system having exact logical coherence with the world of facts, which are described with a certain vagueness, and the operational definitions, which connect both domains and participate in the preciseness of the first and the vagueness of the second.

21. P. W. Bridgman's Theory of Meaning

About the same time when the "scientific world conception" group were arranging their first public meeting, P. W. Bridgman published a book[8] in the United States in which he reacted to the same situation by which this group had been faced. In a broad sense, we can characterize his work also as an attempt to integrate Mach, Poincaré, and Einstein into a coherent picture of modern science. Bridgman's field was not mathematics or symbolic logic but experimental physics. He has been a man of the laboratory who preferred to do things rather than set up a long chain of arguments. His approach is therefore different from that of the Central European group. It was, in a way, more similar to Mach's, who was also essentially an experimentalist. Bridgman found out what was the salient point in the integration of Mach and Poincaré. Reichenbach had explicitly pointed out that what is needed is a bridge between the symbolic system of axioms and the protocols of the laboratory. But the nature of this bridge had been only vaguely described. Bridgman was the first who said precisely that these "relations of coördination" consist in

[30] Hans Vaihinger, *Die Philosophie der "Als Ob"* (1911); English translation by C. K. Ogden (ed. 2, Barnes and Noble, 1935), p. 219. Incidentally, in this book the term "logical positivism" was used for the first time, although in a somewhat different sense from the one it now has.
[31] *Ibid.*, p. 222.

the description of physical operations. He called them, therefore, "operational definitions." This name has been generally accepted. Bridgman was also very definite in stating that a theory which does not contain the operational definitions of its abstract terms is meaningless. In this way he arrived at a concept of "meaning" and "meaninglessness" that was similar to the concept advanced by Carnap and his group.

Bridgman, however, formulated the criterion of meaning in a much more concrete way. He did not restrict himself to the general prescription of how to investigate the meaning of a statement but investigated elaborately the operations that have to be carried out in order to define the meaning of physical terms like "length" or "thermal capacity." By these investigations he found, for example, that the operations by which one can distinguish between heat conduction and heat radiation, or between heat supplied and mechanical work supplied, cannot be performed in all cases. Only if the phenomena investigated are of a simple type are these operations feasible. Therefore, terms like "heat conduction" or "mechanical work" do not have a meaning under all circumstances.

Bridgman has contributed much to the new philosophy which has developed along with twentieth-century science. He has advocated strongly the view that the domain of phenomena within which a word has meaning is restricted, and no word has meaning if we do not indicate the circumstances under which it is used. Bridgman has also pointed out repeatedly that this new "semantic" aspect is bound to have great repercussions upon discourse in politics and religion.[32]

In 1931 Carnap was appointed professor of natural philosophy at the University of Prague. I succeeded in bringing about this appointment, despite the strong opposition of the adherents of traditional philosophy, because of a happy coincidence. At that time the Faculty of Arts and Sciences was divided into a Faculty of Humanities and a Faculty of Science. All professors of philosophy were in the Faculty of Humanities and the Faculty of Science gave no instruction in philosophy. The president of the Czechoslovakian Republic, Thomas G. Masaryk, who had himself been a professor of philosophy, believed strongly in the educational value of philosophy. He insisted that the Faculty of Science should have a philosopher of their own. I suggested Carnap, and as there was no advocate of traditional philosophy left, the

[32] P. W. Bridgman, *Yale Review* 34, 444 (1945).

science faculty agreed. From 1931 on we had in this way a new center of "scientific world conception" at the University of Prague.

22. The Spread of Logical Empiricism

My own interest, which had been for a long time diverted from the problems offered by the philosophy of science, returned now to the object of my earlier years. The intellectual situation was now in a certain respect a similar one. The new science of quantum theory gave rise to a repetition of the crisis that had been precipitated about 1905 by the relativity theory, but with even greater intensity. Again it was maintained that scientific method had failed. The new theories do not even claim to give an "explanation" of the physical phenomena. They claim only to offer mathematical formulas from which the observed phenomena can be derived. The "explanation" is left as a field for metaphysical theories, which would claim to give the "real causes" of things. The argument went mostly that relativity as well as quantum theory give mathematical patterns without any causal justification.

Remembering our old arguments in the Vienna coffeehouses around 1907 about Abel Rey, Ernst Mach, and Henri Poincaré, I devoted some work to applying the newly developed "scientific world conception" to overcome the new crisis. I tried to show that there is not the slightest reason to see in twentieth-century theory an argument for an idealistic or spiritualistic world conception, and that this opinion only arises from a lack of scientific formulation of the new physical theories. This lack has its source in the poor training of physicists in philosophy, which makes them often faithful believers in the metaphysical creeds imbibed in their early youth "from a nurse or a schoolmaster." [33] In Chapters 6 and 7 of the present book I attempt to give an analysis of physical theories on the basis of the new ideas; the scientific argument is carried through consistently without suddenly breaking into vague metaphysical discourse. While these chapters are more or less devoted to a general discussion of modern physics, Chapters 8 and 9 contain a special discussion of modern quantum theory from the same viewpoint, includ-

[33] A. N. Whitehead, *The Principle of Relativity* (Cambridge: The University Press, 1922).

ing some remarks on "determinism" that take up, in a new way, the problem of Chapter 1.

If we look from another angle upon those misinterpretations of physical theories, it is evident that they are not the result of some intellectual inability. Their real source is the urge to find support for a metaphysical creed that, for some reason, one cherishes. And this reason is, as we have already hinted, the fitness of this metaphysical creed to bolster up some political or religious creed that one believes to be indispensable for the well-being of mankind. This sociological aspect has been for many years familiar to me from the discussions of our old Viennese group and, in particular, from the attention that I later paid to the influence of religious and political creeds upon scientific theories in two specific cases: Duhem's presentation of the action taken by the Roman Church against the Copernican theory, and Lenin's attacks on Mach's conception of physics. I have touched upon this aspect in Chapter 5 and have devoted all of Chapter 10 to it. The Copernican conflict is treated in Chapter 13, the specific nature of the Soviet philosophy (dialectical materialism) and, in particular, its relation to positivism and empiricism are described in Chapter 11.

At the time of the meeting in Prague (1929) the Vienna Circle and Reichenbach's group in Berlin were a small number of dissident people hemmed in by the vast ocean of German school philosophy, which was more or less a development of Kantian metaphysics. It was considered to be a specific "German philosophy"—namely, "German idealism" —and philosophies of other types were regarded with a certain suspicion as something "un-German" and "foreign." The workers for a "scientific world conception" had no hope of finding any considerable encouragement in Germany. Neurath described this cultural and historical situation in his small book, "The Development of the Vienna Circle and the Future of Logical Empiricism." [34] Neurath writes that the Kantian influence had been slight in the Universities of Vienna and Prague and that their philosophy avoided the "Kantian interlude" and passed directly from Leibniz to modern positivism. He continues, "The influences of English and French thinkers are frequent and things happen in Austria parallel to what

[34] O. Neurath, *Le Développement du Cercle de Vienne et l'avenir de l'empirisme logique,* French translation by General Vouillemin (Paris: Hermann, 1935).

happens in Warsaw, Cambridge, or Paris, rather than to what takes place in Berlin."

Although German science had developed along international lines and no serious scientist would have objected to any foreign influence, in philosophy things were different. There was a strong tendency to overrate "German idealism" and to minimize British, French, and American philosophical trends. We felt very soon that the future of the "scientific world conception" was to break through this wall and to make contact with "foreign" philosophies. This feeling turned out to be entirely correct and we met friendly interest on the part of American, British, and French thinkers. In the United States there was a natural common ground, the work of the American pragmatists, in particular of C. S. Peirce. Charles W. Morris had cultivated especially the ties between pragmatism and the Central European positivism. He coined for the result of the very close coöperation of these groups the name "logical empiricism," which seems to me to denote the salient point better than any other name. E. Nagel (now at Columbia) and W. V. Quine (now at Harvard) came to Vienna and Prague, as Morris (now at the University of Chicago) had done, to make personal contact with Schlick, Carnap, and the other workers in this field.

In Great Britain our natural link was L. Wittgenstein, whose own education had been half Austrian and half British, and, through him, Bertrand Russell. The brilliant young Oxford philosopher, A. J. Ayer, also came to Vienna and published the most readable book on logical empiricism that has been written in English, and perhaps the most readable book altogether.[35]

In France, the advocates of the "new positivism" were naturally interested in our movement. L. Rougier started his philosophic work on a basis similar to that of Schlick. He took his start from Poincaré, tried to integrate Einstein into the "new positivism," and wrote the best all-round criticism of the school philosophy that I know of, "The Paralogisms of Rationalism." [36]

Marcel Boll, an able physicist himself, saw in the Viennese movement a valuable contribution to a renewed and more vigorous positivism and a support of progressive thinking and

[35] A. J. Ayer, *Language, Truth, and Logic* (London: Gollancz; New York: Oxford University Press, 1936).

[36] L. Rougier, *Les paralogismes du rationalisme* (Paris: Alcan, 1920).

acting. He translated writings of Carnap, Reichenbach, Schlick, and myself into French.

We encountered also a strong interest in a group of French neo-Thomists. The great influence of the neo-Thomist, P. Duhem, upon the Viennese group repeated itself now in reverse. The French general, Vouillemin, recommended our group because we replaced the spelling "Science" modestly by "science." He also translated several papers of the Vienna Circle into French and published a small book, "The Logic of Science and the Vienna School," [37] in which he gave his interpretation of logical empiricism. The French neo-Thomists of this group saw in logical positivism the destroyers of idealistic and materialistic metaphysics, which they regarded as the most dangerous enemies of Thomism.

To organize this international coöperation a preliminary conference was held in 1934 in Prague, at which Charles Morris and L. Rougier participated. The ground was laid for arranging international congresses "for the unity of science," which were to be held every year. They actually met in 1935 in Paris, 1936 in Copenhagen, 1937 in Prague, 1938 in Cambridge, England, and 1939 in Cambridge, Massachusetts, at Harvard University.

23. Teaching the Philosophy of Science at Harvard

In the year 1936, just while the Congress for the Unity of Science was in session at Copenhagen, Professor Schlick was assassinated near his lecture hall in the University of Vienna by a student. At the court trial the attorney for the defendant pleaded extenuating circumstances because the student was indignant about Schlick's "vicious philosophy." Everyone who knew Schlick had been full of admiration for his noble, humane and restrained personality. The political implications of the expression "vicious philosophy" were obvious. The student received a ten-year prison term. When, however, two years later, the Nazi troops occupied Vienna and arrested a great many people, Schlick's murderer was released from prison.

The shots directed at Schlick were a dramatic indication of the dispersal of the Central European positivism that was taking place under the pressure of the advancing Nazi power. At the end of 1938 this process was completed. By far the

---

[37] Le general C. E. Vouillemin, *La Logique de la science et l'école de Vienne* (Paris: Hermann, 1935).

greatest part of the Central Europeans who had worked along the lines of logical positivism had left their countries. The immediate reason was either to escape political persecution, or, in many cases, just the feeling that under the dictatorship of the Nazis there would be no place for a philosophy guided by logic and experience. The majority of the emigrants have lived since in the United States, a smaller part in Great Britain.

When I arrived in the United States in October 1938, I started a lecture tour during which I spoke at twenty-odd universities and colleges on the philosophic interpretations of modern physics. Chapter 7 of this book presents one of these lectures.

Since the fall of 1939 I have had the privilege of teaching at Harvard University not only mathematical physics but also the philosophy of science. This teaching has been a great experience for me and has been of great influence on my philosophical writing. I started with an audience of about fifteen students. Since this was an unusual subject I did not quite know what to tell them. I began by presenting to them the logical structure of physical theories as envisaged by logical empiricism. But very soon I noticed that this was not the right thing to do. The frequent discussions that I had with the students showed me what they really wanted to know. By a process of interaction, a program was finally worked out that was a compromise between what I wanted to tell the students and what they wanted to know.

At that time Harvard University set up its "General Education Program." This was a great help to me since it was based on the deficiencies of the traditional curriculum as felt by the students, the faculty, and the general public. President J. B. Conant urged, in particular, a new approach to the teaching of science. He stressed that science teaching has to be linked up with a presentation of the historical, cultural and psychological background of the work done by the great scientists. This program was later developed in Mr. Conant's book, *On Understanding Science*.[38]

Stimulated by all these factors and particularly by the rapidly increasing interest of the students in the philosophical and cultural implications of science (I had later an audience of more than two hundred fifty), it became more and more

[38] J. B. Conant, *On Understanding Science* (New Haven: Yale University Press, 1947).

clear to me how to work out a program for my students. I now put the greatest emphasis on presenting physics, and science in general, as part of our general pattern of thinking and acting. I presented it on one hand as a logical system that has to be checked by physical experiments and on the other hand as one of the means of expressing man's attitude towards the world, the small world of society and politics and the large world that is our astronomical universe. This more historical approach has been familiar to me since my student years from the meetings with my older friends.

All my papers written after 1940 follow this line. Chapter 11 of this book describes the interaction between the advance in science and the changes in metaphysical systems. Its point is that a great many metaphysical systems are merely abandoned systems of science. In Chapter 12 the Copernican conflict is discussed from the same viewpoint, particular stress being laid on the role that could be played by the intervention of political powers. Chapters 14 and 15, which are closely connected with each other, discuss directly the role that instruction in the philosophy of science is to play in the college curriculum. By the time I came to write them, I had collected a great deal of experiential material about this problem. My point was now that the philosophy of science should, on one hand, give to the science student a more profound understanding in his own field, and on the other hand, be for all students a link between the sciences and the humanities, thus filling a real gap in our educational system.

In all my writing before 1947 I had stressed the point that science gives no support to metaphysical interpretations, of whatever type. I had discussed these interpretations only as reflecting the social environment of the philosopher. However, after that time, as a result of contact with my students and fellow teachers, I became more and more interested in the question of the actual meaning of the metaphysical interpretations of science—idealistic, materialistic, relativistic, and others. For the fact that a great many scientists and philosophers advance such interpretations and cherish them is as firmly established, by our experience, as any fact of physics.

I now began a new series of investigations into the meaning of metaphysics within the framework of logico-empirical and sociopsychological analysis. The first preliminary result of these investigations is published in Chapter 16 of the present book.

In 1940 Professor Harlow Shapley, Director of the Harvard College Observatory, introduced me into the Conference of Science, Philosophy and Religion, which meets every year. This Conference is a group of philosophers, educators, social workers, and ministers of all denominations, and includes a sprinkling of scientists. They are interested particularly in the contributions that each of these fields can make to the understanding and supporting of the democratic way of life. The leaders in this group have been, besides Dr. Shapley, Dr. Louis Finkelstein, President of the Jewish Theological Seminary of America, and Dr. Lyman Bryson, Director of the Educational Department of the Columbia Broadcasting System. From these meetings I have learned more about the attitudes of different groups of people toward science, and what points in the philosophy of science support or are believed to support a certain way of life. The large majority in these meetings has been rather critical of the scientific outlook and its contribution to human welfare.

I addressed this group several times between 1940 and 1947. My contributions centered mostly around the question of whether the "relativism" of modern science is actually harmful to the establishment of objective values in human life. I made an argument to prove that the "relativism of science" has also penetrated every argument about human behavior. "Relativism" is not responsible for any deterioration of human conduct. What one calls "relativism" is rather the attempt to get rid of empty slogans and to formulate the goals of human life sincerely and unambiguously. My contributions to these meetings will be published [39] in due time, under the title "Relativity—a richer truth."

[39] Beacon Press, Boston.

Chapter 1

Experience and the Law of Causality

THE FRENCH MATHEMATICIAN Henri Poincaré, in two books[1] on the philosophy of Science, "Science and Hypothesis," and "The Value of Science," presented the point of view that many of the most general principles of theoretical science—such as the law of inertia, and the principle of conservation of energy—about which one often wonders whether they are of empirical or a priori origin, are actually neither of these, but purely conventional definitions depending on human arbitrariness.

The purpose of the present paper is to extend this conception to the principle that is in a certain sense the most general in all theoretical science, the law of causality. The direct stimulus for this undertaking was given by a book which, as a matter of fact, follows an opposite tendency, the sagacious and in many respects unprejudiced work, "Concepts and Principles of Natural Science," by Hans Driesch.[2] The author sets out to show that the principle of conservation of energy has an a priori nucleus which is no other than the law of causality in its precise formulation. In order to demonstrate the apriority of the energy principle, Driesch presents a series of ingenious arguments which show that experience can never disprove the principle in question. This array of arguments calls to mind in an astonishing way that used by Poincaré for his conception of the energy principle as a convention. The agreement is all the more striking since evidently neither author was influenced by the other. Although the conclusions reached are quite different, the two arguments are very similar. Since that of Driesch is to a large extent applicable to the law of causality, I have found in it new support for my conception of this law, which I felt to be a necessary consequence of the arguments presented in Poincaré's papers.

[1] H. Poincaré, *Science and Hypothesis* (Science Press, New York, 1905; original, 1902); *The Value of Science* (Science Press, New York, 1907; original, 1905).
[2] H. Driesch, *Naturbegriffe und Natururteile* (Leipzig, 1904).

The thesis that we shall try to prove states that the law of causality, the foundation of every theoretical science, can be neither confirmed nor disproved by experience; not, however, because it is a truth known a priori, but because it is a purely conventional definition. We shall take as a basis the form of the law of causality that is freest from undefined and ambiguous expressions and contains only the essentials, referring directly to the data of the senses.

The law states that if, in the course of time, a state A of the universe is once followed by a state B, then whenever A occurs B will follow it.

This statement contains everything that is the real content of the law of causality. It is important to understand that the law can be applied only to the whole universe and not to a part of it. This, however, makes it impossible to test the law empirically. In the first place, one can never know the state of the whole universe, and in the second place, it is in general not certain whether it is possible for a state A of the universe ever to return. If no state A could ever be repeated, the law would be meaningless theoretically, since it refers only to recurring states.

Fortunately, it is not the exact law of causality itself which finds application in science, but a formulation of it that asserts only something approximate. This says that if, in a finite region of space, the state A is at one time followed by the state B and at another time by the state C, we can make the region sufficiently large by adding to it its environment that the state C becomes as close to the state B as we please.

In other words, in finite systems the law of causality is the more nearly valid the larger the system. In the application of the law to a finite system, the answer to the question whether the system is large enough depends on the degree of accuracy required for the occurrence of the predicted effect. This can be shown by a simple example taken from astronomy, the science that has been worked out most rationally. Let us consider the system consisting of the sun and the earth. A state A of this system, defined by a particular distance of separation and relative velocity of the two bodies, is always followed by the same series of states, no matter how often A is repeated; but we must not take the word "same" too exactly. For, in reality, the series of states following A also depends on the distances and velocities of all the other planets and the fixed stars as well, and we must include them in the system.

The more celestial bodies we include, the more accurately is the law of causality obeyed. However, if we take into the system only the planets with their satellites, the accuracy is sufficient for all practical purposes. We see from this example that there do exist finite systems to which the law of causality is applicable.

Whether a given system will behave in this way cannot be known beforehand; for this reason the so-called inductive method has been developed. When an investigator sees "that in a system the state B follows the state A, not once but often, he will say that A is the cause of B." This means nothing else, however, than that the law of causality is applicable to the system under discussion. For an all-embracing system, a single case in which B follows A is enough to enable one to draw conclusions for all times thereafter. For a finite system, however, it is necessary to decide in every case whether the law of causality is applicable. Naturally, such a decision can never be a final one, for the law of causality as applied to finite systems is not the real one, but only a substitute for it. The real law itself is only an ideal which the law for finite systems approaches as a limit as these systems are made larger and larger.

Here we do not wish to concern ourselves with the difficulties arising from the finiteness of empirical systems. It will soon appear that these are relatively unimportant in comparison with arguments that would place the law of causality in a peculiar light even if it were rigorously valid for finite systems, which will be assumed hereafter. We have, then, a finite system for which the law is valid that if the state A is followed once by the state B, then A will be followed every time by B. In this statement there occurs, however, a single word—"state"—that is not explainable directly through any reference to sense data. And the analysis of this word will suffice to demolish this seemingly so strongly built meaning of the law.

What is a "state of a system"? The most obvious explanation would be that by state we mean the ensemble of the perceptible properties of a system. This would be a clear meaning. However, if we take the word "state" in this sense, the law of causality becomes incorrect, as can be seen from simple examples. Let us assume that the system consists of two iron rods, lying side by side on the table, that is, in state A. Left to themselves, they will continue to lie quietly; that is, A is followed by A. If now we replace one of the iron rods by a magnetized one of exactly the same appearance, the initial state, according to our definition of the word "state," will be the same as before, namely, A. The rods will now move toward each other, however; that is, A is now followed, not by A, but by B. In order to be able to say that the law of causality is still valid, we must say that the initial states were only apparently the same. We must include in "state" not only the totality of perceptible properties, but also another, namely, in our example, magnetization. A property belonging to the definition of the state is called a state variable of the system.

How does it come about that we assign to bodies imperceptible as well as perceptible properties? Such properties—electric charge, chemical affinity, and so on—are characteristics that indicate how the body possessing them behaves when brought into certain situations. They are, according to Driesch, "the aggregates of possibilities, regarded as reality."

This, however, means only that if a body in a given situation behaves differently from another body the state of which, in the sense first defined, is the same, we assign to it new state variables in addition to the perceptible ones. This in turn means only that if the law of causality is not valid according to one definition of the state, we redefine the state in such a way that the law is valid. If that is the case, however, the law, which appeared to be stating a fact, is transformed into a mere definition of the word "state." We can express the law in the following form: "By the word 'state' one understands the perceptible properties of a system of bodies, plus a series of fictitious properties, of which so many are included that the same states are always followed by the same states." In this form the "law of causality" no longer looks at all like a law.

Because of the fact that the word "state," which occurred in that form of the law of causality first taken as a basis, is only defined by this law, the latter loses the character of a factual proposition and becomes a definition. Of a definition, however, one cannot say that it is empirical or a priori; it is only a product of human imagination.

The conclusion to which the foregoing reflections lead is that "the law of causality is only the establishment of a terminology." Because this law forms the basis of the whole of theoretical science, the latter itself is also nothing else than a suitably chosen terminology. Whereas experimental science describes the properties of bodies as given by our senses, and the changes in these properties, the task of theoretical science is to provide bodies with fictitious properties the chief purpose of which is to insure the validity of the law of causality. Theoretical science is not research but a sort of remodeling of nature; it is work of the imagination. From this it is clear whence the so-called pure—that is, a priori—science, the possibility of which led Kant to write his *Critique of Pure Reason,* derives its conviction of being right. The principles of pure science, of which the foremost is the law of causality, are certain because they are only disguised definitions.

Pure science states nothing about empirical nature; it only gives directions for portraying nature. All the arguments which Driesch has arrayed so ingeniously for the existence of a pure science show indeed that there are principles independent of our experience, but fail to explain why this is the case. The reasons are completely revealed by the conception presented above.

Thus we see that the latest philosophy of nature revives in a striking way the basic idea of critical idealism, that experience only serves to fill in a framework which man brings along with him as a part of his nature. The difference is that the old philosophers considered this framework a necessary outgrowth of human organization, whereas we see in it a free creation of human imagination.

How often the question has been put: "How can it happen that man can work out all of outer nature, which is, after all, completely independent of his mind?" Are not nature and the human intellect incommensurable things? From our standpoint it is easy to answer that the nature which the human mind rationalizes by means of theoretical science is not at all the nature that we know through our senses. The law of causality and with it all of theoretical science have as their object not empirical nature but the fictitious nature of which we spoke above. The latter, however, is not only the object, but also the work (and work, not in any metaphysical sense, but in the ordinary sense) of man; hence it can of course be completely comprehended by him.

To the fundamental questions of theoretical science, experience and experiment can never give an unequivocal answer. If I wish, I can provide all bodies with state variables that are all qualitatively different, in order to fulfill the law of causality. I can regard heat, electricity, magnetism, as properties of bodies, essentially different from one another, just as is done in modern energetics, and as Driesch does. On the other hand, if I wish, I can get along without introducing qualitative differences. For example, I can introduce only the motion of masses; but then, in order to obtain the necessary diversity, I must take refuge in unconfirmable hidden motions. This leads to the purely mechanical picture of the world, which Democritus dimly conceived as an ideal, and which occurs mostly in the form of atomism. This purely quantitative picture of the universe, striving to manage with a minimum number of qualities, was given its most logical development in the book "Philosophy of Inanimate Matter" by Adolf Stöhr,[3] where even the qualitative specificities still adhering to mechanical atomism were suppressed in favor of purely geometrical-quantitative schemes. This work, as the most radical carrying out of the program of the atomists, occupies a significant place in the literature of natural philosophy. In a quite different way, H. A. Lorentz and his pupils have created a quantitative world picture by breaking away from the mechanistic tradition and introducing as state variables electric charge and electric and magnetic field intensities. Thus arose the electromagnetic picture of the world. Among all these, it is not possible to choose uniquely on the basis of experience. One may be simpler, another more complicated, but none true or false.

We see that it is not at all a scientific question, in the narrower sense, what world picture I make for myself. The world pictures are only more or less different expressions used for the same thing—empirical nature.

Furthermore, the same is true of a question which has long held sway as a so-called question of world conception, the answer to which is above all demanded of the scientist. It is a question that seems to carry with it an infinite number of emotional values, and yet it is only a question of terminology. It is the question (to return at the end to the book of Driesch mentioned at the beginning) whether the phenomena of animal and plant life can be explained by means of the laws of physics and chemistry, the question that is usually summarized in the high-sounding expression, "vitalism or mechanism?"

We are indebted to Driesch for the first clear and unprejudiced formulation of the problem which, following him, and

[3] A. Stöhr, *Philosophie der unbelebten Materie* (Leipzig, 1907).

with reference to what has been said hitherto, we can express as follows: Must we, in order to satisfy the law of causality in the domain of life, ascribe to the body besides the properties (state variables) of physics and chemistry, also other, qualitatively different properties? Driesch tries to show that we must do this, and introduces entelechy, as a state variable peculiar to living bodies. This attempt of Driesch's to show that it is impossible to get along with the state variables of physics and chemistry alone seems to me not entirely convincing. To be sure, Driesch shows that we *can* assume for the living processes a specific state variable, but not that we *must*. For it is not possible to foresee every trick that one might invent in the fiction of hidden combinations of inorganic state variables. In favor of vitalism I should like to remark that, just as I cannot force someone who regards heat as a specific state variable to consider it as a motion of mass particles, so I cannot force the adherents of entelechy to replace it by fictitious state variables. However, that is not very important for the purpose of the present work. What is important is that, from the bio-theoretical works of Driesch, if we examine them from the standpoint adopted by us, it is clear that the question "vitalism or mechanism?" is not a question of fact. It is not a question to which a crucial experiment can answer yes or no. It is rather a question the solution of which depends on the ingenuity of the human imagination and can never be convincing to all men. The question is not: "Is that thus or so?" It is rather: "Can we paint the picture in this or in that style, or in both?"

With the question of world conception in the ethical-religious sense, all this has nothing whatsoever to do.

Chapter 2

The Importance for Our Times of Ernst Mach's Philosophy of Science

THERE IS SOMETHING REMARKABLE about the teachings of Mach. Philosophers often ridicule or disdainfully reject them as the work of a physicist dabbling in philosophy; physicists often deplore them as aberrations from the right path of respectable, realistic natural science. Yet neither physicists and philosophers, nor historians and sociologists, nor many others, can get rid of Mach. Some attack him passionately; others extol him with fervor. There is something fascinating about his simple, straightforward teachings. In spite of their simplicity they are stimulating and provocative. There are indeed but few thinkers who can provoke such sharp differences of opinion, who are so inspiring to some and so utterly repugnant to others. What is there in these doctrines that makes it impossible for anyone, whatever his views may be, to avoid adopting some definite attitude towards them?

This is what I should like to discuss in the present paper. I have formed a fairly definite opinion about the position that Mach occupies in the intellectual life of our times, and this position, I believe, will explain why the battle rages about him so furiously. It is not a question here of the details of Mach's teaching, often individually and historically conditioned, but rather of their nucleus, which is just the focus of the struggle. I will not speak therefore about the general attitude of Mach towards the psychophysical problem, nor about his separate contributions to physics and psychology, but only about his conception of the tasks and possible aims of exact science.

In recent years, among creatively active physicists and mathematicians, there has become noticeable a reaction against the conceptions of Mach. When one of the most outstanding theoretical physicists of our time, Max Planck,[1] and one of the foremost living geometricians, E. Study,[2] charac-

---

[1] M. Planck, *Die Einheit des physikalischen Weltbildes* (Leipzig, 1909).
[2] E. Study, *Die realistische Weltansicht und die Lehre vom Raume* (Brunswick, 1914).

terize these conceptions as being partly misleading, partly incapable of being carried out, and partly actually harmful for science, the fact provides food for thought and cannot be lightly brushed aside.

What an investigator with the markedly constructive talents of Planck dislikes above all in the views of Mach is his judgment of values. For the investigator, every new theory that is supported by experiment is a piece of newly discovered reality. According to Mach, on the other hand, physics is nothing but a collection of statements about the connections among sense perceptions, and theories are nothing but economical means of expression for summarizing these connections. He says:

> The aim of natural science is to obtain connections among phenomena. Theories, however, are like withered leaves, which drop off after having enabled the organism of science to breathe for a time.[3]

This phenomenalistic conception, as it is called, was familiar to Goethe. In his posthumous "Maxims and Reflections" he says:

> Hypotheses are the scaffolds which are erected in front of a building and removed when the building is completed. They are indispensable to the worker; but he must not mistake the scaffolding for the building.

Sounds like "conventionalistic" hypoths. (see Pepper)

And still more drastically:

> The constancy of phenomena alone is important; what we think about them is quite immaterial.

It will be said, however, that Goethe was not really a good physicist, and that we can see in his case an example of how such basic principles hinder the spirit of research. Thus Planck says:

> When the great masters of exact investigation of nature gave their ideas to science, when Nicholas Copernicus removed the earth from the center of the universe, when Johannes Kepler formulated the laws named after him, when Isaac Newton discovered

---

[3] E. Mach, *Die Geschichte und die Wurzel des Satzes von der Erhaltung der Arbeit*, written in 1871. An English translation, *History and Root of the Principle of the Conservation of Energy*, was published in 1911.

gravitation . . . —the series could be long continued—surely, economical points of view were the very last thing to steel these men in their struggle against traditional opinions and dominating authorities. No, it was their unshakable belief—whether resting on an artistic, or on a religious basis—in the reality of their world picture. In view of these certainly incontestable facts, one cannot reject the surmise that, if the Mach principle of economy were really to be put at the center of the theory of knowledge, the trains of thought of such leading spirits would be disturbed, the flight of their imagination crippled, and consequently the progress of science perhaps fatefully hindered.[4]

That these fears in such generality are groundless can be readily seen if one recalls the views of one of the greatest theoretical physicists of the nineteenth century, James Clerk Maxwell, on the nature of physical theories. One need only read the introduction to his essay on Faraday's lines of force (1855)[5] to be convinced that he was completely an adherent of the phenomenalistic standpoint. Yet one cannot say of him that such adherence in any way crippled the flight of his imagination; indeed, quite the opposite. The conception of the relative worthlessness of the theory in comparison to the phenomenon gives to the theorizing of such an investigator something especially free and imaginative.

I am willing to concede that the phenomenalistic doctrine is pleasing to those whose work in physics is descriptive rather than constructive. Many such people, who are capable of describing very neatly definite—even if very special—phenomena, may regard themselves because of this doctrine as being sublimely superior to the imaginative, creative spirit, whose works, after all, are only phantoms and "withered leaves." I do not believe, however, that for these people the philosophy of Mach has crippled the imagination. Rather, it is the case of an imagination crippled by nature, which uses the teachings of Mach as a beautiful cloak to cover its deformity. It may have been cases like these which cause Planck, at the end of the lecture cited above, to hurl at the preachers of the phenomenalistic doctrines the Biblical words: "By their fruits ye shall know them."

Concerning this criterion of the fruits I shall have more to

[4] Planck, *op. cit.*, p. 36.
[5] Published in *Cambridge Philosophical Society Transactions*, 1864, and in *The Scientific Papers of James Clerk Maxwell*, ed. by W. D. Niven (Cambridge: The University Press, 1890), vol. 1.

say. First, in connection with the same Biblical allusion, I should like to introduce a quotation from Pierre Duhem about the value of physical theories. Duhem was the most outstanding representative in France of ideas similar to those of Mach. He said:

> By the fruit one judges the tree; the tree of science grows exceedingly slowly; centuries elapse before one can pluck the ripe fruits; even today it is hardly possible for us to shell and appraise the kernel of the teachings that blossomed in the seventeenth century. He who sows cannot therefore judge the worth of the corn. He must have faith in the fruitfulness of the seed in order that he may follow untiringly his chosen furrow when he casts his ideas to the four winds of heaven.[6]

These remarks of the greatest and most accurate student of the history of physics are perhaps the best answer to the opinion expressed by Planck

> that even our present world picture, although it shows the most varied colors according to the individuality of the investigator, nevertheless possesses certain features that can never be obliterated by any revolution, either in nature or in the human mind.[7]

These enduring features arise, according to Mach, from the fact that all possible theories must give the same connection between phenomena; this very fact guarantees a certain constancy. The known connections among phenomena form a network; the theory seeks to pass a continuous surface through the knots and threads of the net. Naturally, the smaller the meshes, the more closely is the surface fixed by the net. Hence, as our experience progresses the surface is permitted less and less play, without ever being unequivocally determined by the net.

Since, according to Planck and Study, the basic principles of Mach would do nothing but harm to physics, it is fortunate for physics that these principles have never been thoroughly applied by their adherents, even if it is a gloomy sign for the principles themselves. Thus Study says about positivism, as he calls the doctrines of Mach:

> We regard this principle as a perfect utopianism. The possibility

[6] P. Duhem, *L'Évolution de la mécanique* (Paris, 1903), translated into German by Ph. Frank and E. Stiasny as *Die Wandlungen der Mechanik* (Leipzig, 1912).
[7] *Op. cit.*, p. 35.

of its existence is based entirely on the fact that it is disavowed by its own followers at every step. Up to now there has never been any serious attempt to apply it consistently . . . We are dealing here with a question of principle and must therefore distinguish between the theory of positivism and the practice of the (fortunately for themselves) thoroughly inconsistent positivists.[8]

Planck says similarly:

We then attain a more realistic mode of expression . . . which is actually the one always used by physicists when they speak in the language of *their* science.[9]

With biting sarcasm, Study says:

In numerous cases the hypotheses that are basely denounced at the official reception (why not atomistics, too?) are admitted, under a different name and through a back door especially arranged for this, into the sanctuary of science. Such names and corresponding motivations are by no means few. Without any effort the writer collected a full dozen of them: "most complete and simplest description" (Kirchhoff) . . . "subjective means of research," "requirement of conceivability of facts," "restriction of possibilities," "restriction of expectation," "result of analytic investigation," "economy of thought," "biological advantage" (all of these employed by E. Mach).[10]

With equal mockery, Planck remarks:

I should not be at all surprised if a member of the Mach school were to come out some day with the great discovery, that . . . the reality of atoms is just what is required by scientific economy.[11]

Other authors, too, point out the glaring contradiction that exists among the admirers of Mach between theory and practice. A peculiar theory of the nature of physical theories is set up, but as soon as physics really begins the positivist behaves practically like any other physicist. A follower of Mach can proclaim that physics has to do only with relations among sense perceptions, but the preacher of this doctrine speaks as a physicist exactly like any one else, about matter and energy, and even about atoms and electrons.

[8] Study, *op. cit.*, pp. 36, 41.
[9] Quoted by Study, p. 37.
[10] *Ibid.*, p. 37.
[11] M. Planck, "Zur Machschen Theorie der physikalischen Erkenntnis," *Vierteljahrsschrift für wissenschaftliche Philosophie und Soziologie* 34, 497 (1911).

However, it is just this apparently so palpable contradiction that can lead to the understanding of the permanent nucleus of Mach's teachings. Let us listen once more to Study:

The whole situation is a striking reminder of Kronecker's proposal to abolish the irrational numbers and to reduce mathematics to statements about integers; in this case, too, the suggestion has remained programmatic, and for the same good reasons.[12]

The analogy, as I see it, is a very appropriate one. But I should like to give it a different interpretation from that of Study. It is obviously pointless actually to express all theorems of mathematics as theorems about integers. In principle, however, it is highly enlightening to know that all theorems about irrational numbers, and hence also all theorems about limiting values, *could* be expressed as theorems about integers. Once this possibility has been substantiated, the whole of analysis can proceed to develop as usual. But now when a theorem about derivatives is set up and somebody begins to subtilize about it, asking whether this theorem is really in agreement with the "nature" of the differential and going into profound and skeptical deliberations concerning this "nature," he can be told quite simply: "I could express this theorem, if I took enough time, as a theorem about integers; the nature of this theorem is hence no more and no less mysterious than that of the natural numbers."

The situation is quite similar with respect to Mach's physical theory of knowledge. It is not a question of actually expressing all physical statements as statements about relations among sense perceptions. It is important, however to establish the principle that only those statements have a real meaning that *could* in principle be expressed as statements about the relations among our perceptions. To express the law of conservation of energy or the law of equipartition of energy among all the degrees of freedom as statements about relations among perceptions is just as laborious, but also just as superfluous, as to express the theorem that the derivative of the sine is the cosine as a statement about integers. In principle, however, both are certainly possible.

For the inner working of physics it is in most cases practically immaterial whether one has adopted Mach's standpoint

[12] Study, *op. cit.*, p. 39.

or not. Similarly, in Kronecker's lectures on integral calculus there is nothing to be found that differs essentially from the presentation of other mathematicians.

Wherein, then, lies the value of the doctrines of Mach for physics?

My view is that their main value is not that they help the physicist to go forward in his physical work, but rather that they provide the means for defending the edifice of physics against attacks from outside.

One who examines dispassionately the concepts that today are at the basis of the system of hypotheses of physics will hardly be able to assert seriously that the atom, the electron, and the quantum form really satisfactory ultimate building blocks. Every thinker who is somewhat inclined toward logical thoroughness can find many obscurities in these concepts. Into these nebulosities boring doubt can penetrate and try to shake the whole system of physics as the foundation of our scientific world picture. Here Mach steps in and says:

All these concepts are only auxiliary concepts. What is significant is the connection among phenomena. Atoms, electrons, and quanta are only links to represent a connected system of science; they make it possible to derive logically the immeasurable system of connected phenomena from a few abstract principles. But these abstract principles are then only the means to an economical representation. They are not the epistemological basis. The reality of physics can never be shaken by any criticism of the auxiliary concepts.

The work of Mach is therefore not essentially destructive, as it is often represented to be; positivism is not, as Study calls it, a "negativism," but on the contrary is an attempt to create an unassailable position for physics. As a matter of fact, Planck, too, recognizes this when he says:

To it [the positivism of Mach] belongs in full measure the credit for having found again, in the face of threatening skepticism, the only legitimate starting point of all investigation of nature, the sense perceptions.[13]

That Planck condemns so sharply the conception of Mach seems to me therefore to arise from the fact that he considers it only from the viewpoint of its application within physics.

[13] Planck, *Die Einheit des physikalischen Weltbildes*, p. 34.

It must be said, however, that, even when regarded from this standpoint, the phenomenalistic conception has already accomplished something and is perhaps capable of accomplishing still more. In the boundary regions of physics, where general concepts like space, time, and motion play a role, the epistemological position one takes is no longer entirely immaterial. Indeed, it is universally known today that Einstein's general theory of relativity and gravitation grew immediately out of the positivistic doctrine of space and motion, as Einstein himself has discussed in detail in his reference to Mach.[14]

On the whole, however, I will gladly concede to Planck and Study that positivism itself has not done much in clearing up individual questions of physics. But from this it does not follow that positivism is, in general, of no value. The "fruits" of Mach's teachings are indeed not purely physical in character. It will be recalled that in recent years an attempt was made to take advantage of the criticism of the basic physical concepts in order to proclaim the bankruptcy of the scientific world picture. Bearing this in mind, one must ascribe a high value to the effort of Mach to make physics independent of every metaphysical opinion.

H. Poincaré says:

At first glance it appears to us that theories last only a day and that ruins heap up on ruins . . . If we examine the matter more closely, however, we find that what decays is those theories which claim to teach us what things *are*. But there is something in them which endures. If one of them has revealed to us a true *relation*, this relation has been acquired for all time. We shall find it again under a new cloak in the other theories which will reign successively in its place.[15]

In a very determined manner, the French philosopher Abel Rey emphasizes the importance for the general intellectual life of preserving the edifice of physical ideas. He says:

If those sciences which, historically, have had an essentially emancipating effect go down in a crisis that leaves them only with the significance of technically useful collections but robs them of every value in connection with the cognition of nature, this must

[14] A. Einstein, *Physikalische Zeitschrift* 17, 101 (1916).
[15] H. Poincaré, *La Valeur de la science* (Paris, 1905); English translation by G. B. Halsted, *The Value of Science* (New York, 1907).

bring about a complete revolution in the logical art and in the history of ideas . . . The emancipation of the mind, as it has been conceived since Descartes, thanks to physics, is a most fatally erroneous idea. One must introduce another way, and restore to a subjective intuition, to a mystical sense of reality—in short, to the mystery—everything that we believed had been taken away from it . . . If, on the contrary, it turns out that there is no justification for regarding this crisis as necessary and incurable . . . then the rational and positive method remains the best nurse of the human spirit.[16]

Here we have a very clear exposition of the dangers that would arise for the whole world conception from a physics that had no other epistemologic foundations than those auxiliary concepts which are so much exposed to criticism.

Mach himself saw the real value of his theories in the fact that they permitted setting up a connection, as free from contradictions as possible, between physics on the one hand and physiology and psychology on the other. He who still doubts this has only to read the general sections of the *Analysis of Sensations.*[17] Here it is stressed again and again that one must exert oneself to develop physics while using concepts that will not have to be given up in a transition to a neighboring branch of science.

From this effort of Mach to employ only concepts that will not lose their usefulness outside of physics we can understand his opposition to atomistics, which in particular has caused many physicists to turn against him. It is true that atomistics, when applied to physiologic and psychologic problems, easily leads into a blind alley. Such questions arise as: "How can a brain atom think?" "How can an atom perceive green, since, after all, it is itself only a miniature picture of a macroscopic body composed of perceptions?"

I will not deny that Mach allowed himself to be misled by this argument into attacking the use of atomistics in physics more sharply than can be justified. After all, the usefulness of the atomic theories in this limited realm is certainly indisputable. His followers, as is generally the case, often saw in this weakness of the master his greatest strength, and wished to banish the atom entirely from physics. I believe that

---

[16] A. Rey, *La Théorie de la physique chez les physiciens contemporains* (Paris, 1907), p. 19.
[17] *The Analysis of Sensations and the Relation of the Physical to the Psychical,* translated by C. M. Williams and Sydney Waterlow (Chicago, 1914).

one can completely free the nucleus of Mach's teachings from this historically and individually conditioned aversion to atomistics. The atoms are auxiliary concepts just like others that can be employed advantageously in a limited domain. They are not suitable for an epistemological foundation. Once we have adopted this point of view, we are all the freer in employing the concept of atoms wherever it is admissible. I believe that even Planck would not object so much to the kernel shelled in this way. It is then no longer so very strange when one declares the atoms, if not their reality, to be a requirement of economy. They can be the simplest means of representing physical laws without thereby being suitable to form an epistemological foundation.

In general, phenomenalism will neither particularly further nor hinder the physicist in his field of work. Thus Maxwell, who doubtless thought positivistically, wrote the work that laid the foundation for the molecular theory of gases. The phenomenalistic conception becomes a danger only in those cases in which the requirement of economy is not realized with equal intensity. The most noteworthy historical example is perhaps Goethe's doctrine of colors. However, if ones wishes to pass judgment on a person of such strong individuality one must not forget, as A. Stöhr quite correctly points out, that the requirement of economy may mean something quite different for every individual.[18] For one, it signifies a minimum of hypotheses; for another, say, a minimum of different kinds of energy. The former is the case for the extreme phenomenalist Goethe; the latter for the pure mechanist.

It will perhaps be instructive, as a comparative case, to recall a theoretical physicist who, as an immediate student of Mach, really tried to construct a system of physics and chemistry in which no hypothetical corpuscles, whether atoms or electrons, occur, and which embraces all the phenomena known at present. It cannot be denied that Gustav Jaumann in his numerous works has undertaken this task with great constructive force.[19] I do not believe, however, that the result has turned out to be really in the spirit of Mach's teachings. To be sure, it corresponds to the surface requirement that all

[18] A. Stöhr, *Philosophie der unbelebten Materie* (Leipzig, 1907), pp. 16 ff.
[19] G. Jaumann, "Geschlossenes System physikalischer und chemischer Differentialgesetze," *Sitzungsberichte der Wiener Akademie der Wissenschaften*, math.-scientific class, section IIa (1911), and many other papers in the same journal.

atomistics be omitted, but it hardly corresponds to the requirement of economy. A large number of constants are employed about which the theory can make no prediction. The Jaumann system makes it possible only in a very limited degree to derive phenomena, also with regard to numerical values, from a small number of hypotheses. To show the independence of physical research and the epistemologic basis, one can mention that the most energetic attempt to refute the corpuscular theory of electricity, that of F. Ehrenhaft, has no connection whatsoever with philosophic dogmas of any kind.

I believe that I have now made clear to some extent the significance of Mach. In order fully to survey his position in the intellectual life of our times, however, we must find a more remote standpoint, in order to obtain a better view.

If we read the most important work of Mach, his *Mechanics*,[20] we shall find that in no section does he give us so deep an insight into his innermost thoughts and intellectual inclinations as in the wonderful chapter on theological, animistic, and mystical points of view in mechanics. A wind of refreshing coolness blows from these statements. What other authors have treated with vehement blustering, often with a quiet announcement of a small auto-da-fé for the opponent, we see here discussed in a genuinely scientific spirit. Yet throughout the whole chapter there quivers an undertone of suppressed excitement. One encounters there that state of being drunk with soberness which has been attributed to the Age of Enlightenment. Indeed, Mach describes in this age his spiritual home. In the chapter referred to, he says:

For the first time, in the literature of the eighteenth century enlightenment appears to be gaining a broader base. Humanistic, philosophical, historical, and natural science come into contact at this time and encourage one another to freer thought. Everybody who has experienced this upsoaring and emancipation, even if only in part, through the literature, will feel a lifelong melancholy nostalgia for the eighteenth century.

The personal acquaintances of Mach are aware that he was an ardent admirer and reader of Voltaire. One of his former

[20] E. Mach, *Die Mechanik in ihrer Entwickelung, historisch-kritisch dargestellt* (Leipzig, 1883); *The Science of Mechanics; a Critical and Historical Exposition of its Principles*, translated from the second German edition by Thomas J. McCormack (Chicago, 1893).

assistants, Professor George Pick, informed me that Mach most emphatically condemned Lessing's attacks on Voltaire. It is known, too, that Josef Popper, of whom Mach says that for a long time he was the only man with whom he could talk of his physical and epistemologic opinions without precipitating a conflict, wrote a whole book devoted to the defense, indeed the glorification, of Voltaire.

In my opinion, Mach was led in this predilection by a correct estimate of himself. We can understand the role which as philosopher he plays in the intellectual life of the present if we look upon his teachings as the philosophy of enlightenment appropriate to our time.

Since this conception may easily be misunderstood, I must discuss it more fully. First of all, the word "enlightenment" has acquired such a bad connotation that perhaps many will see in this description a disparagement of Mach. We must therefore try to make clear something about the nature of this enlightenment and the reasons for its subsequent neglect.

The first period of enlightenment in modern times began with the downfall of the Ptolemaic world system. Copernicus tried to represent his system with the help of the concepts of the Aristotelian scholastic philosophy. If, however, we read the dialogues of Galileo about the two world systems, we encounter a very different tone. Here the basic concepts of Aristotelian physics were taken up and examined. In the teachings of Aristotle and his school, concepts like "light" and "heavy," "above" and "below," "natural" and "forced" motion, which were usable only for a very limited domain of experiences, were made the basis of all theoretical physics. Galileo showed that it was just this use of concepts outside of their natural realm of validity that prevented the followers of Aristotle from understanding modern physics. I do not mean by this to belittle Aristotelian physics, which was an outstanding contribution for its time; I only wish to show that what was enlightening in Galileo's writings was his setting a limit to the misuse of auxiliary concepts. And it is this protest against the misuse of merely auxiliary concepts in general philosophical proofs that I consider to be an essential characteristic of enlightenment.

Every period of physics has its auxiliary concepts, and every succeeding period misuses them. Hence in every period a new enlightenment is required in order to abolish this misuse. When Sir Isaac Newton and his contemporaries made the concepts of absolute space and time the basis of mechanics, they were able to represent a large domain of physics properly and without contradictions. It does not follow, however, that these concepts form a basis of mechanics that is satisfactory from the standpoint of the theory of knowledge. When Mach criticized the foundations of Newtonian mechanics and tried to eliminate absolute space from it, he was the direct continuer of the work of Galileo. For in absolute space we still had a remnant of Aristotelian physics. And when Einstein joined Mach and in his general theory of relativity really erected an edifice of mechanics in which space and time properly speaking no longer occurred, but only the coincidence of phenomena, the elimination demanded by Mach of the auxiliary concepts of space and time—useful only in a limited domain—was completed. Einstein is the first thinker to found a physics entirely free of Aristotelianism.

In the Age of Enlightenment proper I also see a struggle against the misuse of auxiliary concepts. If we leave out of the discussion the political and social aspects, then, theoretically considered, the criticism at that time was directed against the fact that theologic concepts, which were formed for dealing with certain psychic experiences of human beings, were made the foundation of all science throughout the Middle Ages and even at the beginning of the modern era. These concepts, no matter how appropriate they may be to restore hope and faith to the struggling human soul, are nevertheless only auxiliary concepts limited to this domain and are not suitable to be the epistemologic foundation of our knowledge of nature. This critical point of view emerged with great energy at that time. Today even theologians have adopted the view that the Bible is not a scientific textbook. Indeed, many Protestant theologians, proceeding still further in the direction of enlightenment, now teach that all theologic truths are only statements about inner experiences.

The natural science of the Enlightenment also needed auxiliary concepts for its development. In this way the concepts of matter and atom began to play a decisive role. All at once these auxiliary concepts were being applied to everything in the world; materialism, as it is called, was born. The fact that matter, too, was only an auxiliary concept was forgotten, and people began to regard it as the essence of the world. Soon criticism of this view set in. But although this criticism of the misuse of auxiliary concepts usually serves only scientific progress, here it had an additional effect. Since the ideas of the Age of Enlightenment were not pleasing to the ruling powers, the criticism of the misuse of enlightenment was used to discredit enlightenment itself. Because the rationalists misused auxiliary concepts, it was said of them that their protest against the theologic world picture was unjustified. This view is, of course, logically not tenable, for the fact is that their criticism did not go far enough. However, there are always thinkers who are so constituted that their thinking ultimately leads to the conclusions required by the ruling powers. An attempt was made to overthrow enlightenment by skepticism. Very appropriately Nietzsche says, of the part taken in this work by certain philosophers:

> The philosopher against his rival, e.g., science: now he becomes a skeptic; now he reserves for himself a form of cognition which he denies to the scientist; now he goes hand in hand with the priest so as not to arouse the suspicion of atheism, materialism; he regards an attack on himself as an attack on morality, virtue, religion, order—he knows how to discredit his opponent as a "seducer" and an "underminer"; now he goes hand in hand with the authorities.[21]

In reality, however, only that part of enlightenment was refuted which was not enlightenment. Nevertheless, because of the weight of the authority of those involved, this disparagement of the great achievements of the eighteenth century has had considerable influence. There is perhaps no one among us who did not acquire a prejudice against enlightenment at school during his youth.

I admit, of course, that the great spirits of the Enlightenment, Voltaire, d'Alembert, and the rest, were imitated by many shallow writers who diluted their criticism more and more and descended to intolerable banality, ending up by continuing themselves the misuse of the auxiliary concepts. I admit, too, that this shallowness belongs to the essence of the Enlightenment. Once the misuse of the old concepts has been exposed, there is not much of an original nature left to say. The temptation to dull triviality is strong and the number of those who have fallen victim to it is great.

Nevertheless, all this provides no evidence whatsoever against the philosophy of enlightenment. A man who has

[21] Friedrich Nietzsche, *The Will to Power*, No. 248.

freed himself once and for all from the fears of the usual stigma of heresy will say that the task of our age is not to fight against the enlightenment of the eighteenth century but rather to continue its work. Since that time there has occurred so much exaggerated application of entirely new auxiliary concepts which are useful in limited domains that there is plenty of new work to be done.

To this work Mach dedicated himself. He approved enthusiastically of the eighteenth-century enlightenment. This does not mean, however, that he began to idolize the eighteenth-century concepts like materialism. Rather, in him lived the spirit of those great men; it drove him on to protest against the misused concepts of his time just as they had fought those of their time. Among the concepts that he fought there happened to be many of the favorite concepts of eighteenth-century enlightenment.

This is what I mean when I call Mach the representative of the philosophy of enlightenment of our period. Since his youth was lived during the time of materialism, it is no wonder that so many of his works are devoted to the struggle against mechanistic physics and atomistics.

If we accept Mach's attitude as that of an enlightenment philosopher it will be easier for us to understand many features of his teachings and many of their effects. In the first place, there is their strongly suggestive influence—one might even say their virulence—which, in spite of many contemptuous judgments by professional philosophers, commands attention. Study calls the positivism of Mach

a still completely unsatisfied existence, a kind of philosophical beast of prey, hungry for a victim.[22]

As in the case of the philosophers of the enlightenment, so also in the case of Mach, it developed that the disciples and followers displayed an excessive tendency towards shallowness. Furthermore, to Planck's criterion of the fruits the present opinion provides an answer: the fruits of Mach's teachings are not the writings of his physical and philosophical followers, but rather the enlightenment of minds brought about by them—a fact which even Planck recognizes. By this I do not mean to assert that Mach has no importance in

[22] Study, *op cit.*, p. 24.

other respects. I do think, however, that this is the best summary of his position in the general intellectual life of our times.

In this opinion I am strengthened also by the striking agreement of his views with those of a thinker for whom he cannot have had any great sympathy, Friedrich Nietzsche. This agreement was first pointed out by Kleinpeter.[23] The more one delves into the posthumous works of Nietzsche, the more clearly one observes the agreement, particularly in the basic ideas related to the theory of knowledge. Now Nietzsche is the other great enlightenment philosopher of the end of the nineteenth century. The harmony of his epistemologic views with those of Mach, who had gone through an entirely different course of instruction and whose temperament and ethical ideals were entirely different, seems to me to be evidence for the fact that such views must have penetrated to the enlightened minds of that time.

That great master of language, Nietzsche, formulated these ideas with extraordinary force and impressiveness when he said:

I behold with amazement that science today has resigned itself to being relegated to an apparent world; a true world, be it what it may: in any case, we have no organ of cognition for it. Here one might ask: by what organ of cognition is one led to assume this antithesis? . . . From the fact that a world which is accessible to our organs is also understood to be dependent on these organs, from the fact that we understand a world as being subjectively conditioned, it does not follow that an objective world is in any case possible. Who prevents us from thinking that subjectivity is real, essential? The "in itself" is contradictory conception, to be sure: a "quality in itself" is nonsense: we have the concept "being," "thing," always only as a relation concept . . . The bad part of it is that along with the old antonyms "apparent" and "real" the correlative judgments of value have been propagated: "of little worth" and "of absolute worth" . . .[24]

Elsewhere Nietzsche says:

That things have a quality in themselves, quite apart from any interpretation and subjectivity, is an idle hypothesis: it would presuppose that to interpret and to be a subject are not essential, that a thing detached from all relations is still a thing.[25]

[23] H. Kleinpeter, Der Phenomenalismus (Leipzig, 1913).
[24] Nietzsche, The Will to Power, No. 289.
[25] Op. cit., No. 291.

Nietzsche's most significant expression of the positivistic world conception is probably given in the aphorism, called "On the Psychology of Metaphysics," where he attacks with cutting sharpness the employment of very frequently misused concepts:

This world is apparent: *consequently* there exists a true world; —this world is conditional: *consequently* there exists an unconditional world;—this world is full of contradictions: *consequently* there exists a world that is free from contradictions;—this world is changing: *consequently* there exists a permanent world;—all false conclusions: (blind faith in the reasoning: if there is *A*, there must also be its antithetical concept *B*).[26]

It is not to be denied that the philosophy of enlightenment possesses a tragic feature. It destroys the old systems of concepts, but while it is constructing a new system, it is also already laying the foundations for new misuse. For there is no theory without auxiliary concepts, and every such concept is necessarily misused in the course of time. The progress of science takes place in eternal circles. The creative forces must of necessity create perishable buds. They are destroyed in the human consciousness by forces which are themselves marked for destruction. And yet, it is this restless spirit of enlightenment that keeps science from petrifying into a new scholasticism. If physics is to become a church, Mach cries out, I would rather not be called a physicist. And with a paradoxical turn, Nietzsche comes out in defense of the cause of enlightenment against the self-satisfied possessor of an enduring truth:

The assertion that the *truth is here,* and that an end has been made of ignorance and error, is one of the greatest seductions that there are. Assuming that one believes it, then the will to test, investigate, predict, experiment, is crippled: the latter can itself become wanton, can doubt the truth. The "truth" is consequently more ominous than error and ignorance because it binds the forces with which one can work for enlightenment and knowledge.[27]

Of these forces, however, at the turn of the century Mach was one of the mightiest.

[26] *Op. cit.,* No. 287.
[27] *Op. cit.,* No. 252.

Chapter 3

Ernst Mach and the
Unity of Science

IN THE YEAR 1882 the famous American philosopher and psychologist William James made a tour through Europe and everywhere met scientists interested in his field of work. At the end of October, James came to Prague and met Ernst Mach. James described his impressions of this meeting in a letter he wrote to his wife in America:

Mach came to my hotel and I spent four hours walking and supping with him at his club, an unforgettable conversation. I don't think any one ever gave me so strong an impression of pure intellectual genius. He apparently has read everything and thought about everything, and has an absolute simplicity of manner and a winningness of smile, when his face lights up, that are charming.

I do not want to speak here about the wide activity of Mach in physics, physiology, psychology, and the history and logic of science, to do which would necessitate a series of papers. Instead, I shall speak about Mach's activity only in so far as he may be considered one of the spiritual ancestors of the Unity of Science Movement and, particularly, the real master of the Vienna Circle.

A hundred years after the birth of Ernst Mach we must not forget or underrate the fact that he is still very much alive today. Surveying the opinions of the scientific workers of today, we find many of them who decidedly reject his doctrine. On the other hand, there are a great many scientists who enthusiastically express their full agreement with him. But among the scientists who are acquainted with Mach's doctrine there are very few whose behavior toward him is neutral or indifferent. In spite of this fact, opinions about what are the most characteristic features of his doctrine are very different and sometimes even contradictory.

On the one hand, Mach is described as the most radical opponent of every attempt to introduce into science factors that have any tinge of spiritual tendency. He saw even in a concept which for ages has been in physics as usual as the concept of force a detrimental remainder of the obsolete world picture of primitive man, which was animistic and fetishistic. On the other hand, we are told that according to Mach our world consists entirely of perceptions or complexes of perceptions; that there is no such thing as matter for the building of a world. For this reason Mach has been proclaimed as a champion of the idealistic philosophy within modern science and a leader in the struggle against materialism.

To hint at another difference of opinion: on the one hand, Mach is said to claim that the sole function of science is to record observable facts and to sum them up by economical and suitable formulas. The scientist has, according to Mach, to be on his guard against daring generalizations, through which an animistic or metaphysical element may insinuate itself into science. On the other hand, physicists working in their research laboratories accuse Mach of not recognizing the existence of objective facts. According to these people, Mach maintains that there are only subjective opinions of single physicists, but no real facts; there is no real physical world, the exploring of which was supposed to be the goal of the research work of the physicists. For this reason Mach's doctrine is even alleged to have a paralyzing influence on research work and hence on the progress of science. For only the belief in a real, an objective, world can give to the physicist the mental activity and force needed for his difficult achievements.

Whence these different judgments, sometimes even contradictory to each other, about the chief lines of Mach's philosophy? Why is the essence of Mach's doctrine described by different authors in such different ways? The chief reason for these differences is, I think, that philosophers, and sometimes scientists too, endeavor to discuss Mach's doctrine in the language of traditional philosophy. In this language such terms occur as "idealism," "spiritualism," "materialism," "real objective world," "subjective opinion of the real world." But the point is that it is impossible to describe Mach's doctrine in this language, impossible to describe it at all in terms of traditional philosophy. If we want to form an adequate conception of Mach's doctrine, we must never forget that he always declined the title of philosopher. Mach has been praised by a great many philosophers for this modesty. But I do not think that it was exactly modesty. He wanted rather to draw a conspicuous boundary line between his own doctrine and the doctrine of traditional philosophy.

Of first importance, it seems to me, for an understanding of the chief line of Mach's thought is a passage in the introduction of his book, "The Analysis of Sensations," [1] in which he explains his chief aim in writing the papers that are commonly described as philosophic. Mach starts from the fact that scientists are accustomed, each in his special field, to make use of a certain system of concepts, or, to put it more exactly, of certain technical terms, a certain technical language which is very suitable within this special field, say physics. But this special technical language may become very unsuitable and even misleading if it is applied to the description and formulation of the frontier problems which arise when we pass from one special science to a neighboring science, say from physics to biology or to psychology. Mach's own words are:

> I do not claim the title of a philosopher. I want only to take, in physics, a standpoint which does not have to be abandoned immediately when we look over into the field of another science. For all the sciences ultimately form a whole. What I am stating, I am perhaps not the first to state. Furthermore, I do not want to bring forward my explanation as an extraordinary achievement. I think, rather, that the same line would be taken by anyone who tried to survey a field of science that is not too narrow.

According to Mach this desire to make use of a unified mode of expression in all fields of science is a consequence of the economical design of science. This design implies the comprehension of as many facts as possible by the simplest possible system of propositions.

Since Mach dealt in his papers with so many different kinds of problems in the fields of physics, physiology, and psychology, a great many scientists did not discover what the chief trend of these papers was. In order to find the clue to it, we have to read attentively another passage in the same introduction. Mach says there expressly:

> The basis of all my investigations into the logical foundation of physics as well as into the physiology of perceptions has been one and the same opinion: that all metaphysical propositions must be

[1] E. Mach, *Beiträge zur Analyse der Empfindungen* (Jena: G. Fischer, 1886; English translation, Chicago, 1914).

eliminated, because they are idle and disturbing to the economical design of science.

And Mach's famous book "Mechanics and its Development" [2] begins with the sentence:

"The tendency of this paper is an elucidatory or, to put it more accurately, an antimetaphysical one."

In the reports on Mach's teaching by advocates of traditional philosophy, one may often read that Mach's chief doctrine was that the world consisted of perceptions and not of material particles. But from the passages that I have just quoted, in which Mach expressly describes the chief aim of his investigations, it is clear that these investigations were quite unconcerned with such problems as whether the world consists of perceptions or of matter. This is rather the typical way in which traditional philosophy likes to put a problem. It is just this way of putting a problem that Mach emphatically rejected.

Hence Mach's chief tendency may be described by the phrases, "unification (that is, economical presentation) of science" and "elimination of metaphysics." We shall find that these two aims are very closely connected with each other. And we shall see that the most widely popularized doctrine of Mach, according to which the real world consists of perceptions, was never formulated by him in this metaphysical way. What was really in Mach's mind when he maintained that our world is built up of perceptions or complexes of perceptions was not that this phrase "built up of perceptions" is in any sense a statement concerning a property of the real world, but only that it is a useful means for the unification of science and the elimination of metaphysics. It would be a misunderstanding of Mach's aims to believe that the construction of the world by perceptions, which was merely a means to an end, was the true end of his philosophy. Many of his philosophical interpreters stick fast at this means to an end, "the perception language," and neglect the real purposes of Mach's doctrine, the unification of science and the elimination of metaphysics. For it is just by the presentation of some scientific results in terms of metaphysics that the unification

[2] E. Mach, *Die Mechanik in ihrer Entwickelung* (Leipzig: F. Brockhaus, 1883; English translation, Chicago, 1893).

of science is, according to Mach, gravely imperiled and some-times even frustrated.

If one describes physics as the science of matter, biology as the science of life, psychology as the science of the mind, sociology as the science of the collective mind, metaphysical concepts or words such as "matter," "soul," "collective soul," are introduced, and it is obvious that words like "matter" and "soul," for example, are probably not reducible to the same terms. It is easy to prove that the introduction of expressions of this kind renders impossible the representation of our ex-periences by a unitary system of terms; in other words, it renders the unification of science impossible.

To remove these difficulties Mach suggested the formula-tion of the laws of physics as functional connections among perceptions such as "green," "warm," "hard," including also, of course, the space and time perceptions. Every physical ex-periment consists in observing how the alteration of some per-ception is connected with the alteration of others. If no perceptions touching our own bodies intervene—for example, if there is no altering of perceptions by intoxication of our nerves—we are in the field of physics. If we observe the con-nections between perceptions, including perceptions arising from alteration in our own bodies, we are in the fields of physiology or of psychology. But it is clear that we can no longer prove the impossibility of a unified language of science if we start from Mach's perception language instead of the metaphysical terminology of traditional philosophy, and, we must admit, sometimes even of traditional science.

On the contrary, if we start from Mach's standpoint and formulate all scientific propositions in terms of perceptions, the unification of science becomes possible. Mach never main-tained that our world consisted of complexes of perceptions, but that every scientific proposition was a statement about complexes of perceptions. Whether it be a proposition of physics, biology, or psychology, it can only be proved or re-futed by comparison with observation.

According to Mach, the unification of science is possible, but only by formulating all scientific propositions as proposi-tions about complexes of perceptions, in the widest sense of this word. Every proposition that states something about our observations contains as predicate some term like "green," "warm," "joyful," "painful,"—perception terms, as Carnap calls them. A proposition that is not reducible to propositions containing only perception terms as predicates cannot be checked by experience; it is a metaphysical proposition. Hence to Mach the expression "elimination of metaphysics" means the elimination of all sentences that are not reducible to sentences containing only perception terms as predicates. The elimination from science of metaphysical propositions leaves only sentences of a homogeneous type, namely, sentences with perception terms as predicates. Therefore, if we demand of science an economical representation of our experiences, that is, a representation by a unified system of concepts, we must admit only propositions that are reducible to propositions containing only perception terms as predicates.

This is the real meaning of Mach's doctrine that all propositions of science deal with perceptions. He did not want to make a statement about the question of what the world consists of, but he wanted to point out how the propositions of science had to be formed in order to make possible a unification of science. His result is this: The unification of science is not possible except by the elimination of metaphysical propositions. Then only propositions of a homogeneous type remain. Hence we can form from them a coherent logical system.

The elimination of metaphysics from science was for Mach, as we now understand, not a demand arising from some antimetaphysical mood, but the only means of making possible the unification of science. According to Mach, metaphysics must be eliminated because it is contradictory to the economical function of science.

A great many people were puzzled because Mach's philosophy, which was supposed to be a sort of idealism (similar to the philosophy of Bishop Berkeley), changed so easily, or—to speak in terms of idealistic philosophy—degenerated so easily, into physicalism. We have seen that even the Vienna Circle went over very quickly from the phenomenal language used, following Mach, by Carnap as well as by Schlick, to the physical language claimed by Neurath. In physicalism, which now plays a great role in all papers that start from the viewpoint of logical empiricism (in the most coherent and exact way in the papers of Carnap), a language is used that seems very near to materialism.

So it has been for a great many philosophers a riddle and almost a source of irritation that the opinions within a group claiming to possess a particular sense of logical consistency could oscillate so easily between the extreme poles of human thinking, which idealism and materialism are supposed to be.

But this antithesis, which, according to traditional philosophy, exists between materialism and idealism is not, according to Mach, a scientific antithesis. Mach disliked the use of terms such as "idealism" and "materialism" and if he did use them it was only to reject them. Though he rejected materialism as well as idealism, this rejection does not mean that he tried to take a mediating standpoint between them. For him, both idealism and materialism are systems of metaphysical propositions, not scientific theories. For they can be neither proved nor refuted by experience. Mach had what one might call the instinctive aversion of a genuine scientist to the use of vague terms like "idealism" or "materialism" in science. This aversion sometimes induced him to make statements against one or the other metaphysical system. And his statements were often misinterpreted as statements on behalf of the other system, just as if, by rejecting one sort of metaphysics, he advocated the contrary metaphysics. From Mach's point of view the question of "idealism" or "materialism" cannot be put as a real scientific problem. Every attempt to exploit the achievements of science to bolster up idealistic or materialistic metaphysics is from the beginning doomed to failure.

What Mach felt instinctively we can today formulate in words, if we take the standpoint of logical empiricism, as it was formulated very precisely in Carnap's book "Logical Syntax of Language" [3] and in his paper "Testability and Meaning." [4]

The transition from the supposed idealistic to the physicalistic conception of science took place so smoothly within the Vienna Circle because, according to the doctrine of logical empiricism, the question to be put was not whether idealism and materialism were right opinions about the real world, but only what language, phenomenal or physical, was the more suitable for giving an economical and unitary account of our experiences. Since either of these languages may be more suitable within a limited field than the other, the choice of an accepted language has nothing to do with the question whether our real world consists of perceptions or of

[3] R. Carnap, *The Logical Syntax of Language* (New York: Harcourt, Brace, 1937).
[4] *Philosophy of Science* (1936 and 1937).

matter. What is of essential importance is only the question whether we believe that it is possible to comprehend all fields of science in one and the same language. If the unification of science, in this sense, is held to be possible, as Carnap and the adherents of the Unity of Science Movement maintain, it is of secondary importance whether this unification be achieved in terms of perceptions, as Mach believed and Carnap proved to be right in his first paper, "The Logical Construction of the World," [5] or whether the physical language is to be introduced, as Carnap proclaims in his recent papers in accordance with Neurath's suggestions.

The essential alternative for our conception of science is rather this: Do we, in accordance with traditional philosophy, maintain that the question whether the real world consists of matter or of perceptions, and other questions like it, are scientific questions, or do we, with Mach, eliminate metaphysical questions of this sort from science as disturbing its economical character and put the question just mentioned in the way in which it is put by logical empiricism?

Then we ask, what language is the most suitable as the language of a unified science. From this point of view, the metaphysical question seems to be, as Mach expressed it, an idle one. And the question as logical empiricism puts it, whether the phenomenal language or the physical language is more suitable as the language of unified science, ceases to be a question of profound metaphysical importance and becomes a question of convenience. It is perhaps comparable to the question of what system of symbols is the most suitable for the introduction of a unified symbolism into logic.

If we want to describe Mach's role in the history of human thought and in the development of science in a particularly comprehensive and impressive way, we can do it, it seems to me, by a clear-cut antithesis. The traditional conception of science is connected with a certain opinion about the importance of metaphysics to science. According to this conception, there are two methods of science:

(1) The first method is restricted to recording facts, including empirical rules summarizing facts. The adherents of this method of scientific activity take care not to introduce sweeping generalizations and hypotheses, because by them a metaphysical element may easily creep into science. This kind of scientific activity possesses, according to its adherents, the

[5] R. Carnap, *Der logische Aufbau der Welt* (Berlin, 1928).

advantage that all propositions admitted by science are secured by experience or logic and are clear and intuitive. The scientists of this group are anxious not to introduce vague phrases. But by proceeding in this cautious way only special sciences of small extent are created. Physics and biology and psychology have each collected a lot of facts and rules, but there is no link between these special departments. This conception of science is often referred to as the "positivist" conception, it is not at all in accordance with the conception of the so-called "logical positivism," neither does it agree with Mach's doctrine. This pseudo-positivist conception of science does not satisfy our aspirations toward the unity of science.

(2) Therefore, beside this positivist conception, or more exactly, over it, the metaphysical conception of scientific activity has always existed, because it has been supposed to be better adapted to satisfying our desire for a synthesis of knowledge and the unity of science. According to this conception we can reach the unity we are striving after by the introduction of daring metaphysical generalizations and hypotheses. By means of these metaphysical generalizations the separate sciences can be summarized and unified into a unitary science. The general principles of this unified science are, of course, metaphysical propositions. The most famous metaphysical system, which was supposed to comprehend and represent all special sciences, was the system of Hegel. In this system all separate sciences, such as mathematics, physics, biology, are presented as steps in the self-evolution of the absolute spirit. An example of the sort of metaphysical proposition that serves to achieve the unification of science is Hegel's fundamental theorem of dialectics, namely, "every quantity, if sufficiently increased, turns into a quality." This theorem is supposed to be valid in physics as well as in biology, in biology as well as in history. It is particularly interesting because it continues to play a great role and is not confined to the adherents of Hegel's idealistic metaphysics. This theorem and many like it are taken over into dialectical materialism, the official philosophy of the Soviet Union of today. By means of propositions of this kind the barriers between the separate sciences are broken down and the unification of science is achieved, but only at the price of introducing large systems of very vague propositions. With regard to

such metaphysical propositions a general agreement among scientists would never be reached.

The opinion of traditional philosophy and traditional science has been for ages that scientific activity has only these alternatives: either that only theorems that can be proved by experience or logic are recognized as legitimate in science, in which case the separate sciences remain separated from each other by insurmountable barriers, or that we admit the introduction of metaphysical propositions, in which case the unification of science can be achieved, but we have to deal with propositions that will never be recognized by all scientists.

To put it still more concisely: either *the renunciation of the unification of science* or *the introduction of metaphysical propositions into science.*

The great importance of Mach's activity lies in the fact that he declined to recognize these alternatives. He proclaimed, rather, *the unification of science by means of the elimination of metaphysics.*

It is just this phrase that is the clue to the understanding of Mach's doctrine, and of his papers, which seem to deal with so many subjects and such different fields of science. What always mattered for Mach was the opportunity to accomplish the program that we have just outlined. And it is just this program of Mach that we may adopt as the program of our "Unity of Science Movement," of our Congresses and of our Encyclopedia. If Mach's centenary has been celebrated by so many physicists, physiologists, psychologists, and historians of science we may take a special pride in these celebrations, in which we have a special right to honor him as one of the spiritual ancestors of the "Unity of Science Movement." For, I think, within our movement, the harvest of the seed scattered by Mach is particularly rich and in the strictest accordance with his true intention.

Chapter 4

Physical Theories of the Twentieth Century and School Philosophy

WHAT IS THE SIGNIFICANCE of present-day physical theories for the general theory of knowledge? There are many physicists and philosophers whose answer would be, "Nothing." On what grounds many philosophers give this answer, I cannot and do not wish to investigate here. How does it happen, however—and this question will serve as our starting point—that so many physicists assert that the greatest revolutions in the theories of physics are incapable of changing the principles of the general theory of knowledge? For example, one finds in physical works on the theory of relativity the thesis, often defended with passion, that the relativistic revision of the measurement of space and time has no "philosophical" consequences.

Anyone who has occupied himself to some extent with the historical development of physics will be struck at once by the similarity of this thesis to what took place during the period of those great revolutions in the theories of physics that led from the medieval, scholastic conception of nature to the conception prevalent today, revolutions associated above all with the names of Copernicus, Galileo, Kepler. Thus, one reads that the adherents of the heliocentric theory—at that time considered revolutionary—contended most zealously that the Copernican "revolution" had brought about something that was only mathematically and physically new, that it had made no change at all in the general philosophic conception of the world. At the famous trial of Galileo, when pressure was brought to bear on him to recant his doctrine, it was not a question of his swearing that he no longer believed in the motion of the earth, as one often reads in superficial presentations, which have immortalized the famous misquotation: "Nevertheless, it does move!" What the Inquisition actually wanted of Galileo was only that he confess that the doctrine of the motion of the earth was correct merely as a mathematical fiction, but was false as a philosophical doctrine. We can also find in the standpoint of the Inquisition something corresponding to the modern relativistic conception. According to the latter, we cannot say that "in reality" the earth moves and the sun stands still, but only that the description of phenomena turns out to be simpler in a coördinate system in which this is the case. More than this was demanded of Galileo, however. He was expected to admit that the heliocentric conception was a mathematical fiction, whereas the geocentric one was a philosophical truth. It is readily seen that even this standpoint of the medieval authorities finds its analogue in our times. Today, too, a fictionalistic conception is often presented for the purpose of bringing out more strongly, by contrast, the "eternally valid," "philosophically reasonable" truths. For instance, it is very often asserted by philosophers, and sometimes also by physicists, that non-Euclidean geometry and the Einstein measurement of time are mathematical fictions, whereas Euclidean geometry and absolute time are, in the very nature of things, established truths.

Still more often we find, however, that physicists refuse to make any decisions concerning such questions as time, space, causality, preferring to leave these for the competent specialist, the philosopher or the epistemologist. Since today no one need have the same fears as Galileo, this refusal must arise from a conviction that can be formulated roughly as follows: "There are questions that are so profound that they cannot be solved by the exact sciences." In connection with this point, some believe that there is a special method, the "philosophical," with the help of which such questions as those concerning the nature of time, space, and causality can be answered, while others regard these problems as forever insoluble, as "eternal riddles."

The classical expression of this resignation of the exact sciences was the famous speech of Emil du Bois-Reymond which dates back to 1872 and bears the title "On the Limitations of Natural Science." [1]

This speech, which culminates in the declaration *"Ignorabimus"*—we shall never know—has been quoted countless times—triumphantly by the belittlers of the scientific world conception, with melancholy assent by its adherents. The speech in its essentials has been accepted by most philosophers

[1] *Über die Grenzen des Naturerkennens.*

and scientists as irrefutable truth. In the history of the scientific world conception it has been the scientist's trip to Canossa. If we reflect by what arguments Du Bois-Reymond arrived at his *ignorabimus,* we must reach the conviction, considering the present state of the epistemology of the exact sciences, that it is high time to unroll the question once more, and once again to see whether the despairing point of view concerning scientific cognition is really unavoidable.

Du Bois starts with the thesis:

The cognition of nature is the reduction of changes in the material world to motions of atoms, acted upon by central forces, independent of time . . . It is a psychological fact of experience that wherever such a reduction is successfully carried through our need for causality feels satisfied *for the time being.*

There still remains, however, the question of how matter is able to exert the central forces. This question naturally cannot be reduced again to central forces. To quote Du Bois further:

No one who has given any thought to the subject can fail to recognize the transcendent nature of the obstacles that are here before us . . . Never shall we know any better than today what it is that haunts the space where matter is found. For even the spirit of Laplace could not be any wiser on this point than we . . . Our cognition of nature is therefore enclosed by the two boundaries set up—on the one hand, by our inability to comprehend matter and force, and on the other hand, by our inability to understand mental processes in terms of material conditions.

If we disregard the problem of the connection between the spiritual and the material, since it does not concern us here, Du Bois then sees the limits of our knowledge of the world primarily in the impossibility of understanding the nature of matter and force. He continues:

Within these limits the scientist is lord and master; he dismembers and builds up; . . . beyond these limits he cannot and will never be able to go. With respect to the riddles of the material world . . . *ignoramus;* . . . with respect, however, to the riddle of what are matter and force, and how they are able to think, he must decide, once and for all, on a verdict much more difficult to render: *ignorabimus.*

But what does it mean when we say that a question is insoluble? Let us suppose, for example, that someone has asserted that the problem of a regular transport route to the planet Neptune is insoluble, or that the production of a living organism from lifeless matter is impossible. Despite this assertion, the person making it can describe quite accurately the concrete experience we should have if the problem were solved. We cannot, however, in any way—not even approximately—imagine what we should have to experience in order to be able to say that the problem of the nature of matter or force has been solved, or that one knows, as Du Bois requires, "what it is that haunts the space where matter is found." When, for example, Heinrich Hertz, as is often said, elucidated the nature of light, this was not at all in the sense meant by Du Bois. According to Hertz, light and electromagnetic phenomena are associated with the same equations but have different wavelengths; the nature of light is thereby made no clearer than it was before, since the nature of electricity is also in this sense an eternally insoluble riddle.

Thus there are two types of unsolved and perhaps insoluble problems, which Du Bois characterizes by means of the words *ignoramus* and *ignorabimus*. Anyone who is used to working on the real solutions of problems will feel a certain displeasure when he turns to problems of the second kind. For he is accustomed to proceed with the solution by first picturing to himself the experience corresponding to the completed solution, and then working until he succeeds in bringing about the realization of the desired experience. If, however, we cannot state what this experience is to consist in, have we really set up a problem?

As a matter of fact, we find very often that the physicist, as physicist, declines to work on problems set up in this way; yet in another corner of his soul he admits that such problems might be attacked with other methods—not physical, but "philosophical," as they are called. In seeking the reason why physicists—who as such attach the greatest value to exact formulations of questions—in spite of their displeasure admit the possibility of something quite different, I believe it is necessary to take into account the fact that many physicists, when not working in their own fields, are inclined to a world conception that has become rooted in the educational system through centuries-old tradition, a conception which we will call simply the world conception of "school philosophy."

We do not wish to investigate here the question of why so

many physicists adhere to this school philosophy, in spite of the fact that it was just the critically thinking physicists who contributed most to its shaking; for the causes of this adherence are to be understood only psychologically, and perhaps sociologically. Rather, we wish to find out what the standpoint of the school philosophy consists in, and how it has made so many scientists assent without opposition to the resigned *ignorabimus*.

It is said that the philosophic schools are so far apart from one another in their points of view that it is not possible to perceive among them anything like a unified conception of the world. In spite of these individual differences of opinion, however, I believe that we can see today a common nucleus, which has been handed down through the centuries and, to a certain degree, has crystallized. Along with this there has been developing, at first timidly, then more and more boldly, but even now still quite cautiously, a new world conception, one that is gradually gaining strength with the progress of the exact sciences. In order to introduce some name, just as we called the traditional doctrine the "school philosophy," we will call the new one the "scientific world conception," to indicate briefly that it recognizes no other cognition than the scientific.

The school philosophy, whether it calls itself realism or idealism, is characterized by the possession of a certain conception of what is called truth, hence also of what can be regarded as the real formulation of a problem. The basic ideas of this doctrine of the school philosophy cannot be presented better than by Henri Bergson's introduction to the French translation of the American psychologist, William James's, *Pragmatism*. Bergson says:

For the ancient philosophers there existed a world, raised above space and time, in which all possible truths had dwelt since eternity. According to these philosophers, the truth of human judgments was measured by the degree to which they were faithful copies of those eternal truths. The modern philosophers, to be sure, have brought down truth from heaven to earth, but they still regard it as something that exists prior to our judgments. A proposition such as "Heat expands a body," according to them, would be a law governing the facts: if not ruling over them, at least ruling in their midst; a law actually contained in our experience; it remains for us only to extract it from the latter. Even a philosophy like that of Kant, which assumes that every scientific truth is such only in relation to the human mind, considers the true propositions as given a priori by human experience. Once this experience, in general, is organized by human thought, the whole work of science consists in breaking through the obstructing husk of facts, in the interior of which the truth is housed like a nut in its shell.

It is readily seen that this conception of truth permits every type of question. It makes it difficult, however, to distinguish between sensible and meaningless formulations of problems. For to every question the answer can be found behind the husk of facts if one bores with sufficient energy. In principle, it might then be possible to answer even such questions as those concerning the nature of matter and force. If, however, the shell of the nut is so hard that it can never be bored through, so that the answer cannot be extracted, we call the question "eternally insoluble," and say resignedly, *Ignorabimus*. If we have this conception, we can also pose such questions as those that are most characteristic of the school philosophy: whether the outer world really exists, and whether we can know the world in its true properties. To these questions the realist replies in the affirmative, the idealist in the negative. Neither can adduce any concrete experience as decisive for his answer. Both agree, however, that such a question is a sensible problem.

There is no doubt that this standpoint of the school philosophy makes very difficult the acceptance and understanding of present-day physical theories. For example, from this point of view one can raise the question of what the "real" length of any body is. If the theory of relativity ascribes to a body different lengths with respect to different reference systems, the adherent of the school philosophy will opine that this difference arises from "perturbations" of the measuring instrument, which make the "correct" measurement impossible in practice. This, however, does not prevent one length from being the "real" one as distinguished from the merely "apparent" measured lengths. Of the family of reference systems moving uniformly and rectilinearly with relation to one another, only one can be really at rest, according to this conception. Since according to the relativity theory—and so far it has not been disproved experimentally—it is not possible by any experiment to determine which is the system that is really at rest, for the adherent of the school philosophy this "being really at rest" is a fact that cannot reveal itself in any concrete experience that man can have.

One who considers it obvious that an electron must have at every instant a definite position and velocity—though the measurement of them may be impossible—finds it difficult to understand the basic principles of quantum mechanics. He is forced to interpret the quantum-mechanical calculations, which he uses nevertheless, in such a way that these definite positions and velocities of the electron do not determine its future. Since, on the other hand, the doctrines of the school philosophy in the field of mechanical phenomena require strict determinism, he is forced to assume for the motion of the electron some mystical vital causes, similar to organic life. True, this conclusion will be pleasant and congenial to some people; but I do not believe that it is useful for physical investigation. It does not follow—as many believe—from the theories of modern physics; it arises only from the desire to bring these new theories into harmony with the world conception of the school philosophy.

The objection will perhaps be raised that in most of their investigations physicists are not at all concerned about philosophy, and hence that the school philosophy cannot be a hindrance to the understanding of relativity or the quantum theory. Physicists examine these theories from a "purely physical" point of view and do not know anything at all about the philosophical conception of the world. If one studies closely the reactions of physicists toward the modern theories, however, it will be found that the less they are accustomed to thinking about philosophical questions, the more their thinking is dominated by the traditions of the school philosophy. Experience has also shown that those physicists who declared, for instance, that the relativity theory was nonsense often spoke in the name of "pure, empirical science, free from speculation," but took their arguments chiefly from the school philosophy, not from empiricism. It need not be supposed that one has to make any philosophical studies in order to become acquainted with this world conception. In all knowledge that has come to us from the elementary school, in all metaphors of our language, it is implicitly contained. Its presence is not noticed because traditions, centuries old, make us take it for granted. The pure "empiricist" uses it under the name "common sense." Hence it is no wonder that it is just the physicist opposed to speculation who is easily inclined to the *ignorabimus* of Du Bois-Reymond, with his surrender of the scientific conception of nature.

There are some physicists who do not understand the "restriction to pure empiricism" to mean that so long as one is at the experimenting table one investigates purely empirically, but for the interpretation of the results obtained uses "common sense," that is, the traditional philosophy. It is these physicists who are most active in the movement against the world picture of the school philosophy. They are the physicists who try in the entire realm of their world conception to admit as an element only that which has been concretely experienced, as every physicist does at the experimenting table.

These critically thinking physicists must ask themselves: how are those problems constituted the solutions of which represent advancement, as compared with the problems in the investigation of which scientists have been, figuratively, rotating about their own axes for centuries?

For example, in the past the identity of light and electromagnetic radiation was not known, and now it is known. What does this signify? By means of electrical devices—for example, radio transmitters—and by means of light sources one can produce phenomena that obey the same formal laws, the wave laws, and are differentiated by only one quantity, the wavelength. This recognition of the identity of light and electromagnetic radiation can be expressed as a perfectly definite statement concerning concrete experiences. It is not at all necessary to express it in such a way that something is said about the "nature" of light or electricity. Definite rules assign to the electromagnetic experiences symbols, the field quantities, among which there exist formal relations, the field equations. From given combinations of symbols one can then, using mathematical operations, derive new combinations with the help of the equations. These combinations may be translated into experiences again with the help of the same rules of assignment. Hence, with the help of the theory, which consists of rules of assignment and of field equations, one can draw conclusions about future or past experiences on the basis of given experiences. In this way one has practical control over the experiences. Identity of light and electricity then means an identity of mathematical relations between symbols. From the theoretical point of view, the solution of a problem means the assignment of symbols to experiences, among which there exist relations that can be stated. From the more practical point of view, it means the possibility of obtaining control over one's experiences with the help of this system of relations.

We see then that in no problem of this sort is it ever a question of bringing about an "agreement between thought and object," as the school philosophy says. Rather, it is always only a question of inventing a procedure which, with the help of a skillfully chosen system of symbols, is capable of bringing order into our experiences, thus making it easier for us to control them. Truth cannot be sought outside of our experiences. The aim of the investigation is not the seeking after a "reality hidden in a nutshell." The edifice of science must be built up out of our experiences and out of them only.

Before I go further into a discussion of how much the present physical theories require such a conception of science, I should like to show with the help of a few historical remarks how the edifice of the school philosophy was gradually undermined, and what new conceptions have taken its place. As this development is still in its beginning stage, I shall have to give a somewhat aphoristic presentation rather than a systematic one.

In the city of Prague there lived and wrote the physicist who led most determinedly the struggle against the conceptions in physics that correspond to the reality concept of the school philosophy. Ernst Mach taught in Prague from 1867 to 1895, that is, from his twenty-ninth to his fifty-seventh year. He was professor of experimental physics, first at the then bilingual University of Prague, and after the separation, at the German University. Here he wrote those of his works that are most important for the epistemology of physics: "The History and Root of the Principle of Conservation of Energy" (1871),[2] and "Mechanics in its Development" (1883).[3]

His fundamental point of view was that all principles of physics are principles concerning the relations between sense perceptions, hence principles that state something about concrete experiences. All concepts such as atom, energy, force, and matter are, according to Mach, only auxiliary concepts, allowing one to make statements about sense perceptions in a simpler and more synoptic form than if they were formulated

---

[2] *Die Geschichte und die Wurzel des Satzes von der Erhaltung der Arbeit,* tr. by Philip E. B. Jourdain as *History and Root of the Principle of the Conservation of Energy* (Chicago: Open Court Publishing Co., 1911).
[3] *Die Mechanik in ihrer Entwickelung, historisch-kritisch dargestellt,* tr. by Thomas J. McCormack as *The Science of Mechanics* (Chicago: Open Court Publishing Co., 1893).

directly as statements about the perceptions. In this way, all questions concerning the nature of force, matter, and so on, become meaningless, for these concepts can be eliminated from all physical statements so that only statements about concrete experiences are left. The *ignorabimus* toward the question of the nature of matter and force, according to this conception, has no more justification than if a mathematician were to say: "Science, to be sure, can set up all the theorems about complex numbers, but it will never be able to explain the nature of the complex number. Toward this problem we must modestly acknowledge an eternal *ignorabimus.*" To this contention every other mathematician will respond that the complex numbers have been introduced only in order to make clearer certain statements about real numbers, that basically every theorem from the theory of functions of a complex variable can be expressed also as a theorem about real numbers.

Neither Mach himself nor his immediate students have systematically carried further his point of view and set up, in opposition to the world conception of the school philosophy, a similarly coherent scientific conception. On the contrary, Mach's teaching, through many presentations, has been washed out into something indefinite rather than built up to a consistent scientific conception of the world. It has even been interpreted again in line with the school philosophy, sometimes more realistically, sometimes more idealistically, so that to many—as, for example, to the great anti-Machistic school in Russia, at the head of which stood Lenin himself— it appeared not as the beginning of a new scientific world conception but as a new fashionable form of the school philosophy.

Conceptions similar to those of Mach were presented in France, in part independently, by the physicist Pierre Duhem. In his expositions, Duhem did not equal Mach in breadth of vision, but often surpassed him in sharpness of logic.

From an entirely different direction there arose against the school philosophy a movement often referred to as "conventionalism." Its most important representative is the French mathematician, physicist, and astronomer, Henri Poincaré. He called attention to the fact that physical principles often contain concepts that are defined by these very principles. In such cases the principles can never be tested against experience, since they are disguised definitions, "conventions." Thus, according to Poincaré, the law of conservation of energy is nothing but a definition of the concept of energy. The significance of conventionalism for the understanding of what is expressed by the principles of physics is very great, in my opinion, and perhaps no one among the physicists has contributed as much as Poincaré to the shaking of the school philosophy. In Germany the chief representative of this movement is Hugo Dingler. Through extreme application of conventionalism, however, Dingler has again approached the school philosophy, according to the principle that opposites meet, by attempting to show that certain conventions are the simplest and hence are the only ones justified.

A direct attack against the truth concept of the school philosophy was made by the American psychologist William James in his book *Pragmatism*, which introduced the pragmatic movement that has spread so widely. According to James, the truth of a system of principles—a physical theory, for instance—does not consist in its being a faithful copy of reality, but rather in its allowing us with the help of these principles to change our experiences according to our wishes. According to this view, which essentially agrees with that of Mach, but rejects even more bluntly the truth concept of the school philosophy, every solution of a problem is the construction of a procedure that can be of use to us in the ordering and mastering of our experiences. If, for example, we are familiar with all the means and rules of machine construction, if we know what motion takes place under given conditions, then it is clear that it would not help us further in the slightest if we knew, besides this, the nature of matter and force. If we understand the solution of a problem in the sense of James, then we cannot, in general, consider questions like the latter as scientific formulations of problems.

Henry Bergson, in his introduction to the French translation of James's *Pragmatism*, from which we have taken the characterization of school philosophy, also characterizes very clearly and pertinently the contrasting pragmatic conception of truth and science:

The other conceptions [those of the school philosophy] represent truth as something that was present before the well-defined act of the man who formulated it for the first time. We say he was the first to see it, but it had been waiting for him as America had waited for Columbus. Something had hidden it until that moment from all eyes, had covered it, so to speak, and he had discovered it. Quite different is the conception of William James. He does not deny that reality, at least to a large extent, is independent of what we say or think. But truth, which can only be associated with what we state about reality, appears to him to be created by our statement. We invent truth in order to make reality useful to us, just as we create mechanical devices in order to make the forces of nature useful to us. It seems to me that one might summarize the essence of the pragmatic conception of truth in a formula of the following kind: Whereas for the other conceptions a new truth is a discovery, for pragmatism it is an invention.

The objection has often been raised that pragmatism correctly characterizes only the practical, not the theoretical, significance of science. To this objection James himself replied that next to the interest that man has in breathing freely his greatest interest, which in contrast to most interests of a purely physical kind knows no fluctuation and no failure, is the interest in feeling that he is not contradicting himself, that what he thinks at the present moment agrees with what he thinks on other occasions. As we shall soon see, however, unambiguity or freedom from contradictions is the most essential attribute of every cognition; hence, conflicts between the practical and theoretical conceptions of truth do not arise from the doctrine of pragmatism.

The physicist in his own scientific activity has never employed any other concept of truth than that of pragmatism. The "agreement of thoughts with their object," as the school philosophy requires, cannot be established by any concrete experiment. In practice we encounter only experiences, never an object; hence nothing can be compared with an object. Actually, the physicist compares only experiences with other experiences. He tests the truth of a theory through what one is accustomed to call "agreements."

Thus, for example, one always obtains the same numerical value for the Planck constant h, using various methods. This really means that the quantity h can be constructed in entirely different ways from experiences—as from the experiences of black-body radiation, or those of the Balmer series of the hydrogen spectrum. The theory in which h plays a role then asserts that all the various groups of experiences, which are qualitatively so different from one another, nevertheless should give the same numerical value of h. It is therefore only a question of comparing experiences with one another. This procedure, which the physicist is accustomed to use in his work, has been made by Mach and James into a general conception of the criteria of truth.

In all this it must be admitted, however, that these conceptions possess a certain indefiniteness for the mathematical physicist. He always has the impression that there is a lack of precision. In particular, he finds it hard to take the pragmatic theory of truth quite seriously. This arises partly from the fact that James, and to a certain extent Mach also, failed to set a very high value on the role of formal logic in the construction of the system of human cognition. In fact, in a certain opposition to the misuse of logic by school philosophy, they both emphasized the fluid elements in cognition as against the rigidly logical. Another way of putting it is that, in opposition to the viewpoint of mathematical logic, which to them always smacked of the school philosophy, they presented the viewpoint of evolutionary biology. Because of this the mathematicians and mathematically thinking physicists have often been forced into a certain opposition to the doctrines of Mach and James. Many of them, attracted by the logical garments of the school philosophy, have even behaved in a friendlier way toward the latter than toward the modern tendencies.

It is therefore significant that the school philosophy has also been criticized from quite another side; indeed, that position was assailed which seemed most unassailable, namely, the logic of the school philosophy. The logic employed by philosophers until well into the nineteenth century was not very different from that formulated by Aristotle. In connection with the investigations on the foundations of mathematics, however, there developed in the field of logic a fresh tendency, which shook the old scheme of Aristotle. This movement is represented in Germany, especially, by the names of Schröder, Frege, and Hilbert. Through the use of a symbolism modeled after that of mathematics it gave to logic a flexibility and freedom of movement that it had not possessed before. This made it possible to deal with far more complicated thought structures than could have been handled on the basis of the school logic.

It turns out, in fact—and this is chiefly the work of the English mathematician and logician Bertrand Russell and his students, particularly the Austrian Wittgenstein—that the logic of the school philosophy, because of the narrowness of its scheme, made it impossible from the very start to express certain thoughts. Thus, many of the principles regarded by the school philosophy as being certain were certain only because the contrary did not fit into the scheme of Aristotelian logic.

In this way Russell pointed out that one of the most fateful errors of the school logic was its assumption that every judgment consists in attributing to a subject some property as predicate. If one says, for example, that a body A is moving with respect to another body B, the adherent of the school logic will demand that to one or the other of the two bodies shall belong the predicate of motion. Now Russell has shown that very many judgments consist in stating a relation between two things and cannot be reduced to the statement of a property of a single thing, which is a much more special case. However, to the adherent of the school logic a statement like the following, for example, appears nonsensical: "If two bodies are moving with respect to each other, it is meaningless to ask which one is 'really' moving, that is, to which one belongs the predicate 'being in a state of motion.'"

With regard to the school philosophy, which has taken over the old logic more or less consciously, Russell remarks that it is led by the unconscious conviction that all statements of judgments must have the subject-predicate form—in other words, that every statement must attribute a property to a thing. This conviction has made most philosophers incapable of understanding the world of science and of everyday life. According to Russell, however, most philosophers are less concerned with attaining a true understanding of this world than with showing its unreality in the interest of a transcendental, truly real world.

With the aid of the old logic the school philosophy could easily deduce the absurdity of the pragmatic concept of truth and the relativistic conception of physics. On the other hand, the new logic of Russell and his school was suitable to help build up the purely empirical, and hence still somewhat vague, conceptions of Mach and James into a real system of the scientific world conception that was superior to the school philosophy from the standpoint of formal logic as well.

There were some philosophers with a mathematical-physical orientation who followed Russell but at the beginning cared little for Mach and almost nothing for James. Nevertheless, like the latter, they too discarded the truth concept of the school philosophy. In contrast to the method of pragmatism, however, they not only tried to characterize the system of science in a general and somewhat indefinite way by saying that the system is an instrument to be invented and constructed in order to find one's way among experiences, but also—and instead—they investigated the structure of this instrument. The investigation took place through an analysis of the method by which physics orders the experiences through a mathematical system of formulas. From this most advanced science, as an example, one can get an insight into the requirements that must be imposed on scientific cognition in general.

What then are the elements of which the instrument that we call science or cognition is composed? Here the influence of the mathematical-logical movement becomes felt. The new epistemology says that the system of science consists of symbols. This conception has been most clearly formulated by Moritz Schlick in his "General Theory of Knowledge." [4] Like James, Schlick begins with a determined rejection of the truth concept of school philosophy. He says that

in the past, the truth concept was almost always defined as the agreement of the thought with its objects.

He then shows that the word "agreement" cannot mean here anything like equality or similarity, as in ordinary usage, since between a judgment and the circumstances that it judges there can be no similarity. He continues:

Thus the concept of agreement melts away before the rays of analysis, in so far as it is to mean equality or similarity; and what is left is only a unique correspondence. In this consists the relation of the true judgment to reality, and all those naïve theories according to which our judgments and concepts somehow could portray reality are completely destroyed. There remains for the word "agreement" no other meaning than that of unique correspondence. One must dismiss the thought that a judgment in relation to the facts of the case could be anything more than a symbol, that it could be more intimately connected with them than through mere correspondence, that it is able somehow to describe or express or portray them adequately. Nothing like it is the case. The judgment portrays the nature of what is judged as little as the note the tone, or as the name of a man his personality.

If a person has always known and kept in sight the fact that

---

[4] M. Schlick, *Allgemeine Erkenntnislehre* (Berlin: Springer, ed. 2, 1925).

cognition arises simply through an assignment of symbol to object it would never have occurred to him to ask whether it is possible to have a cognition of things "as they really are" themselves. He would be led to this problem only by the opinion that cognition is a kind of pictorial representation that portrays the things in one's consciousness. Only under this assumption could he ask whether the images really have the same qualities as the things themselves.

It is easy to convince oneself that physical cognition consists in the unequivocal assignment of a system of symbols to experiences. Thus, for example, to electromagnetic phenomena are assigned field intensities, charge densities, and material constants as symbols. Among these symbols there exist formal mathematical relations, the field equations. Symbols that are equivalent to one another according to these relations or to the general logical and mathematical laws can be assigned to the same experiences without violating the uniqueness in the required sense.

If, for example, we start with a definite measured distribution of electric charge on the surface of a sphere, there is assigned to this experience, as a symbol, a definite mathematical function—the charge density as a function of position. If the sphere is left alone and we examine it after a lapse of some time, we measure everywhere the same charge density. To this experience is assigned a constant number for the density. If now the field equations were so constituted that according to them there would be obtained for the calculated charge density after some time a function other than a constant, then we should have a symbol system that would assign to the final electrical state of the sphere various symbols that are not equivalent. Because of this ambiguity we should say that our symbol system, which on the one hand is based on the rules of assigning symbols (here it is the method of measuring electric charges), and on the other hand on the relations among the symbols (here the field equations), gives no true cognition of the electrical phenomena.

Every verification of a physical theory consists in the test of whether the symbols assigned by the theory to the experiences are unique. If, for example, the Planck constant h occurs in the equations, it denotes a definite experience. This can be produced concretely if by means of the equations we express h through so-called "observable" quantities, that is to say, those symbols to which our rules assign concrete experiences.

In this way an experience is then directly assigned to the quantity h. As is well known, one can express h through quantities connected with the observation of black-body radiation and through quantities that arise from the observation of the Balmer series in the hydrogen spectrum. There are thus two experiences apparently denoted by h. These consist in the calculation of its value from two different groups of phenomena. If the two gave different values for h, we should be denoting two entirely different experiences by the same symbol h. We should then have in the system of equations involving h, in conjunction with the rules of assignment (methods of measurement), a symbol system that does not denote the experiences uniquely, and hence represents no true cognition. Through the fact that they both do give the same value of h we recognize the uniqueness of the system of symbols, the "truth" of the theory.

This comparison of the values of a quantity, calculated in different ways from observations, is the only way in which the physicist in his actual work can test the "truth" of a theory. The direct comparison of "observed" and "calculated" values, as it is often called in works on physics, turns out on closer examination to be nothing else than the test of the uniqueness of a symbol system. Suppose, for example, that on the one hand I calculated a current strength from the electronic theory of metals, while on the other hand I "observe" a galvanometer. Then this alleged observation is also only a calculation from another theory, namely, that of the galvanometer. For in reality I observe only the coincidences of pointers and scale divisions, and even these substantiations on more careful analysis would turn out to be results of a theory of the solid body. Even in the limiting case, where a value "is observed as directly as possible"—for example, if it is a question only of the position of a pointer on a scale—it is still calculated from the theories of rigid bodies and light rays, because I observe directly only dancing spots of color and not positions of the pointer. Hence what I usually call the comparison of observed and calculated values is, for example in our case, the comparison of the values of currents given from two different theories for the same concrete experience.

The school philosophy interprets an agreement of this kind —which, we are convinced, is the only criterion of truth for the physicist—in the following way: If for a quantity, for example, *h*, the same numerical value is obtained in various ways, then this quantity has a real existence. If by this expression is understood only what was really substantiated, namely, that the quantity *h* occurring in the equations can be calculated uniquely from phenomena of various kinds, then no objection can be raised against it. However, we must not say then that from the agreement of the results of the measurements we can draw conclusions about the real existence of *h*; for in that case this existence is identical with agreement.

Similarly, no conclusion drawn from physical experience concerning the real existence of the quantum of action, the elementary charge of electricity, or similar concepts, is a scientific conclusion. It finds its justification only in the metaphysical representation of reality given by the school philosophy, according to which the true principles exist before all experience and must be discovered by investigation, as Columbus discovered America.

I believe that the mathematician can get from the following illustration a very good understanding of the difference between the school philosophy, which recognizes metaphysical reality, and the scientific world conception, which uses only constructions based on concrete experiences.

If I have a convergent sequence of rational numbers, having an irrational number as a limit, I can establish a convergence without making use of the concept of the irrational number. That is to say, I need only to establish that the difference of any two rational members of the sequence above a given index can be made arbitrarily small by choosing an index that is sufficiently large. I have therefore before me, if I have defined only the concept of the rational number, a sequence of rational numbers having the property of convergence, but no limit in the domain of rational numbers. As is clear to every mathematician, there is no conclusion by the help of which it could then be shown that a limit of this convergent sequence exists. Rather, the convergent sequence itself is the concrete exhibitable object. Howver, I can now *define* such a sequence as an irrational number. This means that in all theorems involving irrational numbers I can substitute for the latter, sequences of rational numbers. It is not necessary, and is not justifiable logically, to speak of a real existence of irrational numbers, independent of the rational ones.

If we take this as an analogy, then the concrete experiences correspond to the rational numbers and the so-called really existing truths to the irrational numbers. A group of experiences with a system of symbols assigned to it, in which such agreements can be established throughout as we established in the case of the constant h, for example, corresponds to a convergent sequence of rational numbers. The uniqueness of the symbol system can be established within the group of experiences itself without having recourse to an objective reality situated outside, just as the convergence of a sequence can be established without the need of discussing the limit itself.

Likewise, as the concept of the irrational number is first defined by the convergent sequence of rational numbers, so the concept of true existence, say of the quantum of action h, is first defined by the agreements in the whole group of experiences involving h.

Just as the expression "irrational number" is an abbreviation for a convergent sequence of rational numbers, so the concept of a really existing quantum of action is only an abbreviation for the group of experiences which yield one and the same numerical value for h.

It is completely false to say—as is often said—that the agreements of the values of h are explained most naturally by means of the *hypothesis of the real existence* of a quantum of action. In a *hypothesis* one can only state a conjecture about future experiences, not about the "real existence" of a thing corresponding to an assigned name. To state a conjecture of this kind would be exactly as if a mathematician were to say: "The existence of convergent sequences of rational numbers without limits can be explained most naturally by means of the hypothesis that there are irrational numbers." In reality, through such an assertion he would only be giving a new name to convergent sequences without limits. Similarly, through the assertion of the existence of a quantum of action no new fact is stated besides the agreements. Hence, also, *no hypothesis is present.*

I have already spoken about the fact that the development of the scientific conception of nature was retarded by a certain conflict between the mathematical-logical and the biological-pragmatic approach. The latter was greatly lacking in precision, so that even the school philosophy appeared to have many advantages here. Thus, for example, Bertrand Russell in his book, *Our Knowledge of the External World,*[5] in many

[5] Chicago: Open Court Publishing Co., 1914.

points showed greater concurrence with the conceptions of the school philosophy than with those of Ernst Mach. In the German translation of this book, however, Russell remarks in a footnote that he now agrees with Mach on one of the most important points. It seems to me that in the case of other representatives of the Russell movement as well the conviction is gaining ground that a consistent further expansion of the scientific world picture is not to be sought by opposing the Mach conception in favor of the school philosophy for the sake of its apparently more rigorous logic. On the contrary, it appears that this expansion must be carried out with the aid of modern logic by building up the doctrines of Mach to form a system everywhere free from objections on logical grounds.

Although according to modern conceptions logic can produce nothing more than tautological transformations of principles, it is nevertheless indispensable for the construction of a rigorously scientific world picture. The reason is that many of the prejudices of the school philosophy arose from the fact that mere tautologies were regarded as expressions of cognition. A complete survey of all possible tautological transformations therefore offers the possibility of constructing on the basis of Mach's views a scientific edifice that is superior to the school philosophy in its logical precision.

The most determined attempt in this direction was undertaken by Rudolf Carnap. In his book "The Logical Structure of the World," [6] which appeared in 1928, he seeks to build up the whole system of science, starting from concrete experiences. He tries to show that all principles in which physical or psychological objects are involved can be replaced by statements concerning concrete experiences. The rules according to which statements about concepts must be replaced by statements about concrete experiences are called by Carnap the constitution of these concepts. In a scientific statement there should occur only concepts the constitution of which is known. The basis of every science is the system of concept constitutions. The building of this system step by step with the help of the modern logic of Russell is what Carnap calls the logical structure of the world.

According to this conception, a scientific problem can consist only in asking whether a definite scientific statement is true or false. Since, however, every such statement can be

[6] R. Carnap, *Der logische Aufbau der Welt* (Berlin, 1928).

reduced to a statement about concrete experiences if the constitution of the concepts occurring in it is known, every problem that can be called scientific consists in the question whether a definite relation among concrete experience does, or does not, exist. At the same time Carnap shows further that all relations, in the last analysis, can be reduced to statements of a similarity between concrete experiences. Since one can properly assume that every such similarity is confirmable in principle, it follows that every problem that can be scientifically formulated is also soluble in principle.

We see that the consistent carrying through of a purely scientific world conception, as attempted by Carnap, leads us just as far away from the resigned *ignorabimus* as does the pragmatism of James, which is thought out somewhat less logically but in its tendencies has the same goal. Carnap formulates it thus:

Science, the system of conceptual cognition, has no limitations . . . There are no questions the answers to which are impossible for science in principle . . . Science has no boundary points . . . Every statement formed from scientific concepts can be established in principle as true or false.

This does not mean, of course, that there are no other domains of life than science. These domains, however—lyric poetry, for example—are distinct from science. Through the latter itself no problems can be set up that are insoluble by its means.

Wittgenstein says very precisely:

When an answer cannot be expressed, neither can the question be expressed.

Hence, as understood by Carnap and Wittgenstein, the questions beloved by the school philosophy, such as whether the outer world really exists, not only cannot be answered but cannot even be expressed, because neither the positive assertion, falsely called the realistic "hypothesis," nor the negative idealistic assertion can be expressed through constituted concepts. In other words, neither assertion can be expressed as a substantiable relation among concrete experiences. We see here the close relationship between the truth concept of the modern logical movement and that of pragmatism.

A tendency similar to that of Schlick and Carnap is followed by Hans Reichenbach; but Reichenbach departs from Carnap in many points, as in the recognition of the realistic standpoint.

After this survey of the movements that seek to construct a purely scientific world conception through following closely the actual practice of mathematical and physical investigation in contrast to the school philosophy, let us return to our starting point, the question of why physicists often refuse to pass judgment on problems like space, time, and causality, and leave them to the philosophers.

This refusal, we can now say, arises from the fact that these physicists, consciously or unconsciously, cling to the doctrines of the school philosophy, according to which such problems must be solved by methods fundamentally different from those employed by physicists. If a scientist follows these thoughts through logically, he must end up in the blind alley of *ignorabimus*.

If, however, we stand on the ground of the purely scientific world conception, we know that the solution of a scientific problem can only consist in finding out new relations among concrete experiences, or, to express it in another way, in making progress in the unique designation of experiences by a system of symbols.

One can try to fit new experiences into places in the existing system of symbols; this we call purely experimental investigation. The idea that there can be a still purer type of experimental investigation that makes no use at all of symbol systems is, in my opinion, an illusion. To be sure, as Schlick properly points out, one can experience phenomena and can get to know them without using any symbol system; but this is not scientific cognition. For, at best, one could then establish, for example, that today about noon several colored spots were seen in certain combinations, although a more exact analysis would probably show that even in such an utterance there is already an assignment of symbol to experience.

The work of the theoretical physicist consists, in part, in investigating the consequences resulting from the fundamental relations belonging to the symbol system. This is an essentially mathematical task, such as, for example, the integration of the field equations, the fundamental relations among the field quantities. Another part of the work of the theoretical physicist consists in extending the symbol system. Naturally, with the introduction of new symbols new rules of assigning them to experiences must also be introduced.

If, for example, in the investigation of the hardness of a substance one must make a new hypothesis concerning its crystal lattice, this means a change in the symbol system; specifically, in the geometric figure by which the substance concerned is characterized. Everyone will acknowledge that a work of this kind is really a concrete physical work. From such changes in the symbol system there extends a continuous series to those changes that the physicist often feels to be "speculative" or "philosophical," as, for example, the introduction of the Einstein time scale. Here, too, the question is only one of setting up a new rule of assigning the symbols t and t' in our equations to our experiences, as well as of a new relation between the symbols t and t' in the symbol system. One can give no criterion, however, to determine whether a change means a physical cognition or a philosophical one. For the physicist there exist no such limitations. Whether I am dealing with the measurement of hardness or with that of space and time, it is always only a question of assigning a unique system of symbols to experiences. Nowhere is there a point where the physicist must say: "Here ends my task, and from here on it is the task of the philosopher."

This could happen only for a thinker standing on the ground of the school philosophy. He might ask, for example: "When I have exhausted all problems of assigning time symbols to experiences, which among the time scales admitted by the relativity theory is the true, real time?" And that question the physicist cannot answer; it is the philosopher who must pass judgment on it.

It looks as if classical physics has been living on good terms with school philosophy, whereas modern physics, with its relativity theory and quantum mechanics, has at once come into conflict with it. The physicists who feared the break with school philosophy could resolve this conflict only by a kind of doctrine of double truth. They said, in effect: "We physicists speak only of time measurements; hence for us the relativity theory is valid. The philosopher speaks of the *real* time; for him perhaps something else is valid." If this doctrine of double truth was meant somewhat ironically, as was often the case, it was an irony of embarrassment. There are actual cases, however, when it is meant in all seriousness.

The reason that the conflict did not occur during the time of classical physics is simply that, for example, the time concept of the school philosophy had just as much empirical physical origin as that of the relativity theory, the difference being that the former corresponded to the older state of physics, that which we today call the classical. The symbol system with the help of which Newtonian mechanics and Euclidean geometry portrayed space and time experiences was declared by the school philosophy to be *real* space and time, and proclaimed as eternal truth.

If, however, in accordance with the scientific world picture, we regard every problem as merely one of assigning symbols to experiences, then in the designation of the space and time experiences a change is fully as possible as in the rest of physics. Just as this leads to progress in the theory of the solid body, so it also leads to progress in the study of space and time, keeping up with the progress of our observations.

One cannot declare certain parts of the symbol system to be unchangeable for all time. To be sure, one may keep the old Kantian terminology, in a certain sense, and explain space and time as the frames of physical phenomena. But one must bear in mind, as Reichenbach correctly says, that this frame, too, must be always adapted more and more closely to our progressing experience.

The rise of the physics of Galileo and Newton brought about the breakdown of the philosophy of Aristotle, which attempted to show the eternal truth of the physics of antiquity. Similarly, beside the relativity theory and quantum mechanics there cannot exist a philosophy that contains a fossilization of the earlier physical theories.

Just as the views of the school philosophy on space and time make it more difficult to understand the relativity theory, so its conception of causality is an obstacle to an understanding of the new quantum mechanics. I will not go into greater detail here concerning the causality problem; I wish to draw attention to only one point.

Classical physics understood by the law of causality the calculability of future states from an initial state: if the state of the world or of an isolated system is known exactly at one instant of time, then it is known also for all future time. It was regarded as indubitable that with the help of prescribable methods of measurement one could determine the values of the quantities defining the state of a system—if not exactly, then at least approximately. It was assumed that with increasing refinement of the methods of measurement it would be possible to increase the accuracy arbitrarily. Hence, in principle, to such quantities as lengths or field intensities, determining the state, were ascribed exact numerical values.

That people held this conviction so firmly is owing to the belief of the school philosophy that exact values of lengths or field intensities must exist even if they are not yet known accurately to the person performing the measurements. They are hidden in the nutshell referred to by Bergson, and one must break through it to reach the true values.

It is quite natural that we cannot measure the exact length of a rod. If I wish to assert, however, that through refinement of the methods of measurement we can gradually come closer and closer to the exact value of the length, it is first necessary to ask whether we can define what we understand by exact length. For here we often go in a circle. We define as exact value the limiting value approached by the measurements as the method is increasingly defined. In this definition we assume that such a limiting value exists. Its existence can be shown empirically, if at all, only to within an uncertainty of a definite order of magnitude. But in this way we have come no nearer settling the question of the existence of an exact value.

According to the atomistic theory, the length of a rod is nothing but the distance between two atoms. Since an atom is a system of electrons, every such distance can be reduced to a distance between electrons. Every measurement consists in a comparison of the measured body with a measuring rod. But the latter is itself a system of electrons. Hence every measurement of length ultimately leads to the substantiation of a coincidence between electrons. By this, of course, is not meant a coincidence in the literal sense, but something like the phenomenon whereby one electron covers the other when viewed from a definite direction. It does mean, however, that the measurement of length is reduced to the observation of light diffracted or scattered by the two electrons. Now it is clear that differences in length that are small in comparison to the wavelength of the light involved can play no role in this observation. Such differences cannot be observed through any experiment of this sort, hence cannot be regarded as conceivable experience. The possibility of being able to refine arbitrarily the measurement of length by refining the measuring technique can only be based on the hope of being able to produce radiation of arbitrarily small wavelength. The production of such radiation, which must therefore have arbitrarily high frequency, is not very probable, however, according to the observations that led to the formulation of the quantum hypothesis. For then there must be light quanta of arbitrarily high energy and exerting arbitrarily great forces on collision. Moreover, there is another circumstance, first pointed out by Heisenberg, that makes impossible an exact measurement even to within the order of magnitude of the errors that correspond to still attainable wavelengths. If, specifically, one goes to very high frequencies, so that the collision force of the light quantum becomes very great, it is not possible to establish the relative velocity—in our case, the state of rest relative to each other—of the two electrons, for the impulse imparted by the light quantum changes their state of motion in an uncontrollable way; this is the phenomenon that accounts for the Compton effect.

Just as there is no method of measuring the length of a rod with arbitrary accuracy, so too there is no method of measuring the intensity of an electric field with arbitrary accuracy. Every such measurement is based on the observation of the force exerted on a test body in the field. The charge and size of this body are assumed to be so small that they do not disturb the field. This assumption, however, contradicts the atomistic hypothesis, which has no cognizance of arbitrarily small and arbitrarily weakly charged test bodies. Therefore the assumption that a field intensity is measurable with arbitrary accuracy in principle is not justified.

The physicist who starts from the conceptions of school philosophy must say to this argument that there really exist perfectly definite values of lengths, but that nature is so constituted that it prevents us from determining them. There are natural laws especially suited to this purpose. This corresponds entirely to the conception of the relativity theory according to which the absolute velocities of motion of all reference systems exist but the laws of nature are so insidious that they prevent the observation of these velocities. The physicist who wishes to represent this conception of the relativity theory which corresponds to the school philosophy must assume the existence of realities to which no concrete experience corresponds. So, too, the physicist who assumes the existence of exact lengths of bodies must understand by the word "existence" something that no longer has any connection with the empirical sense of this word, which refers to something experienced or, at least, experiencible.

On the basis of this conception, the problem is then put: Is the law of causality valid or not valid in nature? That is, do the initial positions and velocities of electrons determine these quantities for all future time? Even if there were equations for which that were the case, nothing at all is said about real experiences. For we know that we cannot assign positions and velocities of electrons unequivocally to our experiences even by successive approximations. That the law of causality is not valid for our experiences involving the positions and velocities of electrons has been made plausible by the experiments on the diffraction of electrons as they are usually interpreted. If, to wit, electrons fall on a grating, the direction in which a single one is deflected cannot be predicted from its initial position and velocity.

It is often concluded that electrons follow absolute chance in their choice of direction, or even, as one occasionally finds it put in popular presentations, that an irrational element plays a role, a kind of personification of the electron. This follows, however, only if one starts from the picture given by school philosophy, according to which every electron has a definite position and velocity, which nevertheless do not determine its future.

From the standpoint of a purely scientific conception, on the other hand, one will say that there are no individual experiences involving positions and velocities of electrons from which the future of the latter can be predicted unequivocally. Instead, it appears that the probability that an electron will be deflected in a definite direction can be predicted from the experience of the initial experimental arrangement. For these probabilities (the squares of the absolute values of the wave functions) Schrödinger, in his wave mechanics, sets up rigorous causal laws. To the probabilities that occur in these laws and define the state of the system one can therefore assign definite experiences. This theory is called statistical. The statistical element here consists in the manner of assignment of experiences to symbols. Thus to certain symbols, the squares of the absolute values of the wave functions, there are assigned, not individual experiences, but numbers which are obtained by averaging from a great many individual experiences.

The task of physics is only to find symbols among which there exist rigorously valid relations, and which can be assigned uniquely to our experiences. This correspondence between experiences and symbols may be more or less detailed. If the symbols conform to the experiences in a very detailed manner we speak of causal laws; if the correspondence is of a broader sort we call the laws statistical. I do not believe that a more exact analysis will establish a definite distinction here. We know today that with the help of positions and velocities we cannot set up any causal laws for single electrons. This does not exclude the possibility, however, that we shall perhaps some day find a set of quantities with the help of which it will be possible to describe the behavior of these particles in greater detail than by means of the wave function, the probabilities. When we determine a number through a so-called single observation, we really observe even in this case only a mean value; "point experiences" are never recorded. The assignment of symbols to experiences always contains then, strictly speaking, a statistical or, if we like, a collective element. Thus it is always a matter of making the assignment so as to go into detail to a greater or lesser degree.

There can therefore never be the question—which the physicist who is influenced by the school philosophy often thinks must be asked—"Does strict causality hold in nature?" but rather, "What is the character of the correspondence between our experiences and the quantities describing the state of a system, which are subject to rigorous laws?"

We see here, just as in the conception of the relativity theory, that the physicist, if he consciously or unconsciously maintains the standpoint of the school philosophy, is prevented from seeing the present physical theories as assertions about real physical experiences. He is easily led to find in them a mysterious, destructive element, raising philosophical difficulties. He may even find in them a contradiction to common sense.

If we investigate more closely the nature of the epistemology of classical physics and its connection with school philosophy, we find the following:

The general view was that, in the great system of symbols of which the physical theories are composed, there exists a framework which, with our experimental progress, must be gradually filled in. It appeared to be definitely established that all phenomena can be reduced to the motion of material points or the vibrations of a medium; that these material points at every instant possess definite positions and velocities by which all future states are unequivocally determined; that there are time variables with the help of which all phenomena can be most simply represented; and so on. It was believed that while it would be necessary to make many changes during the filling in of the framework, none would be made in the fundamental rods of the framework.

Through the relativity theory and quantum mechanics this conviction has been shaken. We know that even in those parts of the symbol system that form the framework, much has had to be changed and still more will have to be. We are in general no longer convinced, as we were formerly, that the parts of the symbol system forming the frame are already approaching a definitive form. This does not imply the acceptance of any skeptical standpoint, but only the rejection of any distinction between the various portions of the symbol system.

Every physicist is convinced that with experimental progress, with progressive refinement of the measuring technique, we will admit finer and finer structures and will always have to introduce new variables to describe the state of a system. Similarly, he must be convinced that there does not exist for all eternity a rigid framework which is characterized by the trio of space, time, and causality, and in which no experience can change anything. He must be convinced rather that for these most general rules of assignment exactly the same must hold as for the more special rules, the dependence of which on the progress of human experience is not doubted.

Classical physics led to the opinion that this framework was, in its essentials, completed. Hence it could be proclaimed by the school philosophy as eternal truth. Our modern theoretical physics, which admits progress in all parts of the symbol system, is skeptical only when viewed from the standpoint of the school philosophy. From the standpoint of the purely scientific conception, which takes only experiences for granted and looks upon the symbol system constructed for them as a means or an instrument, there is nothing skeptical in it. Would it show skepticism if we asserted that the ultimate machine for traveling through space does not have to resemble the present airplane, not even in its most important parts; that it must have in common with the latter only one thing, the ability to fly?

And now let us return to the question put at the beginning of this paper: What is the significance of the physical theories of the present day for the general theory of knowledge? From the standpoint of the school philosophy they signify a disintegration of rational thought; hence they are only rules for representing the results of experiments and not cognitions of reality, which are reserved for other methods. For those, however, who do not recognize these nonscientific methods, *the present physical theories strengthen the conviction that even in questions such as those concerning space, time, and causality, there is scientific progress, along with the progress in our observations;* that it is therefore not necessary beside the thriving tree of science to assume a sterile region in which reside the eternally insoluble problems in the attempted solution of which men have been only rotating about their own axes for centuries. *There are no boundaries between science and philosophy,* if one only formulates the task of physics in accordance with the doctrines of Ernst Mach, using the words of Carnap:

To order the perceptions systematically and from present perceptions to draw conclusions about perceptions to be expected.

Chapter 5

Is There a Trend Today Toward Idealism in Physics?

IT IS GENERALLY RECOGNIZED that modern exact science, the creation of which in the age of Galileo and Newton led to the great expansion of our technical civilization, is distinguished from ancient and medieval science by the fact that the psychic, anthropomorphic elements are being eliminated more and more from science. In place of the medieval doctrines of "the most perfect orbit," "the position appropriate to a body," "the difference between celestial and terrestrial bodies," and the like, we now have the mathematically formulable laws of Newton's principles, in which only observable and measurable quantities occur. There is no doubt that the physics of Galileo and Newton has created a gulf between body and mind which did not exist in the anthropomorphic, animistic science of the Middle Ages. This separation of the two became unpleasant to those who were interested in a science that would account for the behavior not only of inanimate bodies, but of all bodies in nature, including the human body. Thus arose the problem of explaining the mind on the basis of mechanistic physics, a problem which many have discussed, but without ever making any real advance, and which is actually only an apparent problem. Its insolubility in this form, which was really obvious to all, led many scholars to have a deep dislike for mechanistic physics and to derive a malicious pleasure from every difficulty that the latter encountered. R. Ruyer is quite right when he says:

> That, basically, many scholars are tortured by the burden of this original sin, mechanistic physics, is strikingly shown by their reaction whenever the mechanistic or quantitative conception of physics appears to suffer a setback. The most philosophical minds, far from being disturbed by this setback, hope every time to find in it an opportunity for introducing once more the subjective. This was the case with the discovery of potential energy, gravitation, and the degradaton of energy, as well as chemical affinity.[1]

One need not be surprised, therefore, if the recent revolutions in the field of theoretical physics, the creation of the

[1] R. Ruyer, *Revue de Synthèse* 6, 167 (1933).

126

relativity and quantum theories, were received by the scholars whom Ruyer called "the most philosophical minds" with the same feelings as the preceding theoretical overturnings, such as the degradation of energy. Indeed, today one can hardly open a periodical or book dealing with the development of our general scientific ideas without meeting such expressions as "the end of the age of Galileo," "the failure of mechanistic physics," "the end of the hostility of science toward the spirit," "the reconciliation between religion and science." There is even a book on modern physics, by Bernhard Bavink, entitled "Natural Science on the Path to Religion." [2]

Some are of the opinion that the new physical theories of the twentieth century have bought about a change in the general conception of the world as important as that caused by the physics of Galileo, which replaced the animistic conception of the Middle Ages by the mechanistic one of modern times. In the same way, the new physics is supposed to form a bridge from the "mechanistic world conception" of the eighteenth and nineteenth centuries to the "mathematical conception" of the twentieth century. The latter is thought to be nearer, in a certain sense, to the medieval, animistic conception than to the mechanistic one, because in mathematics there resides an "ideal" or "spiritual" element, and a "mathematical world" is not as foreign to the spirit as is a mechanical world. This view was presented in all solemnity by General Smuts in his opening address at the celebration of the centenary of the British Association of Science on September 23, 1931.[3] He said, among other things:

There is the machine or mechanistic world view dominant since the time of Galileo and Newton, and now, since the coming of Einstein, being replaced by the mathematician's conception of the universe . . . If matter is essentially immaterial structure or organization, it cannot fundamentally be so different from organism or life . . . or from mind, which is an active organizer.

First, we must ask from the standpoint of the logic of science whether the physical theories of the twentieth century really contain any spiritualistic elements and, second, we must ask with what processes outside of physics the demand for a spiritualistic conception of nature is generally found to be associated. Let us begin by touching briefly on the second

[2] B. Bavink, *Die Naturwissenschaft auf dem Wege zur Religion* (Frankfurt am Main: M. Diesterweg, 1933).
[3] *Nature* 128, 521 (1931).

question in order to be able to consider the first in greater detail.

It is certainly no accident that the culmination of the mechanistic conception of nature, as it is found, say, in the work of Laplace, coincided with the triumph of the French Revolution. It is certainly no accident that since that time the struggle against the "ideas of 1789" has almost always coincided with a criticism of this conception of nature, a longing for a more idealistic or spiritualistic theory. The struggle against the "ideas of 1789" has been crowned in recent years by the fact that in a series of countries, especially in Italy and Germany, a directly opposite world conception has prevailed politically. This conception has a philosophic basis that is in sharp contradiction to the mechanistic conception of nature and urges a more "organismic" picture of the world, by which is meant a partial return to the spiritualistic or animistic doctrines of the Middle Ages, just as the new conception of a state is connected with that of the Middle Ages. The adherents of this antimechanistic, organismic conception of nature strive to show that in the exact sciences "spontaneously," "from purely scientific considerations," a revolution has taken place. According to their argument, on the basis of the relativity theory and quantum mechanics one can set up a conception of nature in which the mind again plays a role, and which is compatible with an "antimechanical, organismic, independent" biology.

As a typical example, a work of B. Bavink may be quoted. Bavink has a thorough knowledge of physics and biology and is an outstanding representative of the "organismic conception of nature." He maintains that

today there reigns within the circle of the sciences a willingness to tie once more the threads of science to all the higher values of human life, to God and the soul, freedom of will, etc.—threads that seemed almost completely severed; it is a willingness the like of which has not been present for centuries. That this change should take place at the present time is a coincidence almost bordering on the miraculous, for this change has in itself nothing to do with political and social transformations; it manifestly arose from purely scientific motives.[4]

Whether or not the last sentence is correct is exactly the question we are trying to answer.

[4] B. Bavink, "The Sciences in the Third Reich" (in German), *Unsere Welt* 25, 225 (1933).

On the other hand, in Russia, since the founding of the Soviet Union, a system has been established that seeks its philosophic basis in the "dialectical materialism" of Karl Marx as adapted by Lenin. I do not wish here to discuss the relation between this "dialectical materialism" and what one is accustomed to call "materialism" in Germany and France. I want only to call attention to the fact that in countless articles in the philosophical and political journals of present-day Russia, the tendency toward spiritualism which is often found as an accompaniment of modern physical theories is interpreted as one of the "phenomena of decadence" of science in capitalist countries.[5] In these articles the following line of thought often appears: in western Europe science, to be sure, is still making progress on individual problems, such as the formulation of laws of atomic processes, just as capitalist economy is still progressing technically. However, just as the life of the industrial population is shaken more and more by crises which finally make a generally acceptable solution impossible, so science, in spite of its progress in details, cannot produce a satisfying general picture of the processes in nature. In working on such a general picture it no longer proceeds scientifically, in the modern sense. Rather, it borrows from the animistic, spiritualistic physics of the Middle Ages and interprets modern theories in this light, because the intellectual trends dominant in political life obscure the scientific theories by wrapping them in a spiritualistic fog.

In spite of the tremendous conflict between the "materialistic" Soviet Union and the states based on the organismic conception of the world, they all agree on the fact that the tendency toward spiritualism in modern physics corresponds to the ideology of the new organismic state. By some this tendency is welcomed as a necessary consequence of modern physics; by others it is condemned as an adulteration of it. That the representatives of both groups comprehend physics in this way is a fact that is as well established empirically as the best observations of experimental physics, a fact which we must therefore take into account in any consideration of modern physical theories.

I wish to say at once that the result of our investigation will be as follows: *In the process of eliminating the "animistic," nothing has been changed in the slightest by the*

---

[5] As a recent example may be cited A. K. Timiriazew, "The Wave of Idealism in Modern Physics in the West and in Our Country" (in Russian), *Pod znamenem marksizma*, 1933, no. 5.

modern physical theories. This process continues irresistibly forward as before. He who would interpret physics by means of "psychic factors" had at the time of the physics of Galileo and Newton the same justification as today. The role of the "psychic" has remained exactly the same. Hence, if there does exist today a greater tendency toward spiritualistic interpretation, it is connected only with processes that have nothing at all to do with the progress of physics.

The arguments that are supposed to show that psychic factors play a greater role in modern physics than in the physics of Newton are of various kinds. In one group it is claimed that the role of the "observing subject" in the relativity and quantum theories can no longer be eliminated from physical statements, as was still the case in "classical physics." This argument is often put as follows: Whereas in classical physics expressions like "length of a rod" or "time interval between two events" assert something about "objective" facts, in the Einstein relativity theory such expressions have a meaning only if the observer to whom they refer is specified. One can only say, for instance, "This body has a length of one meter with respect to this particular observer." It appears, therefore, that every physical statement possesses a psychological constituent. In popular literature on the relativity theory writers often even go so far as to compare the various lengths of a rod for various observers with the optical illusion that arises when one draws two straight lines of equal length but places different ornaments at their ends, producing the illusion of different lengths.

This conception, in its "scientific" as well as its "popular" form, is based on a complete misunderstanding of the relativity theory. Wherever in the theory of relativity reference is made to an observer, a physical measuring instrument can be substituted. It is asserted only that the results of the measurement will be different according as the motion of the measuring instrument is different. But in this there is nothing psychological, at any rate not any more than in classical physics. The role of the observer is in both cases exactly the same: he merely substantiates the fact that in a certain instrument a pointer coincides with a division mark on a scale. For this purpose the state of motion of the observer himself is quite immaterial. In the theory of relativity, as well as in classical physics, it is assumed that such a substantiation is "objective," that there can never arise any difference of opinion in connection with it. Naturally, it remains "subjective" in the sense that some observer is necessary for it. Here "objective" means "the same for all subjects," or "intersubjective."

Similar considerations have also been associated with the quantum theory. According to this theory, as Heisenberg showed, the position and the velocity of a given particle can never be exactly determined simultaneously. If one makes use of an experimental arrangement that allows the position to be measured very accurately, the exact measurement of velocity by means of the same experimental arrangement is impossible. It is then held that whereas in classical physics a statement about the position and velocity of a particle was a statement about an objective fact, without any psychologic elements, in the quantum theory one cannot speak of the position and velocity of a particle, but only of what is given by a certain measurement. Thus every statement about particles involves the observer himself, and hence contains a psychologic element. To this argument we must reply as I have just indicated in the discussion of the relativity theory, pointing out that in quantum mechanics, too, what matters is never the observer, but only the instruments of observation. The role of the human being as observer is limited here again to establishing whether or not a pointer on a scale coincides with a division mark. This observation, however, is regarded here, just as in classical physics, as something "objective," or better, as something "intersubjective." What one can learn from the relativity and quantum theories in this connection is only what is also given by a consistent presentation of classical physics: every physical principle is, in the final analysis, a summary of statements concerning observations, or, if one wishes to speak in a particularly physical way, concerning pointer readings.

We have thus seen that the new role of "observer" in physics *cannot* be used in favor of a tendency toward a more spiritualistic conception of physics. There exists, however, a whole series of other arguments which are customarily used to establish the approach or "return" of physics to the "organic, idealistic" conception of nature. Such arguments run somewhat like this: "Quantum mechanics contains a teleological element," or "The indeterministic interpretation of the quantum theory makes room for free will." Here we shall not consider these questions, but shall speak of a still more general argument for the "spiritualistic character" of modern physics. This is an argument which in recent years has been repeated so often and by scholars of such prominence that there is danger that many, through becoming accustomed to such lines of thought, will accept them as justified—indeed, as obvious. These ideas have perhaps received the most extensive dissemination in 150,000 copies of a book by the outstanding physicist and astrophysicist, J. H. Jeans. Jeans depicts the present situation in physics as follows:

Today there is a wide measure of agreement, which on the physical side of science approaches almost to unanimity, that the stream of knowledge is heading towards a nonmechanical reality; the universe begins to look more like a great thought than like a great machine. Mind no longer appears as an accidental intruder into the realm of matter.[6]

Jeans bases his opinion that nature is to be regarded as something "spiritual" essentially on the assertion that modern physics has shown that one cannot give any mechanical representation of natural processes, although one can give a mathematical representation. He says:

The efforts of our nearer ancestors to interpret nature on engineering lines proved equally inadequate . . . On the other hand, our efforts to interpret nature in terms of the concepts of pure mathematics have, so far, proved brilliantly successful.[7]

In the laws of mathematics, in contrast to those of mechanics, of machinery, Jeans sees, however, a spiritual element. If nature behaves according to mathematical laws, it must be the work of a mind which can create mathematics, like the human mind, but is more comprehensive. Jeans is so strongly convinced that the movement toward idealism is connected with the present state of theoretical physics that he keeps in view the possibility that, with a change of the theories of physics, there may again develop a movement away from idealism. Thus he says in a later book:

So far the pendulum shows no signs of swinging back, and the law and order which we find in the universe are most easily described—and also, I think, most easily explained—in the language of idealism. Thus, subject to the reservations already mentioned,

---

[6] J. H. Jeans, *The Mysterious Universe* (Cambridge: The University Press, 1930), p. 158.
[7] *Ibid.*, p. 143.

we may say that present-day science is favorable to idealism . . .
Yet who shall say what we may find awaiting us round the next
corner?[8]

Similar views are presented by Sir Arthur Stanley Eddington, in his book *The Nature of the Physical World*.[9] While
there is in this book a great deal that is beneficial in furthering
the understanding of modern physics and in bringing its
results to a wide circle of readers through a concrete and
lucid presentation, yet it has numerous sections which Eddington himself regards as bold interpretation of present-day
physics to which many will perhaps take exception, and which,
in my opinion, form obstacles to the task of fitting physics
into a self-consistent picture of the processes of the whole of
nature. Eddington, like Jeans, believes that these views are
matters of faith and that it is impossible to force one by
proof to accept them. That is certainly true. However, what
can be shown clearly, in my opinion, is that these idealistic
views have nothing at all to do with modern physics. If anyone wanted to accept them, he could have done so just as well
in connection with the physics of Galileo and Newton, which
is not less "mathematical" than twentieth-century physics.

The arguments of both Jeans and Eddington depend on the
contrast between a physics that reduces everything to mechanics (that of Galileo and Newton) and one that bases
everything on mathematical formulas (the physics of Einstein
and the quantum theory). How can one formulate clearly
the distinction between a "mechanical" and a "mathematical"
basis for the processes of nature? Newtonian physics reduces
all phenomena to the equations of motion for mass points
between which there act central forces, that is, to a system of
differential equations. The mechanics of Einstein changes
these differential equations in a few respects which give essential differences only for very high velocities, and points out
that the equations so changed have mathematically the same
form as the geodesics in a curved (non-Euclidean, Riemannian) space. In place of one system of differential equations,
another occurs. Why then is one theory called "mathematical,"
the other "mechanistic"? Surely similarity to the geodesics
cannot be the only reason, for Newtonian physics can also
be brought into this form without any difficulty.

[8] J. H. Jeans, *The New Background of Science* (Cambridge: The University
Press, 1933), p. 296.
[9] Cambridge: The University Press, 1928.

Adhering to the concrete interpretation of physics as a representation of observable facts, we can try to summarize the difference between "mechanical" and "nonmechanical, mathematical" physics approximately as follows: By means of Newtonian mechanics we can describe the motions of bodies with which we deal in everyday life, so long as they have also the velocities that are encountered in daily experience. To this class of bodies belong the ordinary tools such as hammers and tongs, but also such things as steam engines, automobiles, and airplanes. During the reign of the physics of Galileo and Newton it was believed that in time it would be possible by means of these same equations to describe also the motions of the smallest particles of matter, such as atoms and ions, as well as the motions of celestial bodies during arbitrarily long time intervals and with arbitrarily high velocities. In other words, it was believed that all processes of nature, in the large and in the small, could be covered by the same laws that had been established for the motions of "bodies of average size with moderate velocities." This belief has been shaken by the development of physics in the twentieth century. We know today that the motions of bodies with velocities comparable to that of light can be described only with the help of the relativity theory of Einstein, the motions of the smallest particles in the atoms only with the help of quantum and wave mechanics.

If we understand by mechanics the doctrine of the motion of "bodies of average size with moderate velocities," then we can rightly say that modern physics has established the impossibility of a mechanical basis for the processes of nature. If we say, however, that the mechanical foundation has been replaced by a mathematical one, it is, in my opinion, a very inappropriate mode of expression. We ought to say, rather, that the place of a special mathematical theory, that of Newton, has been taken by more general theories, the relativity and quantum theories. The opinion that a special mathematical theory could represent all the processes of nature has turned out to be false; that is all. But from this fact no contrast between the propositions "Newtonian physics = mechanics = materialism," on the one hand, and "modern physics = mathematics = idealism," on the other hand, can be deduced.

Newton, in his *Mathematical Principles of Natural philosophy*,[10] replaced the matter filling the world and acting

---

[10] I. Newton, *Philosophiae Naturalis Principia Mathematica* (1687), tr. by A. Motte (1729), rev. by F. Cajori (University of California Press, 1934).

through pressure, collisions, and fluid vortices, as pictured by the Cartesians, by small masses, almost lost in vast empty space and acting on each other only through forces at a distance. When this work was published, the new theory was hailed by many of his followers as a triumph over the materialism of the "Epicureans."

As proof, one need only read the famous controversy between Leibniz and Clarke,[11] in which Clarke defends Newton's teachings against the attacks of Leibniz. Clarke says in his first reply:

> Next to the corruptible dispositions of human beings, it [the disavowal of religion] is to be ascribed first of all to the false philosophy of the materialists, who oppose the mathematical principles of philosophy [i.e., Newton's] . . . These principles, and indeed only they, show matter and the body as the smallest and most insignificant part of the universe.

Hence at that time Newton's followers, in so far as they were adherents of spiritualistic metaphysics, extolled his teachings as "mathematical" and "spiritual" in contrast to materialism. Today those with analogous philosophic inclinations say that Newtonian physics was "materialistic," but that Einstein has again brought in a "mathematical," "spiritual" element in place of the mechanical one.

We have already seen that the assertion that the laws of nature are not "mechanical" but "mathematical" means only that the laws are expressed not by means of the special mathematical formulas of Newton, but by means of the more general formulas of the relativity and quantum theories. When, however, we say, not that the formulas used to describe nature are mathematical, but that the world *is* mathematical, it is difficult to say what we mean. By mathematics, considered concretely, we can only understand a system of formulas or propositions. With these formulas are to be correlated the observations that we make of the processes of nature, if the formulas are to represent physical theories. The processes themselves, however, do not consist of these formulas. In an assertion such as "The world is basically mathematics," the word "is" can only be used in a mystic sense, as it occurs perhaps in the sentence "This architecture or this music is pure mathematics."

[11] *A Collection of Papers, which Passed between the Late Learned Mr. Leibnitz, and Dr. [Samuel] Clarke, in the Years 1715 and 1716* . . . (London: J. Knapton, 1717).

In order to make his views clear, Jeans must speak of the world architect; he represents him, not according to Newtonian physics as a kind of engineer, but according to modern physics as a kind of mathematician. Since engineers also produce their work according to mathematical formulas, Jeans has to indicate the distinction between the engineer and the world creator somewhat as follows: The engineer fits his formulas to the observations, whereas the creator invents formulas at will and then constructs the world according to them. Jeans brings in here the difference between "pure" and "applied" mathematics. The engineer is an applied mathematician, the world creator a pure one. Jeans tries to show it in this way: The man who works in pure mathematics invents formulas and propositions without any regard to the question of practical application; later, it turns out that the physicist or engineer, by means of the results obtained by the pure mathematician, can represent the processes of nature, of which the pure mathematician knew nothing when he devised his theory. This can only be explained by saying that the processes are themselves the work of a pure mathematician, and the theoretical physicist who finds these formulas for representing observations is only rediscovering the ideas of the pure mathematician who created the world. The creations of the demiurge must accordingly agree to a large extent with those of a human pure mathematician.

The assertion that the world is built according to the principles of "pure" mathematics is to be found not only in the work of Jeans. It is very often used in setting up mystical conceptions of the world. If one wants to be clear as to its meaning, one must first of all obtain clarity as to the meaning of the propositions of "pure" mathematics in general. According to the conception of B. Russell and L. Wittgenstein, which is also that of the Vienna Circle, the propositions of pure mathematics are not statements concerning natural processes, but are purely logical statements concerning the question of what assertions are equivalent to one another, which can be transformed into one another by formal transformations. The propositions of pure mathematics, therefore, remain correct, no matter what the natural processes may be; these propositions can be neither confirmed nor refuted by observations, since they state nothing concerning the real processes of nature. Mathematical theorems, as is often said, are of an analytic character.

For example, if I prove the theorem "The sum of the angles of a triangle is equal to 180°" as a proposition of pure mathematics, I prove only that from the axioms of Euclidean geometry, including the axiom of parallels, it follows by logical transformation that the sum of the angles of a triangle is equal to 180° if the straight lines and points of which it consists have all the properties ascribed to them by the Euclidean axioms. That is to say, if for a concrete physical triangle I can establish by observation the validity of the Euclidean axioms, then the sum of the angles is equal to 180°. In other words, the statements "The sum of the angles is 180°" and "The axioms are valid" are only two expressions of the same thing, two statements with the same content (where, of course, the proposition of the sum of the angles is only a part of the content of the whole system of axioms). Once this has become clear, the world, whatever it may be, will always obey the propositions of pure mathematics; the assertion that it obeys them says nothing at all about the real world. It says only what is self-evident, that all statements about the world can be replaced by equivalent statements.

Something else must obviously be meant, however, when Jeans and so many others say that the world is constructed according to the principles of "pure" mathematics. As an example, the following is adduced: Mathematicians—Christoffel, Helmholtz, Ricci, Levi Cività, and others—long ago built up the theory of the curvature properties of Riemannian space. When Einstein set up his general theory of relativity, he found this whole branch of mathematics ready for him. Although it was invented without any intention of its being used in physics, Einstein was able to apply it in his theory of gravitation and general relativity. One must therefore assume that the creator built the world according to those principles of pure mathematics. Otherwise it would be an inconceivable coincidence that such a complicated branch of mathematics, developed for quite other purposes, could be used for the theory of gravitation.

We have already seen that this assertion cannot mean that the world is built according to the propositions of the Riemannian curvature theory or of the absolute differential calculus invented by Ricci and Levi Cività; for these propositions, like the proposition of the sum of the angles and all other propositions of pure mathematics, are only statements of how one can express the same thing in different ways. The assertion, therefore, can only mean that the concepts and definitions of pure mathematics—the geometry of Riemannian spaces—created certain structures—the Christoffel three-index symbols, the Riemannian curvature tensor—which could be utilized in the Einstein theory of gravitation. This, however, is the same, although perhaps on a higher level, as saying: "The concepts of the square or the square root or the logarithm have come out of pure mathematics; it is therefore amazing that they also occur in the formulas of physics." If we now use the possibility of representing the world according to Einstein, with the help of the Riemannian curvature tensors, as proof that the world was created by a mathematician, we might have said with the same justification, back in the time of Newton, that the world must have been created by a mathematician; for in Newton's formulas the chief role is played by the "square of the distance," and the concept of the square of a number originated in geometry and was introduced without any regard for physics. If we consider the matter from this standpoint, that is, if we speak not of mathematical theorems but of mathematical concepts, a little reflection shows that the distinction drawn by Jeans between engineer and mathematician, or between "applied" and "pure" mathematics, cannot be maintained.

As a matter of fact, concepts such as those of Riemannian curvature have always been invented for the purpose of representing some problem of concrete reality, for describing processes of nature. The concepts of Riemannian geometry all go back to the problem of describing the motion of a real rigid body in general coördinates; one need only recall the work of Helmholtz on the facts at the basis of geometry.[12] Riemann, Christoffel, and Helmholtz set up certain mathematical expressions which are equal to zero in the case of the motion of a rigid body, according to the usual laws of physics. When Einstein proceeded to formulate the deviations from these laws, it was clear that he had to begin with the expressions that gave the properties of rigid bodies, according to classical physics, in a form valid for all coördinate systems. If there existed any deviations expressible independently of the coördinate system, it had to be possible to express them so

[12] "Über den Ursprung und die Bedeutung der geometrische Axiome" (1870), translated as "On the Origin and Significance of Geometrical Axioms," in Helmholtz, *Popular Lectures on Scientific Subjects*, series 2, tr. by E. Atkinson (London: Longmans, Green, 1881).

that the quantities which in the old physics had the value zero were now different from zero and took on values depending in a simple manner on the distribution of matter. If such a simple dependence did not exist, then there could exist no laws independent of the coördinate system, as Einstein required. If such laws did exist, it had to be possible to express them through the concepts that were at hand for representing the motion of a rigid body. But this gives no evidence that the world creator was a "pure mathematician." The only thing that must be regarded as a real and astonishing characteristic of nature is the fact that there do exist, in general, simple laws for the description of nature. This, however, has nothing to do with the distinction between "mechanical" and "mathematical."

If today expressions with spiritualistic coloring are used to a greater extent than in the nineteenth century, this has no connection with any "crises in physics" or with any "new physical conception of nature." It is rather associated with a crisis in human society arising from quite different processes. In opposition to the materialistic social theories there have come into the foreground movements based on an "idealistic" picture of the world. These movements seek support in an idealistic or spiritualistic conception of nature. Just as at the end of the nineteenth century analogous movements made use of energetics, the electromagnetic picture of matter, and so on, to prophesy the end of "materialistic" physics, so today the relativity and quantum theories are being used. All this, however, has no real connection with the progress of physics.

Chapter 6

Mechanical "Explanation" or Mathematical Description?

WHEN THE PHYSICS of Galileo and Newton put an end to the animistic period, it received the honorary title "mathematical." At that time Newton wrote the *Mathematical Principles of Natural Philosophy*. A pronounced antimaterialistic tendency was ascribed to this work, because in it palpable impacts of masses upon one another were replaced by a pure mathematical formula, the law of attraction. The physics of Galileo and Newton did not come to be called "mechanistic" until it had become customary to use the treatment of mechanics as a model for every other field.

The Newtonian mechanics was looked upon more and more as the standard type of a theory. Helmholtz, for example, said:

To understand a phenomenon means nothing else than to reduce it to the Newtonian laws. Then the necessity of explanation has been satisfied in a palpable way.

It was completely forgotten that in Newton's own day his theory was looked upon as a set of abstract mathematical formulas, which needed a mechanical explanation to satisfy man's desire for causality. Newton himself recognized this need, but he declined to take part in satisfying it himself, when he made the now well-known remark, *"Hypotheses non fingo."* But men like Huyghens and Leibniz never considered the Newtonian theory a physical explanation; they looked upon it as only a mathematical formula. Thus even at the very beginning of the development of mechanistic physics, it was not easy to define precisely the distinctions between a "mechanistic" and a "mathematical" theory.

Much later a contradiction began to be noticed between "mathematical" and "pictural," [1] and it was asserted that only the reduction to mechanics guaranteed a theory that provides a

[1] We here translate the German word *anschaulich* by the English *pictural*, which we take to imply, as the German does, both the ordinary visual perception of objects and the mental visualization of them. See also Chapter 7.

140

pictural representation and that without this pictural character no real understanding was possible. It was claimed, for example, that Maxwell's field equations of electrodynamics are not pictural, if they are not illustrated with a mechanical model.

There were two motives involved in the resistance to the abandonment of mechanism. First, there was no inclination to renounce the "explanatory" value that was ascribed to mechanistic theories only; second, it was feared that the abandonment of mechanistic explanations would lead to a return to medieval animistic anthropomorphic science.

But in speaking of this desire for picturization we ought to be clear as to the actual meaning of the term. The mechanical laws describe for us the ordinary experiences of daily life—the use of tools, automobiles, firearms, as well as the movements of the planets. We find it desirable to interpret all other experiences by analogy with those that are most familiar.

The physics of the nineteenth century showed that this wish cannot be fulfilled. Electromagnetic phenomena cannot be reduced to the same mechanical laws that govern guns or tools. Nevertheless, the laws concerning electromagnetic phenomena may be considered in a broader sense as also pictural. We can verify experimentally the validity of such physical laws as, for example, Maxwell's field equations if we can derive from them a result that is directly observable experimentally. The experiment consists in observing the position of the pointer of an ammeter or of some other measuring apparatus, or the displacement of some colored spot. But these are precisely the kind of observation that we use to verify the laws of ordinary mechanics. In the end only gross mechanical events, which certainly are pictural, are derived from the equations of the electromagnetic field, and this holds in all physics, including that of the twentieth century. In this sense physical laws must be pictural if they are to have any scientific meaning at all, for otherwise they are not experimentally verifiable. The fundamental equations by themselves need not be pictural, since they cannot be submitted to any direct experimental verification.

For a long time efforts were made to set up a mechanical explanation of Maxwell's theory. There was always the feeling that without it, something essential to the understanding of electromagnetic phenomena was missing. Heinrich Hertz finally cut the Gordian knot, so to speak, when he said:

"Maxwell's theory is nothing else than Maxwell's equations. That is, the question is not whether these equations are pictural, that is, can be interpreted mechanistically, but only whether pictural conclusions can be derived from them which can be tested by means of gross mechanical experiments."

These words gave birth to what we call today the "positivistic conception" of physics. Positivistic physics thus replaced mechanistic physics. The mechanistic explanation could now be abandoned as a foundation, without at the same time renouncing the achievements of the epoch of Galileo and Newton. If a positivistic conception of physics was accepted, the rejection of medieval animism was as complete as in mechanistic physics. In place of the mechanical model there was the mathematical formula with its experimentally verifiable results. In this sense, it may be said that the positivistic conception replaced the mechanistic interpretation with a mathematical one. Before anything was known about the relativity or the quantum theories, before, therefore, even the "rebirth of idealistic physics in the twentieth century," Hertz, Mach, Duhem and others had already seen that the essential point in every explanation of nature is not the mechanical model but rather the construction of mathematical relations.

The historical error is often made of connecting the struggle of Mach and Duhem for the positivistic physics with their aversion for atomism, so that a victory for atomism was considered a defeat for positivism. In reality the champions of atomism, Maxwell and Boltzmann, were exactly of the same opinion concerning the general nature of a physical theory as Hertz and Mach. The difference in their views about the value of atomistic theories arose only because they differed in their estimates of the convenience with which the actually known physical phenomena could be derived from these theories.

A few quotations from the writings of Maxwell and Boltzmann will at once clear what they thought concerning the structure of physical theories and their connection with experience.

In the introduction to his treatise, *On Faraday's Lines of Force,* Maxwell expressed himself quite clearly on these questions. Boltzmann says in the notes to his German translation of this paper:

Maxwell's introduction proves that he was as much of a pioneer in the theory of knowledge as he was in theoretical physics. All the new ground in the theory of knowledge that was broken in the next forty years, is already clearly marked out in these few pages; indeed the very ideas are illustrated. Later epistemologists treated all this more fully, but also with greater bias. They set up rules for the future development of a theory after it had already developed and not before, as was the case with Maxwell.

Maxwell describes how he first found a convenient mathematical formulation of the laws of electricity and magnetism that were already known, and then used the mathematical concepts so created for the construction of the new laws:

In order therefore to appreciate the requirements of the science, the student must make himself familiar with a considerable body of most intricate mathematics, the mere retention of which in the memory materially interferes with further progress. The first process therefore in the effectual study of the science, must be one of simplification and reduction of the results of previous investigation to a form in which the mind can grasp them. The results of this simplification may take the form of a purely mathematical formula or of a physical hypothesis.[2]

But Maxwell by no means thinks that there is an essential antithesis between a "purely mathematical formula" and a "physical hypothesis." He judges them only according to their practical exchange value, and finds that each of them has its advantages and disadvantages. Hence he looks for a kind of theory that is more general than either and that combines the advantages of both without the disadvantages. This more general sort of theory Maxwell finds in the physical analogy. It comprehends both the physical hypothesis, in which an analogy is drawn between electromagnetic events and a mechanical model, and a mathematical formula, which points out an analogy between the phenomena of electricity and certain mathematical relationships that are given by the electromagnetic-field equations.

Maxwell continues:

In the first case [of a purely mathematical formula] we entirely lose sight of the phenomena to be explained; and though we may trace out the consequences of given laws, we can never obtain

[2] J. C. Maxwell, *On Faraday's Lines of Force, Transactions of the Cambridge Philosophical Society* 10, part 1 (1855); *Scientific Papers of James Clerk Maxwell* (Cambridge University Press, 1890), vol. 1, p. 155.

more extended views of the connections of the subject. If, on the other hand, we adopt a physical hypothesis, we see the phenomena only through a medium, and are liable to that blindness to facts and rashness in assumption which a partial explanation encourages . . . In order to obtain physical ideas without adopting a physical theory we must make ourselves familiar with the existence of physical analogies. By a physical analogy I mean that partial similarity between the laws of one science and those of another which makes each of them illustrate the other. Thus all the mathematical sciences are founded on relations between physical laws and laws of numbers, so that the aim of exact science is to reduce the problems of nature to the determination of quantities by operations with numbers. Passing from the most universal of all analogies to a very partial one, we find the same resemblance in the mathematical form between two different phenomena giving rise to a physical theory of light.[3]

In the introduction to his lectures on the theory of gases Boltzmann's view is brought out very clearly. In one place he says:

The question as to the fitness of the atomistic philosophy is naturally wholly untouched by the fact stressed by Kirchhoff that our theories about nature bear the same relation to it as symbols to the things symbolized, as letters to sounds or as musical notes to tone, and by the question whether it may not be expedient to consider our theories as pure descriptions so that we may always recall their relation to nature. Therefore the question is whether the pure differential equations or atomism will one day turn out the more complete descriptions of phenomena.[4]

[3] *Ibid.*, pp. 155 f.
[4] L. Boltzmann, *Vorlesungen über Gastheorie* (Leipzig: Barth, ed. 3, 1923), vol. 1, p. 6.

Chapter 7

Modern Physics and Common Sense

ALMOST EVERY new physical theory has to face the common-place accusation that it stands in contradiction to everyday experience or, as it is sometimes put, that it contradicts common sense. The heliocentric system of Copernicus is perhaps the most famous example of a theory that has been charged with being in contradiction to the evidence of our senses. For on the one hand, many of us have grown accustomed to believing that our eyes disclose to us the earth is at rest with the sun and planets revolving around it. On the other hand, the Copernican theory, established since the time of Galileo, maintains that the sun is at rest and the earth revolves around it, "in contradiction to this immediate testimony of our eyes."

Although this accusation has been made in innumerable books, articles, and lectures, it is difficult to understand what could be meant by a physical theory's being in contradiction to the evidence of our senses. Such a contradiction could occur only if the theory implied propositions about directly observable matters which were not confirmed by actual observations. This, however, is not the case for the Copernican theory. In point of fact, the content of our observations on sunsets and sunrises can be deduced from the heliocentric theory as well as from the geocentric one. It must therefore be noted that our sensory observations are not adequately formulated in such a proposition as "We see immediately that it is the sun which is moving and not the earth." For when we formulate our direct observations of the solar motions we obtain statements like the following: "The distance between the sun and the horizon increases from morning to noon, and decreases from noon to evening." And such propositions can obviously be deduced from the Copernican as well as from the Ptolemaic theory. Consequently, the charge of a contradiction between a given physical theory and the evidence of our senses cannot be supported, if we understand by "evidence of our senses" the propositions that can be deduced from the theory and checked by experiment.

145

Our preference for the heliocentric theory rather than the geocentric one is based on the following two points. First, the heliocentric theory makes it possible to calculate more simply the observable positions of the planets in their orbits than does the geocentric theory. Second, generalizations, such as Newton's laws of motion, can be made much more easily on the basis of the heliocentric theory than on the geocentric one. Such facts of observation as the perturbations of the planetary orbits could be shown to be consistent with the geocentric theory only by using formulas and computations that would exceed the powers of a human mathematician. On the other hand, starting from Newton's laws of motion these perturbations can be calculated with the help of relatively simple formulas within the framework of the heliocentric theory.

So much for the logical issues involved in the charge. There is, however, an obvious psychologic reason why people continue to make it. If we consider only the facts of everyday experience, such as the daily rising and setting of the sun, moon, and stars, we discover that they can be deduced from the geocentric theory with great ease. To deduce from this theory the facts concerned with the movements of the planets is still possible, though highly inconvenient and involved. If now we also consider the phenomena of perturbation, we find that to deduce them from the geocentric theory is practically impossible, and that the Copernican theory alone is capable of handling them. On the other hand, the deduction of everyday phenomena like sunrise and sunset can be performed more easily and simply from the geocentric theory than from the more "artificial" heliocentric theory—especially if we take the latter in its completely developed form as given by Newton, so that it becomes adequate for encompassing the phenomena of planetary perturbation.

We may therefore formulate the difference in function of the two theories in the logical system of science as follows: If we are concerned with the deduction of phenomena occurring in the narrow domain of everyday experience, it is convenient to use the geocentric theory. But since the scope of the facts falling within the province of this theory is very restricted, if we seek a theory that will embrace as many phenomena as possible (including phenomena remote from daily experience), we must make use of the heliocentric theory.

Because the geocentric theory is more convenient for handling familiar phenomena of daily life, it is often called an "intuitive" or "visualizable" theory. Indeed, many people have the impression that they fully understand this theory by a direct, immediate observation of facts, and that no logical gap separates it from the content of our naïve sensory observations. However, all these characterizations of the theory mean nothing more than that a relatively simple chain of deductions connects it with the observable phenomena of daily life.

On the other hand, because the deduction of our most familiar observations from the heliocentric theory is not as simple as in the case of the geocentric one, there is a common impression that the former is not connected closely with everyday experience. It has therefore been called an "abstract" or "nonintuitive" theory, apparently because the facts of experience upon which it rests occur only in the context of scientific research, as when we use astronomical intruments to determine the exact positions of the stars.

This familiar distinction between "intuitive" and "abstract" theories is, however, often misunderstood and misused. Thus, it has been said that "intuitive" theories are the only sound ones, because they alone serve as a stimulus to the physicists to carry on fruitful research. They have also been said to offer a true representation of the real world in terms of faithful pictures or images, thus furthering the scientist in his search for the truth. On the other hand, "abstract" theories, which employ mathematical formulas rather than the method of pictorial representation, have been characterized as impediments to scientific progress. It has been said of them that they can at best register knowledge already achieved, but that they are of no help in the discovery of new knowledge.

These alleged differences between intuitive and abstract theories are regarded as particularly significant by followers of Kant and other adherents of German idealistic philosophy. For intuitive or visualizable theories have been claimed to be *"anschaulich"* in the sense specified by Kant. Now in everyday German the word *Anschauung* simply means the observation of an object, especially a visual observation, for example, the visual perception of a table. But for Kant and other idealistic philosophers it frequently has a half-mystical meaning. Thus, when they speak of an *"innere Anschauung"* or "internal intuition" of the properties of a triangle, for example, they do not mean to refer to a visual perception of a triangle, but to some mental act of concentration upon the triangle, which itself exists only in the mind as an image. We shall translate the term *innere Anschauung* by the English word "picturization," and *anschaulich* by "pictural." According to the Kantian philosophy, we are supposed to be able to "see" directly in this mental act such things as that the sum of the angles of a triangle must be equal to two right angles. Accordingly, this alleged power of picturization is claimed to be able to establish the essential properties of triangles without appealing to empirical tests and without regarding the theorems of geometry as propositions consisting of observation terms —where "observation" is used in the familiar sense of observation through the senses. In this way Euclidean geometry was "proved" to be the only legitimate geometry. The non-Euclidean geometries were alleged to have been demonstrated to be false, because their theorems were not guaranteed by picturization. In opposition to these dicta, we must note, however, that the propositions of non-Euclidean geometry can be formulated in observational terms just as the Euclidean propositions can be, and that the alleged absurdity of the former arises only from the fact that they are required to be "tested" by an internal intuition.

These ambiguities in the meaning of "intuition" or *Anschauung* have made it possible for the intuitive theories of physics to acquire a special importance in the eyes of philosophers and even of some physicists. In the Germany of 1939, for example, the differences between intuitive and abstract theories were linked up with differences between races. Intuitive theories were associated with the characteristics of the Nordic race, while the abstract ones were taken as expressing the peculiarities of the Mediterranean races, especially of the Semites, though sometimes even of the French. Naturally, since the Nordic race was regarded as the superior group, intuitive theories were also superior to the abstract ones.

But the preceding discussion of the differences between the heliocentric and the geocentric theories makes clear just what the difference between these two types of theory really signifies. What is usually called an "intuitive" or pictural theory is simply a theory very well adapted to formulate in a simple and convenient manner our everyday experiences; an abstract theory, on the other hand, attempts to cover a more inclusive domain of phenomena, and does not hesitate therefore to formulate the familiar facts of daily life in a somewhat complex manner.

If we are once clear about the differences between the geocentric and heliocentric theories, we are prepared to understand and evaluate the objections often raised against more recent physical theories, such as the theory of relativity or the quantum theory. These objections tend, in the main, to allege that the new theories are too abstract and that they use conceptions very far removed from those employed in everyday experience. Indeed, some physicists have argued that the newer conceptions are too remote from the notions employed by physicists themselves in their laboratory researches.

Our previous analysis supplies us with a clue for evaluating these objections. The laws formulated by so-called classical physics are obtained from the study of material bodies and optical phenomena as these occur either in everyday experience, or in physical experiments carried on under conditions not very different from the circumstances of everyday experience. With the help of these laws, the behavior of bodies and of light in these domains can be expressed in a simple and useful way. Until the end of the nineteenth century these laws have been supposed to govern all the phenomena of the physical world, from the smallest bodies, like electrons, to the largest ones, like suns and stars, and from motions with low velocities to motions with the velocity of light. But the development of physical research at the end of the nineteenth century and the beginning of the twentieth showed that the laws of classical physics are valid only for small velocities and large bodies—to speak more exactly, for masses far greater than the mass of an electron, and for velocities far less than the velocity of light.

Now to express the behavior of things that do not occur in daily experience, such as small particles with large velocities, we require a generalization of classical physics and new types of physical law. These new laws are naturally more complex than the laws of classical physics, especially if we compare them in their applications to phenomena of common experience; in these domains the laws of classical physics are limiting cases of the new laws of relativity and quantum physics. On the other hand, there is no sense in saying that these new laws, when applied to phenomena, such as those within the hydrogen atom that do not occur in daily experience, are more complex than the classical laws, because the classical laws do not apply to these phenomena at all. Consequently, only in the sense indicated is it correct to say that the laws of classical physics are more closely related to everyday experience than are the laws of twentieth-century physics, namely, the laws of relativity and quantum physics.

It is evident, therefore, that from the standpoint of the logical analysis of science the difference between intuitive and abstract theories is a very superficial one. That distinction does not play the important role in science that philosophers and laymen influenced by orthodox philosophy suggest it does.

A glance at the history of science also reveals that the alleged wide gap between these two kinds of theory is not understood in the same manner at every period of the history of science. Thus, at the time of its discovery, Newton's theory of motion was regarded as an abstract, merely mathematical theory; in our own day, however, it is often cited as an example of an intuitive theory, especially when philosophers wish to establish the abstract character of the theory of relativity and of quantum mechanics by contrasting them with an intuitive theory. In truth, however, the alleged difference between Newtonians and relativistic mechanics depends only on the undeniable fact that the difficult and complicated calculations and deductions required for understanding Einstein's theory of relativity are not required for understanding the phenomena of everyday experience. For these phenomena can be formulated with the help of the more simple Newtonian theory of mechanics. Hence the statement that a theory like Einstein's is abstract and nonintuitive simply means that it is more complex than is necessary for a theory that need describe only the facts of daily experience.

It is often maintained that whether a given scientist will be more inclined to use an intuitive rather than an abstract theory is a function of his personality. These psychologic factors are sometimes taken to be facts of individual psychology, sometimes of race or of nationality. It seems to me, however, that the importance of such psychologic considerations has been exaggerated. Such psychologic factors seem to play little role in the work of the great masters of science to whom we are chiefly indebted for the present state of the sciences. Some masters of science exhibit a "double personality."

For example, the great English physicist J. Clerk Maxwell employed elaborate mechanical models in his work, as well as abstract mathematical theories. He discovered many new facts with the help of both types of theory, and was himself firmly convinced that there is no fundamental difference between these two types from the point of view of the logical analysis of science. Indeed, he emphasized the fact that both abstract and intuitive theories are special cases of a more inclusive type of formulation of physical facts, namely, formulation or representation by analogies. And if we examine the work of Boltzmann and other great physicists interested in the logical structure of science, we find them regarding physical theories in the same characteristic way.

We may therefore sum up our considerations on the differences between abstract theories and those alleged to be intuitive and comprehensible to common sense. Intuitive theories try to preserve so far as possible the method of representation invented for handling most simply the facts of daily life. Such theories are therefore comprehensible to everyone who is concerned with those facts and are thus comprehensible to so-called common sense. Mechanical images or models are particularly cherished in this context, and conservative minds will perhaps always prefer using this method of representation.

But the progress of physical research reveals facts that cannot be adequately covered by such intuitive theories. Progressive physicists therefore try to find new ways of representation, new theories which are adequate for as broad a domain of facts as possible, irrespective of whether the new methods supply the simplest representation of the facts that occur in everyday experience. It is thus possible that a new theory, although the simplest one thus far invented for handling subatomic phenomena, turns out to be quite complicated for representing such phenomena as apples falling from trees. For this reason such a theory is alleged to be incomprehensible to common sense, and conservative minds are always reluctant to accept it.

It is thus evident that the difference between the so-called two types of theory has little to do with psychologic difference between those physicists who like to reason abstractly and mathematically and those who like to use concrete images or models. If we examine carefully the work of modern physicists engaged in research on the quantum theory, we discover that the psychologic fact that some of them prefer mathematical formulas while others prefer geometric imagery does not account for their attitude to the quantum theory. For the majority of physicists accept that theory, while only a minority denounce it, claiming that their "mental constitution" forces them to regard quantum theory as incomprehensible to common sense and as an unsuitable basis for laboratory research. Indeed, representatives of both psychologic types are found among those physicists who have contributed to the progress of quantum theory.

The common impression that there is a profound gap between these two kinds of theory may perhaps be due to the fact that the fundamental propositions of science are often formulated in what Carnap calls the "material idiom" instead of in the "formal idiom." Thus, if we ask whether the physical world consists of bodies situated in space whose motions are governed by laws, or of purely mathematical properties of a four-dimensional space-time continuum, we have formulated the question in the "material idiom" or "material mode." So formulated, it leads to innumerable disputes of a metaphysical character. We can avoid such disputes by stating the question in a consistently scientific form, using the "formal idiom." When so stated it becomes the following: Do the fundamental propositions of physics (i.e., its most general laws) contain only terms of the thing-language, or do they contain also terms that do not occur in the thing-language?[1] It is important to observe that even if the second alternative should be the case, the terms not occurring in the thing-language are *reducible* to terms in the thing-language; for otherwise the propositions containing them would be neither confirmable nor refutable in experience. It is clear, therefore, that when the question has been stated in this way, the difference between abstract and intuitive theories has ceased to have the fundamental character often attributed to it. For when the

---

[1] The term "thing-language" is used by Carnap in the description of the world of our sense experience, as an alternative to "phenomenal" language. The latter decomposes our impressions of the physical world into elementary sensations, such as those of small areas of red or blue. The thing-language speaks of complexes of sense impressions as they occur in our everyday language, like "table," "chair," "man."

formal idiom is used, the difference simply amounts to the difference between propositions containing only thing-terms and propositions containing other than thing-terms which are, however, reducible to thing-terms.

Since it is just our everyday experiences that are most conveniently formulated by the so-called intuitive theories, especially those using the language of mechanical models, the outstanding characteristic of such theories is that they give rise to the introduction of a thing-language. And certainly an intellectual effort is required to overcome the reluctance to using a language that is not a thing-language, however useful such a new language might be for formulating the laws of physics about facts discovered by recent research. Accordingly, we can extract one grain of truth from the claim that intuitive theories (especially mechanical ones) are the only genuine physical theories that are compatible with the requirements of the laboratory scientist. This grain of truth lies in the postulate that every physical theory must contain only such terms as are reducible to terms of the thing-language. This postulate, stated in other words, simply means that every physical theory must be tested in terms of propositions that deal with the facts of everyday experience.

The theory of relativity has often been described as abstract, in contrast with theories about the ether, which are said to be intuitive or pictural. For the latter theories introduce a matter-like ether, which is asserted to behave in many ways like the bodies of everyday experience, while relativity theory, on the other hand, introduces only abstract, disembodied formulas. Similarly, quantum mechanics, like relativity theory, is said to introduce a system of purely mathematical formulas, which cannot be interpreted either in terms of waves, particles, or any other visualizable things.

Nevertheless, it is easy to see that the difference between classical mechanics and relativity mechanics has nothing to do with the supposed difference between a "natural" and an "artificial" or "sophisticated" theory. To characterize the difference between classical and relativistic mechanics in this way is as incorrect as a similar judgment on the difference between the geocentric and heliocentric theories in astronomy.

Classical mechanics is very convenient for describing and predicting motions of bodies with velocities small in comparison with the velocity of light. Such comparatively slow motions include the movements of bodies we observe daily, even the movements of the celestial bodies such as the sun, moon, and stars. In order to describe these motions it is convenient to introduce the term "length of a body" without specifying any frame of reference with respect to which this length is to be measured. Similarly, we use the expression "two events occur simultaneously" without requiring the specification of a frame of reference in order that the expression should have a definite meaning.

However, the situation becomes altered if we try to describe and predict the motions of bodies having velocities comparable with the velocity of light, for example, the β-rays of radium, or cathode rays. In order to formulate in the simplest way the laws governing such rapid motions, it is found most convenient to drop the term "length of a body" and introduce the new term "length of a body A with respect to a body B," where B has a determinate velocity with respect to A. The definition of the "relative length of a body" will consist in the description of the procedures of measurement involved, just as in the case of the definition for the so-called "absolute length" of a body. Since all these procedures of measurement are described in the thing-language of daily life, there is no occasion to regard one of these definitions as more abstract than the other. The definition of "relative length" involves the use of observation terms just as does the definition of "absolute length," the sole difference being that the first definition is slightly more complicated. The use of "relative length" in the description of the motions of bodies occurring in daily experience would complicate those descriptions unnecessarily; but it would not make them either too abstract or unintuitive. On the other hand, were we to use the term "absolute length of a body" in describing the behavior of bodies having velocities comparable with that of light, we would also greatly complicate our descriptions; that is to say, our system of physics dealing with such bodies would become very inconvenient if we persisted in using the term "length of a body" according to the formative rules by which the syntax of the language of classical physics is determined. The most familiar and popular example of such a complication is the necessity of introducing the terms "ether" and "velocity with respect to the ether" into the system of physics. These terms, however, remain in a sense isolated from most other terms of physics, simply because no experiment can be set up by which we could determine the magnitude of this "velocity with respect to the ether."

Einstein's theory of relativity in effect introduces new formative rules into the system of physics for the use of the term "length of a body." According to these rules the term "length of a body" can occur in sentences only if the sentences also contain such qualifying expressions as "with respect to a specified reference frame." In this way superfluous terms like "velocity with respect to the ether" can be eliminated from the language of physics, while at the same time the laws governing high velocities like those possessed by β-rays can be formulated in a very simple way.

Similar considerations hold for the term "simultaneously." In classical mechanics it is used in accordance with a certain set of formative rules which do not require that sentences containing the term also contain the qualifying phrase "with respect to a specified frame of reference." In relativistic mechanics we employ a different set of formative rules; according to these rules the term "simultaneously" may be employed only if the indicated qualifying phrase also occurs.

These syntactical differences between classical and relativistic mechanics are often expressed in ways that easily lead to misunderstandings. Thus, it is sometimes said that classical mechanics considers simultaneity in an "absolute sense" while relativistic mechanics does so in a "relative" sense. It is advisable, however, to state the matter intended by using the "formal idiom," and to express the difference in terms of the different formative rules according to which the word "simultaneous" is used in classical and relativistic mechanics. For if we talk of "simultaneity in an absolute and in a relative sense" we are easily led to the meaningless question whether absolute simultaneity *exists* or not.

It is clear that there is no difference between these two sets of formative rules in their being "abstract" or "intuitive" on the one hand, or "natural" or "intuitive" on the other. The sole significant difference between them is that the language of classical mechanics together with its formative rules is more convenient for discussing motions of bodies that occur in daily experience, while the language of relativistic mechanics and its distinctive formative rules is more suitable for formulating the more inclusive field of phenomena which contains bodies with high velocities.

Anyone who supposes that the formative rules of relativistic syntax are artificial, nonintuitive, or abstract in comparison with the rules for classical mechanics can readily convince himself of the contrary by imagining himself in a world in which the phenomena of daily experience occur in a way somewhat different from the way they usually do. It will then be evident that both in the case of quantum physics and in the case of relativity theory, the laws alleged to be in accordance with "common sense" will be of quite different type from what is usually maintained.

Let us, therefore, in the manner of H. G. Wells, imagine a world in which the flight of a tennis ball cannot be formulated and predicted in terms of Newton's laws. Thus we may suppose that the path taken by a ball is not determined by the way in which it is struck with the racket. We also suppose that the only law which can be established in this world simply states *with what percentage* balls struck in a certain way take a determined direction with a determinate velocity. Tennis matches could be organized in this world just as well as in the ordinary Newtonian world, and skilled players would return served balls more often than those not skilled. Although the game would be played in accordance with the ordinary rules of tennis, it would be evident to a careful observer that even the most proficient players would often not succeed in sending the ball in an intended direction even when the ball is struck in the appropriate way.

In such a world neither the familiar man-in-the-street with his well-known common sense, nor the laboratory physicists with a critical attitude toward all "abstract" theories, would claim it to be a matter of common sense that the laws governing the motions of tennis balls should be formulated in terms of the expression "the position and velocity of a tennis ball at the moment after it is struck." For such an expression would not occur in any of the laws with the help of which the direction of flight of a struck ball could be predicted. Indeed, in this imagined world the laws would require a specification of the way in which a ball is struck, but would have no use for the specification of the velocity a ball acquires on being hit. In brief, even everyday experience in this world would not be formulated in laws containing the expression "ball with a determinate position and velocity." The expression would not be employed in the language of daily affairs, and would be taken to be as meaningless for everyday experiences as it in fact is in the actual world of atomic physics. For in this imagined world tennis balls behave in the fashion of the atoms and their nuclei of our actual world.

The impression often current that the language of quantum physics is artificial and contradictory to common sense arises from the fact that this language is unnecessarily exact for use in the affairs of daily experience. If, however, the things in daily experience behaved as tennis balls would behave in our imagined world, this language would be the one most suitable for discussing even the most familiar matters. In that case no one would dream of claiming that the language of quantum physics is artificial or that it is incompatible with common sense. It would be accepted as a very natural language indeed, and would be judged to be as convenient and suitable for everyday matters as quantum mechanics is now taken to be for the phenomena of atomic nuclei.

Chapter 8

Philosophic Misinterpretations of the Quantum Theory

1. The Origin of Philosophic Interpretations of Physical Theories

As SOON as any new physical theory appears, it is used to contribute something toward setting the controversial questions of philosophy, the questions on which philosophers have been working for centuries without coming a single step closer to their solution. Numerous examples of such use suggest themselves. When J. J. Thomson showed that every electrically charged particle possesses inertia just as a mechanical mass does and gave a formula for calculating the mechanical mass of a particle from its charge and size, people deduced from this result arguments to prove that all matter is only a phantom. They found in it an argument *for* the idealistic world view and *against* materialism. Similar interpretations were suggested when energetics arose and phenomena were represented as energy transformations rather than as arising from collisions of masses. The theory of relativity then introduced four-dimensional non-Euclidean space instead of the three-dimensional Euclidean space in which the directly observable processes of everyday life take place. Later, wave mechanics described physical processes with the aid of the probability concept, which has been often said to be a purely spiritual factor, instead of with the aid of mass particles. Everywhere it appears that the spiritual element is replacing the grossly material.

Such interpretations were attached with especial intensity to Niels Bohr's theory of the complementary nature of certain physical descriptions, from which it was hoped that arguments for vitalistic biology and for free will might be obtained.

If one scans all such interpretations, the empirically establishable fact is found that they all further a movement toward a certain world picture. It is not a case of different

158

world pictures being involved; the same one keeps coming up again and again.

Through the work of Galileo and Newton, anthropomorphic medieval physics was expelled from conscious intellectual life. There remained, however, an unfulfilled longing to bring about the unity of animate and inanimate nature which had been present in medieval physics but was missing in the newer physics. There was left only one problem, for which no satisfactory solution could be envisaged: to understand the processes of life in terms of physics. For that was the necessary condition for a unified conception of nature after the disappearance of the anthropomorphic conception of physics, which had fitted in so well with the vitalistic conception of life.

Every crisis in the history of physical theories is associated with a certain lack of clarity in their formulation, and this unfulfilled longing bursts forth with great strength from the unconscious. Efforts were made to complete the new physical theories by "philosophic interpretations" in order to proclaim the imminence of a return to the anthropomorphic physics of the Middle Ages and a consequent reëstablishment of the lost unity of nature. Spiritualistic physics was to hold the possibility of embracing the living processes also.

The assertion is often heard that there is also a philosophic interpretation of physical theories in the service of materialistic-metaphysical picture of the world. However, this symmetrical conception of spiritualism and materialism is a very superficial one. A "materialistic metaphysics," in general, does not exist today as a living intellectual current. At most, it is represented for the domain of physics by those philosophers or scientists who wish to make as wide a gulf as possible between physics and biology, in order to obtain in the field of the living or the social processes free play for a spiritualistic metaphysics.

If, on the other hand, one understands by materialism the belief that all processes of nature can be reduced to the laws of Newtonian mechanics, then this is not a philosophic principle but a physical hypothesis. True, it is a physical hypothesis that has been shown to be wrong, but a physical statement it remains. This false hypothesis is not accepted today by any of the philosophic schools that one is accustomed to designate polemically as "materialistic"—neither by the "dialectical materialism" of Soviet Russia, nor by the "physical-ists" that have come out of the Vienna Circle.

The process of the philosophic interpretation of physical theories in the service of the spiritualistic conception of the universe can be analyzed both psychologically and logically. From the psychologic standpoint, the following, roughly, has been established: The physicist, like every other educated person, acquires the remnants of prescientific theories as a "philosophic" world picture, which in our cultural circles consists mostly in a vague idealism or spiritualism as it is usually learned from lectures on general philosophy. The principles of this philosophy are unclear and difficult to understand. The physicist is happy if he finds in his science any propositions that have in their formulation some similarity to propositions of idealistic philosophy. He is often very proud that his field of work helps him throw some light on the general doctrines that are so important for this world picture. Thus even the slightest similarity in the wording is enough to induce the physicist to offer a proposition of his science as support for the idealistic philosophy.

If J. J. Thomson speaks of "real" and "apparent" mass, the philosophically educated physicist is eager to bring this mode of expression into connection with the distinction between a "real" and an "apparent" world. The statement that mechanical mass is only "apparent" mass is then taken as confirmation of philosophic idealism, according to which matter is only an illusion.

Of greater scientific interest is the logical structure of these philosophic misinterpretations. The process of thought leading to them consists of two steps. First, physical propositions that are really statements about observable processes are regarded as statements about a real, metaphysical world. Such statements are meaningless from the standpoint of science, since they can be neither confirmed nor contradicted by any observation. The first step is therefore the transition to a meaningless metaphysical proposition. In the second step this proposition, by means of a rather small change in wording, goes over into a proposition which again has a meaning, but is no longer in the realm of physics; it now expresses a wish that people should behave in a certain way. This proposition is then no longer metaphysical, but has become a principle of morality, of ethics, or of some other system of conduct.

One can adduce numerous examples of such processes involving two steps. As the simplest, we choose the well-known example of the electromagnetic mass. J. J. Thomson formulated the purely physical proposition that every electrically charged body possesses mechanical inertia, which can be calculated from the charge. To this has been added the hypothesis, likewise physical, that the *entire* mass of the body can be calculated in this way. Philosophers then expressed this as a metaphysical principle by saying: "In the real world there is no mechanical mass at all." This principle obviously has no scientific content. From it there follow no observable facts. As the second step, it was asserted that the material world, as a mere illusion, is unimportant in comparison to the world of the spirit, and that therefore man in his actions can or should neglect any changes in the material world and should devote himself to his spiritual perfection.

When influential groups express such wishes, the fact has a great importance for human life, of course, and possesses a meaning, but there evidently exists no logical connection with the electromagnetic theory of matter, and the whole thing arises only through this misinterpretation with its two steps.

The essential part of the misinterpretation is the passage through the "real" metaphysical world. The misinterpretation can therefore be avoided only if one tries to set up a direct short circuit between the physical principle and the moral principle. This can be done, for example, through the consistent use of the "physicalistic language," which Neurath and Carnap have suggested as the universal language of science.

As understood in Carnap's "logical syntax," the source of these misinterpretations is always the use of the "material mode of speech." The contrast between "apparent" and "real" mass is made to appear as a statement about a fact of the observable world, whereas it is really a syntactic rule about the use of the word "real." Only the formula for the connection between electric charge and inertia is a statement about the observable world.

Quite the same logical structure is possessed by the misinterpretations of the relativity and quantum theories. The first has been employed to provide a basis for the belief in predestination, the second to give scientific arguments for "spontaneity of action" and "freedom of the will."

2. The Complementary Conceptions
of Quantum Mechanics and Their Interpretations

The philosophic misinterpretations of quantum mechanics can be best understood if we remember that the same tendencies are at work here as in the interpretation of previous theories, and that the process takes place along exactly the same lines, both psychologically and logically.

First we must make clear the meaning of the complementarity conception in physics.

One often reads the following formulation: "It is *impossible to measure the position and the velocity* of a moving particle simultaneously." The world, therefore, just as it is according to classical mechanics, is filled with particles having definite positions and velocities; unfortunately, we can never attain a knowledge of them. This presentation, in which the states of the particles play the role of the "thing in itself" in idealistic philosophy, leads to innumerable pseudo problems. It introduces physical objects, namely, particles with definite positions and velocities, about which the physical laws of quantum mechanics say nothing at all. These objects play a role similar to that of the reference system that is absolutely at rest, which some wish to add to the theory of relativity but which never occurs in any physical proposition. In both cases the reason for this addition is that such expressions were found useful in the earlier state of physics, and the school philosophy had made of them constituents of the "real world"; therefore they must be kept forever.

Another way of representing the situation consists in saying that particles "in general *do not possess definite positions and velocities* simultaneously." This mode of expression appears to me to have the difficulty that the combination of words "particle with an indefinite position or velocity" transgresses the syntactic rules according to which the words "particle," "position," and "indefinite" are ordinarily used in physics and everyday life. Of course, there would be no objection if a new syntax were introduced for these words for the purposes of quantum mechanics. In that case, expressions like "particle with an indefinite position" could be employed inside of physics without any danger. And there exist many correct works on the quantum theory in which this is the case. However, gross misunderstandings arise as soon as this way of speaking is used in matters where it is no longer a question of the quantum theory. We can bring about this transition to other fields only by regarding the particle with an indefinite position as a constituent of the "real world"—and then we are right in the midst of the philosophic misinterpretations that were described in Section I.

I believe that, as a starting point for a correct formulation of the complementarity idea, one must retain as exactly as possible the formulation set forth by Bohr in 1936.

Quantum mechanics speaks neither of particles the positions and velocities of which exist but cannot be accurately observed, nor of particles with indefinite positions and velocities. Rather, it speaks of experimental arrangements in the description of which the expressions "position of a particle" and "velocity of a particle" can never be employed simultaneously. If in the description of an experimental arrangement the expression "position of a particle" can be used, then in the description of the same arrangement the expression "velocity of a particle" can *not* be used, and vice versa. Experimental arrangements, one of which can be described with the help of the expression "position of a particle" and the other with the help of the expression "velocity" or, more exactly, "momentum," are called *complementary* arrangements, and the descriptions are referred to as *complementary* descriptions.

If one adheres strictly to this terminology one will never run the risk of falling into a metaphysical conception of physical complementarity. For it is clear that nothing is said here about a "real world," nor about its constitution, nor about its cognizability, nor even about its indefiniteness.

A great seduction to metaphysical interpretations lies in the frequently occurring formulation of complementarity according to which the "space-time" and the "causal" descriptions are said to be complementary. In this way the fact is often hidden that this again only means the complementarity of position and momentum, or of time and energy. By "causal description" we understand here only the description by means of the principles of conservation of energy and of momentum, which does not quite agree with what is usually understood by causality. In popular presentations, among which are those of some physicists, this is not always set forth clearly. This lack of clarity arises from the use of the expressions "space," "time," and "causality," which as a kind of trinity play a somewhat mysterious role in idealistic philosophy. If by "space-time description" is meant simply the assignment of coördinates and time, by "causal description" the application of the conservation principles, then this beloved terminology can be retained, of course. But it then loses the charm of the mysterious and can no longer be used to pave the way for a transition from physics to idealistic philosophy, thereby favoring those misunderstandings described in Section I.

If we are once in the midst of metaphysical formulations, we can easily come to rather crass misinterpretations. As an example, I shall give one by a very prominent physicist. A. Sommerfeld says (*Scientia*, 1936):

> If we treat the human body physiologically, we must speak of a corpuscular localized event. To the psychic principle we can assign no localization, but must treat it—and this is also the opinion of psycho-physiologists—as if it were present more or less throughout the body, just as the wave is connected with the corpuscle in an unspecifiable way.

Here we may see with great clarity how every metaphysical formulation of a statement of physics can be used with great ease to support a statement of idealistic philosophy that only sounds somewhat similar.

To express the idea of complementarity for physics in closest association to Bohr's formulation, so that it will not lead to any metaphysical misinterpretations but yet can be carried over to fields outside of physics, one will have to proceed somewhat as follows:

The language in which occur statements like "The particle is at this place and has this velocity" is suited to experiences involving gross mechanical processes and cannot be employed satisfactorily for the description of atomic processes. However, one can give a group of experimental arrangements for the atomic domain in the description of which the expression "position of a particle" can be used. In the description of these experiments—and in this consists the idea of Bohr— the expression "velocity of a particle" can *not* be used. In the atomic domain, therefore, certain parts of the language of gross mechanics can be used. The experimental arrangements, however, in the description of which these parts can be used, exclude each other.

Meaningless metaphysical propositions immediately arise if one says that "reality" itself is "dual" or displays "different aspects."

3. Complementarity as an Argument for Vitalism and Free Will

Many physicists and philosophers have tried to make use of Bohr's doctrine of the complementarity of physical concepts in order to obtain arguments for the impossibility of an understanding of biology and psychology in terms of physics. Here we can distinguish something like a psychologic and a biologic argument. The first runs approximately as follows: If one seeks to describe a psychic state in terms of introspective psychology, the state is so strongly altered by self-observation that it is no longer the original state. It is not possible to be angry and at the same time to observe and describe one's anger. The existence of a psychic state is incompatible with its observation.

The second runs something like this: If one wishes to describe the state of a living organism by means of physical quantities, the measurement of these quantities requires such a severe disturbance of the organism that it must be killed. The description of a living being through physical variables is incompatible with its ilfe.

The psychologic argument is basically a good one. It is a long-recognized doctrine of every positivistic conception of science, including that of A. Comte, that one cannot found any logically connected psychology on principles obtained through self-observation. One must go over to an objective observation of human actions and movements of expression, as required by American behaviorism, and in accordance with the logical analysis given by Carnap and Neurath of the statements concerning psychic processes.

If psychology is formulated in terms of behaviorism or physicalism, the psychologic argument coincides with the biologic one.

If one applies the Bohr idea of complementarity, one can formulate the role of self-observation in psychology somewhat as follows: There are certain experimental arrangements in the field of psychology that can be described with the aid of propositions and expressions obtained from self-observation. There are other situations in our life that cannot be described with these expressions. In this there is no contradiction. As in physics, so in psychic life there are complementary situations, and complementary languages for their description.

Taking this complementarity into consideration, one will easily see what can be gained for the understanding of *free will* from the analogy to the quantum theory. Even before Bohr's discovery of complementarity, M. Planck had advanced the following argument for the compatibility of free will with physical causality: If a man could calculate his future actions from the present pattern of the physical world, this knowledge would react on his present state—for example, on the molecules of his brain—and thus change his state. Hence there is no predictability of the future. Hence free will cannot be in contradiction to the physical causality of occurrences in the human body.

From this it only follows that a man cannot calculate his future actions from the results of self-observation. It might still be possible, however, for one to calculate beforehand the actions of other men, and to do so even from purely physical observations.

If one applies here Bohr's idea of complementarity, one can give to the whole matter a firmer logical structure. One can then say: Certain situations of human behavior are described with the help of the expression "free will"; under other experimental conditions this expression cannot be used. We are, therefore, dealing here with complementary situations and with complementary descriptions, but not with any contradictions. Bohr himself pointed out that his considerations of complementarity cannot be used to provide an argument for "free will"; they can only yield a useful representation of the epistemologic status of the problem.

It seems to me, however, that there is also a certain objection to the use of the words "free will" for the description of certain situations, corresponding to the experimental arrangements in physics. Expressions like "position of a particle" are expressions taken from the physics of everyday life which, because of complementarity, remain suitable for atomic physics only in certain special situations. Likewise, "free will" would have to be an expression from the psychology of daily life which in scientific psychology could be employed only under certain experimental conditions. This, however, seems to me not to be the case. "Free will" is not an expression from the psychology of daily life; it is rather a metaphysical or theological expression. In everyday life "freedom" is never anything other than "freedom from external coercion," or at most "freedom from intoxication and hypnosis." This has nothing to do with the philosophic conception of freedom of will. If it is correct to say, following Bohr, that the expression "free will" can be used advantageously for the description of certain situations, this expression can refer only to the quite unphilosophic concept drawn from the psychology of everyday life. Hence from this use no conclusions can be drawn about the philosophic freedom of will. It is only necessary to put to oneself the question whether, for the general situation in which the concept of free will is used in practice, any change has been created by quantum mechanics and the complementarity concept. By this I mean, of course, the application of the freedom concept to the question of the responsibility of a criminal, and to the related question of the harshness or lightness of the punishment. One need only formulate precisely the whole idea of complementarity and follow through carefully the whole chain of ideas up to the punishment of the criminal to see at once that no consequences follow here for the problem under consideration. It is therefore very questionable whether it is appropriate to use the expression "free will" in the applications of the complementarity idea to psychology.

If, however, in accordance with the new conceptions of behaviorism and physicalism, psychology is based on principles containing, not statements about self-observation, but statements about the behavior of experimental subjects, then the complementarity considerations in psychology as just described drop out, and psychology becomes a part of biology. In that case the psychologic argument of Bohr reduces to the biologic one. It is, therefore, a question of whether the behavior of living organisms can be represented by laws in which only physical variables occur.

If one wishes to describe a living being physically, one must specify the state of each of its atoms: this is Bohr's starting point. The observations required for this description, however, involve physical disturbances of the organism that are so great as to be fatal. The states of the atoms of an inanimate body can be specified within the limits imposed by the Heisenberg uncertainty relations, whereas the large protein molecules with which life is associated are destroyed by disturbances that would allow atoms to continue to exist.

Experiments by which the living organism may be described in terms of the functions that characterize it as living are therefore carried out under experimental conditions quite different from those of experiments on the organism as a physical system. According to Bohr, it is a question here of "complementary" experimental arrangements, which are described in "complementary languages." Therefore, to describe the phenomena of life in a language which is not that of physics or chemistry is logically free from objections and does not constitute a lapse into a spiritualistic vitalism.

This way of putting the matter, as given by Bohr, is very different from that of most of his "philosophic interpreters," and is certainly tenable. In so far as its usefulness is concerned, some remarks can be made. The whole argument derives its force from the fact that it is an analogue of the argument that led from classical to quantum physics and justified the statement that atomic processes cannot be described in the language of classical physics. In order to establish limits for the appropriateness of this analogy we shall therefore compare two lines of thought.

First, in the transition to quantum physics one reasons as follows: According to classical physics, one must be able, in principle, to devise experiments permitting the measurement of the positions and the velocities of individual particles with arbitrary accuracy. But our knowledge of atomic processes—for example, the Compton effect—shows on closer analysis that the possibility of such measurements is contradicted by experience. Hence atomic phenomena cannot be described in the language of classical physics.

If we wish to extend this reasoning from the inanimate to the animate, we must accept it as an experimental fact that an observation by physical means, sufficiently accurate to enable one to describe exactly the physical state of the individual atoms of a living body, represents so great a disturbance that it kills the organism. It follows then that classical physics, aided by quantum physics (of inanimate atoms), is inadequate for the description of the phenomena of life, since it is incompatible with the application of physics to the living organism that the latter should be killed by every act of exact measurement.

The strength of the quantum theory lies in the fact that no hypothesis about the atom based on classical physics could be found that was in agreement with the experimentally testable behavior of observable bodies. If the testing of a hypothesis about atoms through direct measurements of their mechanical state (position and velocity) had not been in contradiction with empirical facts, the hypothesis would have remained within the framework of classical physics. Since, however, quantum mechanics does involve contradiction, it goes beyond classical physics.

If we wish to retain the same chain of ideas for the transition from inanimate to living bodies, then empirical evidence must be presented to show that the exact physical observation of the atoms of a living body is incompatible with the known empirical laws for the behavior of living bodies and with the physical hypothesis about their atomistic structure. As long as this evidence has not been submitted, it follows only from Bohr's train of thought that in biology, in the present state of our knowledge, the complementarity mode of expression is possible and perhaps even desirable. In contrast, for the transition from classical physics to quantum mechanics one can conclude that in atomic physics the complementarity mode of expression is necessary.

4. Summarizing Remarks

From all that has been said, it is clear that Bohr's complementarity theory does not provide any argument for free will or vitalism. Likewise, one cannot derive from it any new conception about the relation between the physical object and the observing subject, if we understand the words "object" and "subject" in the sense in which they are used in empirical psychology. In presentations of quantum mechanics in which reference is made to this new role of the observing subject, the word "subject" is understood in quite another sense. By "subject" is always meant the measuring arrangement, which can be described in terms of classical physics. What was shifted by the quantum theory was the relation between the object of atomic theory—the atom or electron—which cannot be described by means of classical physics, and the measuring instrument, which can be described classically. The observing subject, in the sense of empirical psychology, has no other task than to read off the measuring instrument. The interaction between measuring instrument and observing subject can be described classically, as far as we can say from the present state of physics. The boundary line between the classical and the quantum-mechanical descriptions lies between the electron and the measuring instrument. Since within the region of classical description it can be displaced arbitrarily, the boundary line can also be drawn between the measuring instrument and the observer. But thereby nothing new is expressed, since within the classical region the position of the section is arbitrary.

The great importance of Bohr's complementarity theory for all branches of science, especially for the logic of science, seems to me that it starts out with a language that is generally understood and accepted, the language used to describe the gross mechanical processes of motion. Its significance lies in the fact that in its use all men are in harmony. In physics this language is used in such expressions as "position of a particle," in the sense of gross mechanics. Atomic processes, however, cannot be described in this language, as the new physics has shown. Bohr has demonstrated in a careful analysis of modern physics that certain parts of the language of everyday life can nevertheless be retained for certain experimental arrangements in the field of atomic phenomena, although different parts are required for different experimental arrangements. The language of daily life thus possesses complementary constituents which can be employed in the description of complementary experimental arrangements.

There is no doubt that this idea is also a fruitful one for logical syntax in general and deserves to be applied to other branches of science. One would have to start out in psychology with the language of everyday life and see whether, in the transition to more subtle problems, this language could be retained. One might perhaps start with the "physicalistic" "protocol language" of Carnap and Neurath and see whether any parts of it are particularly suitable for describing certain situations. Perhaps the symbol language of psychoanalysis is a suggestion of such a partial language. The phenomenal language of which Carnap often spoke in his earlier works must be dropped as a general language, but perhaps, as a constituent of a general language in the sense of the Bohr conception, it can provide a satisfactory description for certain experimental situations.

Chapter 9

Determinism and Indeterminism in Modern Physics

WHEN PHILOSOPHERS describe their standpoint with regard to a new physical theory, their attitude is usually one of the following three: (1) the new theory contradicts the correct philosophic system and is therefore false; (2) the new theory is a brilliant confirmation of the correct philosophic system and is therefore to be welcomed; (3) the new theory can be used for more or less important improvements in the correct philosophic system and therefore possesses a certain value.

When the physicist attempts to continue outside of physics his manner of forming principles and of verifying them through experiments, he comes to the conception of science called logical empiricism. This conception has become fairly well known in recent years, especially through the work of the Vienna Circle. It is from this point of view that I wish to examine a book[1] by Ernst Cassirer, since this is the point of view most closely associated with the thinking of the physicist.

No doubt many will demand a so-called "immanent criticism" of a philosophic work. I believe, however, that such a demand usually signifies only a plea of extenuating circumstances, and in the case of a book as important as the present one would be even derogatory. For, at best, the result of immanent criticism of a book is the acknowledgment that even if it is nonsense, it does have method.

Such rather scholastic criticism I will not attempt. Instead I want to consider how one must judge Cassirer's exposition from the standpoint of logical empiricism, according to which only those statements may occur in science that can be justified through logical derivation or empirical tests.

According to this conception, philosophic principles, which are not scientific in the above-mentioned sense, form a system of isolated propositions from which there are no logical bridges to the system of scientific propositions. Hence a sys-

[1] E. Cassirer, *Determinismus und Indeterminismus in der modernen Physik; historische und systematische Studien zum Kausalproblem* (Göteborg: Elanders Boktryckeri Aktiebolag, 1937).

171

tem of philosophic principles can never be either confirmed or refuted by new physical theories. Strictly speaking, neither can it undergo any improvement. There is often the appearance of improvement, but it can arise only from the fact that an agreement in emotional coloring is taken for a logical agreement. This is frequently made possible because the physical principles are formulated in a metaphysical, rather than a purely physical, language. In such a case, however, one should not say, for example, that a physical theory is in contradiction to a philosophic system, but rather that the metaphysical formulation of the theory appears to be irreconcilable with the philosophic principles under discussion.

When one reads this book by Cassirer one gets at once the impression that the foregoing considerations about the relation between scientific and philosophic principles do not apply to it. Most of Cassirer's assertions about the new physical theories are acceptable throughout from the standpoint of the physicist and its extension into logical empiricism. I might say even more. Cassirer's statements about the new quantum mechanics are less full of metaphysical prejudices and contain fewer transitions from physical to metaphysical language than some statements made by physicists in their professional writings or in speeches on festive occasions. Cassirer's statements are almost all scientific statements, as understood by logical empiricism. Isolated systems of propositions, such as those that play the chief role in the school philosophy, hardly occur. Hence there cannot arise any apparent contradiction between physical and philosophic principles. What does induce in me a critical state of mind is a certain background against which the presentation is brought into relief, a background which is distinctly separated from the basic assertions, but which through its terminology, foreign to science, makes me feel again and again that the author regards all that he says as only rather superficial utterance, the deeper meaning of which he intimates but does not wish to discuss.

For this reason I have designated Cassirer's mode of thinking, which is to be seen not only in his present writing but also in his earlier works, a "disintegration process within the school philosophy."

This remark in my book "The Law of Causality and its Limits" [2] has often been looked upon as an unfavorable criti-

2 P. Frank, *Das Kausalgesetz und seine Grenzen* (Vienna: J. Springer, 1932); *La Loi de causalité et ses limites* (Paris: Flammarion, 1936).

cism of Cassirer's point of view. Quite the opposite is the case. In the book mentioned I wanted to show that the "disintegration" of the school philosophy forms a necessary preliminary condition for the progress of science from the individual sciences to a unified science. Precisely in the case of the present book it can be made clear what the disintegration process that Cassirer carries out consists in, and, furthermore, we can also see how this process remains *within* the school philosophy, at least in its emotional background. Practically considered, Cassirer's conception of the principles of physics is almost exactly that of logical empiricism. However, at the end the sharply drawn contours are a little blurred in the direction of transcendental idealism—which is perhaps only a question of style. It seems to me that this shading of the outlines is a little dangerous, since we know that the reader is often influenced more by the emotional undertone of an exposition than by its logical and empirical content.

Some of the basic conceptions of Cassirer are in a remarkable manner related to, or almost coincident with, the conceptions formed by the logical empiricism of science. Cassirer repeatedly points out that science creates auxiliary concepts, such as force or atom, in order to be able to formulate conveniently the theories it has set up at a certain time, but that at later times these auxiliary concepts freeze into essences, "ontological concepts," which are retained even if they are no longer very convenient in the state of science at that time. This, however, is precisely the criticism leveled at the existence concepts of the philosophers by the Vienna Circle, so often attacked as "anti philosophic."

In my essay on the death of Ernst Mach,[3] I characterized as the enduring nucleus of Mach's teachings his struggle against the "idolization of auxiliary concepts." The French Catholic philosopher J. Maritain, at the Thomistic Congress in Rome in the summer of 1936, characterized as a great service that was essential also for Catholic philosophy the fact that the aim of the Vienna Circle and of the whole movement of logical empiricism was "to disontologize science."

The disintegration of the school philosophy in Cassirer's work is revealed very clearly in his general conception of the law of causality. He believes that there is no such law that can

[3] P. Frank, "Die Bedeutung der physikalischen Erkenntnistheorie Machs für das Geistesleben der Gegenwart," *Naturwissenschafter* **5**, 65 (1917). This essay is Chapter 2 of the present book.

be formulated like a definite law of nature. In his opinion the law of causality asserts only that there exist, in general, laws of some sort in nature. Kant tried to formulate causality also with respect to its content, by asserting, for instance, that for every process there exists another "which it follows according to a rule." Cassirer rejects not only the very special world formula of Laplace, but also the far more general formulation of Kant; there remains only the formal requirement, also attributable to Kant, that nature be describable with the help of simple rules. Here, however, there is left hardly any contradiction to Ernst Mach's purely positivistic conception of science.

Another fundamental feature of Cassirer's conception is that the form of the law of causality and the concepts of what one calls an "object" mutually condition each other. This also is a basic thesis of logical empiricism, and one that has been taken over from positivism. It is only that logical empiricism gives to this thesis a more formal turn: the form of every physical law depends on what variables are introduced to describe the state of a system. It may happen that with respect to some variables for a certain domain of phenomena there exist deterministic laws, but not for other variables. This consideration leads, in the extreme case, to the conventionalistic assertion that through the introduction of certain variables, the law of causality can be made valid; this assertion, however, states nothing at all about nature but is merely a "definition of the state of affairs." That is to say, in the language of Cassirer, that through the introduction of an appropriate concept of the "object" one can always bring about the validity of a law of causality. Like the positivists, Cassirer escapes this conventionalism only by requiring that the causal laws be "simple." The concept of simplicity remains exactly as vague in his case as in the case of the positivists. And the requirement of the "existence of natural laws," which, according to Cassirer, constitutes the real content of the general law of causality, involves that indefinite concept of "simplicity" in a very fundamental way. The assertion that the general law of causality can be expressed only vaguely was one of the essential theses of my book "The Law of Causality and its Limits," which was therefore termed "hyperskeptical" and "antiphilosophic" by many. Exactly this character, however, is possessed by Cassirer's conception of causality, which I have therefore designated approvingly as "disintegrating." Since Cassirer understands by determinism only the requirement that simple laws exist in nature, he cannot find any contradiction, of course, between this requirement and modern quantum mechanics. In place of the laws of classical physics we have there other equally exact laws. Cassirer's presentation is therefore not a criticism of modern physics from the standpoint of "philosophic determinism," but neither is it an attempt to improve "philosophic determinism" with the help of modern physics. What Cassirer does is to conduct an investigation on the question of how the rules and laws of physics have changed their form in recent years because of quantum mechanics. This investigation is carried out with a thorough knowledge of the subject. Except for a few obscure points, it is in agreement with modern physics and, naturally, can never come into contradiction with its principles. For Cassirer does not set up any philosophic deterministic laws as judges over the principles of physics; rather, he is prepared to consider every exact law as fulfilling the deterministic postulate.

Surely this conception is completely tenable, and surely it is more useful for understanding modern physics than are the attempts of many philosophers to formulate the law of causality more precisely and then to interpret physical theories so that they fit into this scheme. An example of such a method is the well-known, in many respects sagacious, book by the physicist and philosopher Grete Hermann, "The Philosophic Basis of Quantum Mechanics." [4] She starts out with Kant's special formulation of the law of causality and tries to formulate the principles of quantum physics in accordance with it, in such a way that for every process there exists another one which the first follows according to some rule. She is then forced, however, to introduce as "cause" a process which, aside from the effect for the sake of which it was introduced, cannot be observed, so that the law of causality becomes a mere tautology. Such a fruitless procedure is avoided by Cassirer through his very general comprehension of determinism. Nevertheless, many distinctions between classical and modern physics are perhaps lost by it. To express the law of causality, following Laplace, as the possibility of predicting future processes is also fruitless unless one says how the states of a physical system are to be described. One can try, however, to formulate the possibility of prediction in accordance with experimental possibilities, on the understanding that one describes only such processes as can be actually carried through. For example, one can say that, according to classical physics, by a sufficient refinement of the aiming mechanism one can strike the center of a target to within any desired degree of approximation; whereas, according to the quantum theory, if one bombards the target with electrons it will never be possible to suppress their scattering below a certain degree. We can therefore say in a certain sense that in the field of observable processes the new atomic physics is no longer deterministic in the same way as classical mechanics.

In its general features, Cassirer characterizes quite appropriately the change in physical laws due to modern physics by saying that now it is not the concept of "thing" but the concept of "law" that stands in the foreground, and that the so-called physical reality, the physical object, is only created by the law which we obtain from observation. He says:

We no longer deal with a being, self-contained and absolutely determined, from which we directly read off the laws, and to which we can attach them as its attributes. What really forms the content of our empirical knowledge is rather the aggregate of observations which we group together in a certain order, and which we can represent through theoretical concepts of laws according to this order.

As far as the dominion of these concepts extends, so far extends our objective knowledge. There is "objectivity" or "objective reality" because, and in so far as, there are laws—not conversely. From that it follows that we cannot speak of a physical "being" otherwise than subject to the conditions of physical cognition, including its general conditions as well as those special conditions that are valid for its observations and measurements.[5]

Reading such deliberations, one comes to think that Cassirer accepts completely the positivistic conception of the quantum theory, according to which concepts like "position" or "velocity" of a particle can be used only under certain experimental conditions, while the formulas of physics only give directions for bringing such observations into relation with one another.

[5] E. Cassirer, *op. cit.*, p. 164.

The reader of Cassirer's book is further strengthened in this opinion when he comes to the statement:

If it turns out that certain concepts, like those of position, velocity, the mass of a single electron, can no longer be filled for us with a definite empirical content, they must be eliminated from the theoretical system of physics, no matter how important and fruitful their contributions may have been.

Often Cassirer even employs a terminology that is linked with the nineteenth-century positivism of Pierre Duhem:

We choose the concepts in such a way that through them the phenomena will be described as completely and unequivocally as possible, that through them the phenomena will be preserved. This requirement of σωξειν τα φαινομενα goes back to the dawn of scientific physics.

However, when Cassirer tries to describe the real role of such concepts as particle, position, and velocity in quantum physics, he expresses himself rather vaguely. He presents the more or less provisory formulations of various physicists—Schrödinger, Heisenberg, Dirac—but does not decide in favor of any one of them as logically the most satisfactory. It seems to me that it is best to adopt the latest formulations of Niels Bohr, which he gave at the second Congress for the Unity of Science, held in Copenhagen in 1936, and which are fully compatible with the formulations of logical empiricism. Bohr said there quite clearly that concepts like "position of a particle" and "velocity of a particle" are expressions of every-day language which can be used in atomic physics only under special experimental conditions; moreover, "position" and "velocity" can be used only under conditions which are mutually exclusive. The term "particle" never occurs in atomic physics equipped with all the properties that it has in everyday language and in the physics of macroscopic mechanical processes. In the description of many experiments there does occur a particle which sometimes has a definite position, sometimes again a definite velocity. The fact that in such cases the term "particle" is used at all is due to the connection with the motion of large bodies. Actually, however, this term is used in a somewhat different sense, or, more exactly, according to different syntactic rules.

From the lectures that were held at the aforementioned

Congress, it is clear that in the complementary conception of atomic physics it is only a question of introducing a *new syntax* for the words "position" and "velocity of a particle" which is different from that of everyday language.[6] In this connection Strauss pointed out that it is not at all a question of introducing mysterious new *objects* like "particles without a definite position." [7] All these lectures made it plain that, although there may exist a difference between the view of Bohr and that of the adherents of logical empiricism with regard to the application of the complementarity principle to biology and psychology, there is certainly no difference in their ideas on the meaning of complementarity in physics.

It seems to me that Cassirer started out with a formulation of the complementarity conception in atomic mechanics that was somewhat vague, both from a physical and from a logical standpoint. This defect crops up now and then also in his general discussion. It can easily be shown that there are many places in Cassirer's book that cannot be understood from the standpoint of logical empiricism, a fact which is connected, in my opinion, with his leaving the scientific analysis prematurely and going over to metaphysics. One gets an inkling of this transition in statements such as:

> But a concept like that of material point, from the very nature of the matter, can never be understood as the copy of a physical object; it is "form" the meaning and content of which consist in their usefulness for the theory, in their ability to lead to simple and rigorous laws for phenomena.

What does it really mean to call the material point a "form"? Evidently it means in the language of physics that the statements in which the term "material point" occurs must have a definite syntactic form in order to be suitable for the representation of observations, and that this syntactic form in quantum mechanics is no longer the same as in classical mechanics and in everyday language. Cassirer, however, does not use the word "form" expressly in the sense of "syntactic form." As he uses it, it is a reminiscence of the Kantian terminology, in which space and time are "forms of experience." Here the word "form" is taken neither in the sense of "spatial form" as in everyday language, nor in the abstract sense in which, say,

[6] See the lecture of M. Strauss.
[7] See, besides the lecture of N. Bohr, those of M. Schlick, V. Lenzen, and myself.

one speaks of the "form of a mathematical equation," but in a quite specific sense which really occurs only in Kantian philosophy and may lead to serious misunderstandings. If one calls the material point a "form," one is making use of a language that does not fit well into the scheme of physical propositions. To be correct, one ought to say: " 'Material point' is an expression which, combined with other words according to definite syntactic rules, is appropriate for the representation of observations."

It is easy to see that Cassirer, in other places, really expresses himself as if, behind the world of relations which the theory sets up among observations by the help of its symbols, there existed another "real" world which we can approximate only imperfectly.

Immediately after the statement quoted above, that outside of the connections among observations one cannot speak of a "physical being," Cassirer says:

This "being" has thus lost its ultimate permanence. It is to some extent included in the process of physical cognition and is to be considered only as a limit to which this process tends, but which is never quite reached.

The "real world," that characteristic fiction of every school philosophy, remains in Cassirer's conception as a "limit." It would be consistent, however, to take this role from it also, for even in this respect one cannot speak of it in a scientific way.

No sooner has Cassirer spoken of this "limit" than he again makes statements in a quite positivistic sense. One sees here very clearly the disintegration of the school philosophy, which, however, has still left untouched a certain dark background, namely that "limit" and those "forms."

That this (in my opinion not entirely consistent) critical attitude toward metaphysics prevents him from representing the scientific sense of quantum physics with complete clarity is to be seen in several places in Cassirer's book.

Cassirer represents the facts stated by the Heisenberg uncertainty principle in the following way:

According to the conditions under which the observation is made, the object shows us to some extent a different aspect. We obtain, according to the choice of the measuring instrument and the use we make of it, various pictures of the event. No single observation can open up and hold out to us at one time the totality of possible aspects. Through every particular measuring arrangement certain features of the event are, so to speak, screened from us, as for example the wave nature or the particle nature of light, whereas others are brought out in their place. What the thing is in an absolute sense, outside of the circumstances of observation as realized in the various experiments, is something about which we no longer obtain an answer.

Through this mode of expression Cassirer depicts the situation in quantum mechanics as though it were a question of things that are absolute, but that cannot be comprehended in all their aspects with *one* measuring arrangement. In this way he brings into physics terminology from the philosophy of transcendental idealism, which is entirely foreign to Bohr's complementary doctrine in its physical form. Quantum physics say only that with certain experimental arrangements concepts like "particle with a definite position" or "particle with a definite velocity" can be defined. in other words, the physical processes that occur with these experimental arrangements can be predicted through statements in which one refers to "a particle with a definite position" or "a particle with a definite velocity," but there is no arrangement for which one can predict processes through statements involving "a particle with a definite position *and* velocity." This, however, does *not* mean that there are particles of which, because of the defectiveness of our apparatus or because of malicious natural laws, we cannot measure all the characteristics (position and velocity); it means rather that such combinations of words as "a particle with coördinates x, y, z, and velocity components v_x, v_y, v_z" must not be introduced into the language of physics. If we were to say that the things corresponding to such combinations of words nevertheless exist as absolute, but unknowable, things, we should be going over into pure metaphysics and destroying every bond with experience, which is surely not Cassirer's purpose.

Cassirer thus characterizes often very pertinently the scientific-logical structure of the laws of quantum mechanics, but then he always formulates them again in the language of idealist philosophy, thus robbing them of their clearly delineated scientific meaning and opening the door to misinterpretations in the direction of an absolutistic metaphysics.

That Cassirer basically does *not* accept this metaphysical interpretation of the quantum theory is to be seen from the determination with which he rejects the opinion that from this theory any conclusions can be drawn in favor of free will or even of moral responsibility. Much more clearly than many physicists have done, Cassirer sees through the deceptiveness of all such arguments and characterizes them very appropriately. He says, for example:

In itself it would be very bad for ethics and its dignity if it could not maintain authority except by watching for gaps in the scientific elucidation of nature and, so to speak, creeping into these gaps.

In these words Cassirer ably characterizes the repeated attempts of philosophers and many physicists to use the lacunae in science for the introduction of supernatural factors.

At another point he says:

If the idea of ethical freedom were threatened by these ideas [of rigorous natural laws], it could get no help from quantum mechanics. As far as as this problem is concerned it is immaterial whether we think that a natural phenomenon is governed by rigorous dynamical laws or whether we assume merely a statistical regularity. For even from the latter standpoint it would be determined to such an extent that the ostensible freedom, the free will, could find no refuge in it. An act which, from the physical standpoint, is to be regarded as not completely impossible, to be sure, but as improbable in the highest degree, is one that need not be taken into consideration in the domain of our will.

And quite tersely and precisely:

The problem of nature and freedom remains the same whether we take the general laws forming the concept of nature as dynamic or as statistical laws.

This separation of the question of natural laws from the question of ethical freedom is treated by Cassirer in a way that is very similar to that of Schlick in his *Problems of Ethics*,[8] which was attacked as being extremely positivistic. Also the rejection of the use of gaps in the laws of physics for introducing spiritual factors arises from positivistic lines of

[8] M. Schlick, *Fragen der Ethik* (Vienna: Springer, 1930); tr. by David Rynin as *Problems of Ethics* (New York: Prentice-Hall, 1939).

thought and is to be found in a quite similar form in my book "The Law of Causality and its Limitations."

This attitude of Cassirer toward the question of the relations between quantum mechanics and ethics must be valued all the more highly in view of the fact that there have been many physicists who supported enthusiastically this misuse of the quantum theory, and sometimes even initiated it. As a contrast to Cassirer's rigorously scientific argument on this question I should like to bring up a few sentences from a lecture by the famous English physicist J. H. Jeans. He says:

> The plain average man . . . believed, among other things, that he was free to choose between the higher and the lower, between good and evil, between progress and decadence. To many, Victorian science seemed to challenge all such beliefs. It knew nothing of higher nor lower, progress nor decadence; it knew only of a vast machine, which ran on automatically and of its own inertia, as it had been set to run on the first morning of the creation . . . We now begin to think that this challenge was a mistaken one, that the universe may be more like the untutored man's common-sense conception of it than had seemed possible a generation ago, and that humanity may not have been mistaken in thinking itself free to choose between good and evil, to decide its direction of development, and within limits to carve out its own future.[9]

At the end of his book Cassirer indicates of what use his philosophy of quantum mechanics may be. He believes that the change of viewpoint between wave theory and particle theory which the quantum theory brings about within physics is analogous to the change of viewpoint that takes place when one goes over from scientific considerations to ethical or esthetic ones. This analogy has been suggested also by many physicists, such as P. Jordan and Grete Hermann, and even by Bohr, although very cautiously and with many restrictions. Whether one looks upon it as deep and fruitful or as merely superficial is more a question of guessing future developments than of scientific argument.

To summarize: Cassirer's book is to be welcomed from the standpoint of logical empiricism as a highly successful attempt to continue the adjustment of the traditional idealist philosophy to the progress of science, which in my opinion can

[9] J. H. Jeans, "Man and the Universe," in *Scientific Progress* (London: G. Allen and Unwin, 1936), pp. 37 ff.

end only with the complete disintegration of the traditional philosophy. The ingenious arguments of Cassirer, presented in clear, understandable language, will be read with great benefit by every physicist and will be useful in correcting many misinterpretations of modern physics. For the adherent of the school philosophy the book signifies, like many previous writings of Cassirer, a way out of an impasse.

Chapter 10

How Idealists and Materialists View Modern Physics

WE KNOW today that nature can be described and understood not "mechanistically" but only through abstract mathematical formulas. Great significance has been attached to this revolution for the philosophic world view. The argument is that since a mathematical formula is something purely mental, the world can no longer be understood in a materialistic sense. Materialism must be superseded by idealism. The physics of the twentieth century is a victory for the "spiritualistic" or, as it is sometimes less clearly expressed, idealistic world view.

This viewpoint has its representatives among both the idealists and the materialists. The former rejoice at the unexpected aid they have received for their world view from the progress of science itself. The latter blame modern physics for abandoning the paths of progress marked out by Galileo and Newton and promoting the return to the dark views of the Middle Ages.

We will cite from the writings of a few English and German authors to illustrate the point of view of the idealists, and from the works of Soviet authors, the apprehensions of the materialists.

In his well-known book *The Mysterious Universe*, the famous British physicist, Sir James Jeans says, for example:

The signal for the revolution was a short paper which Einstein published in June, 1905. And with its publication, the study of the inner working of nature passed from the engineer-scientist to the mathematician . . . The essential fact is simply that *all* the pictures which science now draws of nature, and which alone seem capable of according with observational fact, are *mathematical* pictures . . . Nature seems very conversant with the rules of pure mathematics, as our mathematicians have formulated them in their studies, out of their own inner consciousness and without drawing to any appreciable extent on their experience of the outer world . . . Our remote ancestors tried to interpret nature in terms of anthropomorphic concepts of their own creation and failed. The efforts of our nearer ancestors to interpret nature on engineering lines proved equally inadequate . . . It would now seem to be beyond dispute that in some way nature is more closely allied to the concepts of pure mathematics than to those of biology or of engineering . . . In any event, it can hardly be disputed that nature and our conscious mathematical minds work according to the same laws. She does not model her behavior, so to speak, on that forced on us by our whims and passions, or on that of our muscles and joints, but on that of our thinking minds . . . The concepts which now prove to be fundamental to our understanding of nature . . . seem to my mind to be structures of pure thought, incapable of realization in any sense which would properly be called material . . . To my mind, the laws which nature obeys are less suggestive of those which a machine obeys in its motion than of those which a musician obeys in writing a fugue, or a poet in composing a sonnet . . . The universe can be best pictured . . . as consisting of pure thought, the thought of what, for want of a wider word, we must describe as a mathematical thinker.[1]

The physicist and astronomer Jeans has here made use of this turn from a "mechanistic" to a "mathematical" understanding of physics to favor a religiously tinted metaphysics. When the professional German philosophers, on the other hand, deal with this revolution in science, we find them erecting a "scientific" metaphysics on this foundation.

To illustrate this tendency we will quote a few passages from B. Bavink's *Science and God*. The author stresses that the fundamental laws of physics are today statements about probability.

But a mathematical probability is not a physical reality like a temperature or field strength or what not. With this new interpretation, the whole material notion of substance disappears in our hands. What remains then of the plain, real, hard, sharp, heavy, etc. matter? A certain probability depending on formal mathematical laws, that energy or impulse are observable at a certain world-point.

The physicist of today has learned—an enormous advance from the point of view of his world-view—that his atoms or electrons or what not, are no longer to be regarded as rigid lumps of reality, from which no path can be found into the mental and spiritual sphere; he sees, on the contrary, that all these structures are forms in perpetual flux, which are only of

[1] J. H. Jeans, *The Mysterious Universe* (New York: Macmillan, 1930), pp. 106, 135, 138, 143, 145 ff.

interest even to him as regards their form. With this view, every variety of materialism is superseded.[2]

In this mathematical conception of nature, Bavink, like Jeans, sees the foundations of an idealistic philosophy of physics and hence of science as a whole. The only difference is that Bavink uses somewhat more technical philosophic terms.

One task Bavink proposes for an idealistic philosophy of nature is the following:

It still remains to be shown how the material world is to be deduced from the purely psychical data. It is obvious that spiritualism has hitherto always failed in this respect. It has never succeeded in deducing even the properties of a hydrogen atom from data of this kind. What is new in the present situation is the fact that such a proposal no longer appears so completely absurd as it did even twenty years ago. For that which hitherto presented an insuperable obstacle, namely the "rigid lumps of reality" of ordinary atomic theory, has been resolved into pure form, and a mathematical form is in itself something psychical, it belongs, as Plato already saw, directly in the realm of the Logos, which is behind all things . . .
There it stands; the hard, cold sober world of matter with its atoms, the existence of which is today proven beyond a doubt. It is impossible to pass it by, and it is time for all idealists finally to accept this fact and give up their fruitless attempts to avoid it. Matter will only be finally subjugated by mind when we are really able to understand it as the product of psychical powers. Merely to postulate this as a fact, which is all that spiritualism has hitherto done, is not of the slightest use; matter and its worshipers, the materialists, simply laugh us out of court saying: here is a single atom, the simplest of all, the hydrogen atom. Show us what you can do! Show us how we are to understand it as the product of purely psychical potencies—then we will believe you. Now it appears as if spiritualism today can actually pass this test. I will not maintain that it has already passed it, but I believe it to be undeniable that it is very close to doing so, and has every prospect of success.[3]

Some professional philosophers look upon modern physics as a direct return to the anthropomorphic, animistic physics of the Middle Ages, as it was practiced by Aristotelian scho-

[2] B. Bavink, *Science and God*, English translation by H. S. Hatfield (London: Bell, 1933), pp. 68, 71.
[3] *Ibid.*, pp. 93, 95.

lasticism. Thus Aloys Wenzl, Professor at the University of Munich, says in his essay, "Metaphysics of Modern Physics":

And in this manner the human struggle for insight in the world will have described a circle, or more correctly a spiral. The examination of nature began with an anthropomorphic representation of the material world, in that souls were ascribed to material things, and the relations between them were viewed as expressions of psychic relationships of love and hate. The tendency to reification led farther and farther away from such early representations, freed physics more and more from such images and of necessity led ever closer to a mathematical examination of nature. For there are only two possible ways of making the facts and the laws of experience meaningful. They must either be treated according to psychologic laws or associated with the ideal forms of mathematics. Modern physics has followed the second method to the very limit. But if more is desired, if assertions about their meanings are to be made, the mathematically expressed relationships must be explained, which would be a return, on a much higher plane, to be sure, to the original method, if not in physics, then in metaphysics[4].

When we notice how a philosopher of the twentieth century "explains" the physics of his day, we will see that the "idealistic" explanation is not so far removed from the "spiritualistic" or mystical. In the same essay, Wenzl says:

It is clear that the concept of matter has changed completely . . . Only the mathematical method itself actually defines the sphere of the material world . . . But we can no longer associate an idea of something dead, with this material world. If we do wish to make an assertion about its essence, it is much sooner a world of elemental spirits which are bound in their relationships and their formation of wholes to certain rules of the spiritual realm which are mathematically comprehensible; or to put it in other words, it is a world of lower spirits whose reciprocal relationships can be expressed in mathematical form. We do not know what kind of relationship this mathematical form signifies, but we do know the form. Only the mathematical forms themselves or God could know their inner significance. A very alert metaphysician might explain them at best by analogy to known psychic relationships.[5]

---

[4] A. Wenzl, "Metaphysik der Physik von heute," *Wissenschaft und Zeitgeist* (Leipzig: Meiner, 1935), No. 2, p. 30.
[5] *Ibid.*, pp. 28, 29.

All these utterances show what great hopes the supporters of idealism have had in the crisis in physics of the twentieth century. But just as some political systems adopt idealism as the foundation for their philosophy, so the supporters of Marxism acknowledge materialism as a foundation for their world view. When we read the writings of the spiritual leaders of Russian Marxism, we see that the crisis in physics and its utilization as propaganda for idealism are viewed with concern and alarm.

Lenin published in 1908 a book under the title "Materialism and Empiriocriticism: Notes on a Reactionary Philosophy." [6] In the fifth chapter, entitled "The Latest Revolution in Science and in Philosophical Idealism," Lenin speaks of the changes brought about in the conception of matter by the energetic and electromagnetic theories. The physicists inclined toward idealism often formulate the results of these new conceptions as follows:

> The atom is dematerialized. Matter disappears.

And the Russian philosopher N. Valentinov in his book "Ernst Mach and Marxism" (1907) draws the following inference with reference to a world view:

> The assertion that a scientific explanation of the world is found in straight materialism, is now no more than a myth, and a foolish one at that.

Says Lenin:

> There is not the slightest doubt about the association of the new physics, or rather a certain school of the new physics, with the school of Mach and other types of a modern idealistic philosophy.
> The nature of the crisis in modern physics consists in the overthrow of old laws and fundamental principles. Objective reality outside of consciousness is rejected and materialism is replaced by idealism and agnosticism. Matter has disappeared. This is the way basic and typical difficulty created by the crisis is expressed.

Even in the year 1922 when Lenin was already at the head of the Soviet Government of Russia, he was much concerned about the dangers for materialism that might and did arise out of the crisis, thereby imperiling the foundations of Commu-

[6] English translation (New York: International Publishers, 1927).

nism. At that time it was the relativity theory that played the most important part in the crisis in physics.

On December 3, 1922 Lenin wrote in the journal *Under the Banner of Marxism:*

> We must keep in mind that as a result of the revolution taking place in science today, reactionary philosophic schools and tendencies are likely to arise. Therefore, the journal *Under the Banner of Marxism* must be concerned about this revolution in modern science; otherwise, fighting materialism would be neither fighting nor materialism.
>
> If the great majority of middle-class intelligentsia stand behind Einstein, who is not taking an active part in the fight against materialism, then this holds not only for Einstein, but for most of the great scientists since the end of the nineteenth century.

We find the same apprehensions and the same fight if we examine textbooks that have been introduced in Soviet colleges for teaching materialism. Thus we find in the textbook *Dialectical Materialism:*[7]

> The attempts made to think of motion without matter and of force without underlying substance are laying the foundation for idealism and clericalism. At the present time we see the furthering of these same idealistic tendencies. As a result of their association with Einstein's theory of relativity many are inclined to imagine motion without matter.

And again:

> In place of the old unchangeable atoms there has appeared a system of moving electrons. Therefore, say the "Machians," matter has disappeared. But actually, more exact principles are replacing primitive physical laws. Yet the followers of Mach say: There is no objective knowledge . . . The latest quantum mechanics strengthens the concept of causality, and makes corrections in the old concept. The Machians, however, declare that causality has disappeared.

In the Russian materialistic literature there is a great deal of criticism of the new physical theories, particularly quantum mechanics, on account of their mathematical and formalistic nature. In effect, the line of approach is much like that of

[7] M. Mitin, ed., *Dialekticheskii Materializm* (Moscow Philosophical Institute of the Communist Academy, 1934), vol. 1, pp. 111, 55.

the German and English idealists—such as Bavink and Jeans—except that the materialists are naturally critical about the replacement of mechanics by mathematics as an "idealistic" trend. I will cite as evidence an article entitled "Chemistry and the Structure of Matter" which appeared in a Russian literary journal, *Krasnaya Nov.* The author, Orlov, says:

> Quantum mechanics is today still under the spell of the fetish, mathematics. This means that the method of quantum mechanics is of a formal mathematical nature. The mathematical pattern permits the building of a bridge that unites empirical facts furnished by spectroscopy with the behavior of electrons, atoms, and molecules. But up to now we have no physical explanation for the formulas of quantum mechanics. Instead of that, it is often proposed to abandon the search for an interpretation of physical laws and to replace physical representations with abstract mathematical symbols. It is in this that the fetish, mathematics, consists.

It is remarkable how often scientists with sympathies for idealism, philosophers with scientific inclinations but of a spiritualistic background, and advocates of materialism as a tool for achieving political goals agree with one another in so many essential points.

We have seen in Chapters 5 and 6 that the transition from mechanistic to mathematical physics was the result of the positivistic conception of science and that it had nothing to do with the twentieth-century tendency toward idealism and metaphysics.

But it may well be, and is often maintained, that positivistic physics contains an element of spiritualism or idealism. Positivistic physics consists in the last analysis of propositions about observations or perceptions. But then, so it is often said, it asserts something about the psychic. It has completely abandoned materialism and has become a science of the mind, exactly like psychology. In fact, Ernst Mach built up all the sciences out of relationships among sensations.

Many, therefore, look upon positivistic physics as a variety of subjective idealism, which declares that science can never assert anything about the actual world, but only about subjective sense impressions. In the above-mentioned book, *Materialism and Empiriocriticism*, Lenin represented Mach's doctrine as a direct continuation of Bishop Berkeley's philosophy. He also blamed this doctrine for depreciating the actual world and for promoting the view that behind the world of sense impressions, about which alone science can assert something, lies the real world, which, however, is inaccessible even to science. According to this view, Mach seeks to strengthen the belief that the real world can only be explored through extrascientific or superscientific sources of knowledge such as metaphysics and religion.

This view of Mach's doctrine, however, is completely contradicted by Mach's actual intentions. To be sure, it must be admitted that his terminology may sometimes be the cause of such confusion. Also many of his disciples were in effect inclined toward idealism, perhaps because of pressure to conform to the prevailing official philosophy, according to which everything smacking of materialism was strictly taboo.

For Mach himself, however, the sensations with which he built up the entire science were in no contradiction to the actual world that seemed inaccessible to reason. For him these sensations, which to avoid confusion he very often termed "elements," were the building material he wished to use to create a unified system of science; this could be accomplished if one crossed from one field of science to another, say from physics to physiology.

For Mach, there was no way in which the difference between the apparent world and the real world could be scientifically formulated. Yet the gross mechanistic philosophy stood in no logical contradiction to Mach's conception. The bodies of daily experience with which mechanism constructed its world were also nothing else than a complex of sensations like sight and taste. The question whether there really is a matter (a thing-in-itself) that is different from the sensation has no meaning for science, since no experiment can be performed that might possibly settle the question. Every proposition about a gross material thing can also be expressed about sensations. Thus the whole of mechanistic physics can be translated into the language of Mach. A logical contradiction exists only between a metaphysically conceived Machism, which is then subjective idealism, and a metaphysically conceived materialism, which accepts only matter as having existence. But this doctrine was invented by idealists to refute materialism, and was, in any case, hardly representative of the thought of scientifically minded materialists.

The school philosophers (see Chapter 4) did not have to

wait for the relativity and quantum theories of the twentieth century to misconstrue the transition from mechanistic to mathematical theory. They succeeded in doing this with the physics of the nineteenth and earlier centuries. On more than one occasion they made use of the explanation of Mach's doctrine as subjective idealism. It was even simpler than that. Wherever they saw something mathematical they tried to explain it as an idealistic element inside materialistic physics.

Hermann Cohen, for example, the leader of the neo-Kantian school of Marburg, says that mechanics has acquired a more spiritual character when such subtle mathematical concepts as the differential calculus had to be used to formulate its laws.

In the critical supplement to the seventh edition of F. A. Lange's "History of Materialism" (vol. 1, pp. 504 ff.) Cohen says:

The road of research leads straightway to idealism. Materialism is being destroyed at the roots of physical concepts, and it is mathematics that is leading in the emancipation, which promises to be a lasting one . . . Reality is the Real in mass, force and energy—the reality of infinitesimally small quantities. There are no other means by which we could even denote the real of mass and force for Newtonians, or the real of electric charge for dynamicists; much less can we explain these realities in another way. There is no other means than the differentials. The infinitesimal is not only the origin of every quantity but also the origin of being itself, of the real . . . At the roots of physical concepts materialism was destroyed and the liberation was achieved by mathematics. The old Platonic union of physics and mathematics has proved its eternal strength. The mathematical ideas . . . offer the solution of the fundamental question of philosophy—the question, What is science?

But we have seen in Chapter 5 that the idealistic interpretation of science, when taken seriously, is the first step in the return to the animistic anthropomorphic science of the medieval scholastics.

Positivism, on the other hand, particularly logical positivism, prevents the crisis in the mechanistic philosophy from spreading to the scientific world view as a whole. It shows that the abandonment of mechanistic physics does not imply the need for a return to the anthropomorphic physics of the Middle Ages. And right here something has happened that seems rather paradoxical. All those that advocate a return to pre-Galilean science, whether it be under the name of "idealism," "holism," or "organicism," or even under the name of "race" or "nation," fight with great ardor for the retention of the mechanistic philosophy in the field of physics, and condemn the positivistic physics as an aberration.

Evidence for this can be found by merely turning the pages of the "Journal for the Whole of the Natural Sciences," which was published in Germany under the Nazi government from 1935 on. Its purpose was to fight against positivism in science. Its main line of attack was to encourage the struggle of "German" science against "French rationalism" and "English empiricism." Organismic philosophy is generally regarded as specifically "German."

A few passages from K. Hillebrand's programmatic article, "Positivism and Nature," may be cited here. They will make clear how an overestimation of mechanistic physics served in the fight against positivism and in behalf of organismic science.

Mechanism was a planned world picture constructed upon a principle; positivism accepts without choice every experience into the sum of its experiences. It accepts to be sure mechanistic explanations, as the equivalent of sense perceptions, but it denies as a matter of course the significance of every explanation, and gladly disavows them, for its aim is only description . . . I therefore ask, is not the principle advantage of positivism over mechanism tied up with as great a disadvantage? Is it really necessary or even pleasing to exchange a pictural concept of a mechanistic explanation for a pure mathematical formula, which transcends all perception? The breakdown of mechanism into positivism—very interesting as intellectual history—is an event, it seems to me, that is at present almost everywhere entirely misunderstood. And yet the principles of scientific method will never be determined without its clarification.

And now the author embarks upon an inspired glorification of mechanistic physics. He says:

He who understands the running of a machine, say a clock, based on the complete dependence of rigid bodies on spatial conceptions, has genuinely satisfying knowledge. It is the mistake of positivism that it is able to take this intention of Democritus as just one among other arbitrary hypotheses. It is also unfortunate for the development of positivism that it retains the objectivistic bias of mechanism and has surrendered its only virtue, its pure, clear picturization.

As is almost always the case with those favoring an idealistic-organismic science, the enthusiasm for the mechanistic physics in its most obsolete form is coupled with a strong aversion for the application of non-Euclidean and multidimensional spaces. Hillebrand continues:

> Mechanism is Euclidean science. Relativism of non-Euclidean spaces, on the contrary, is the favorite child of positivism. A four-dimensional space or a space with curved radii is just as logical for pure abstract thought as the Euclidean; indeed the dissolution of space and time into mere abstract mathematical formulas seems to be a distinct gain to this other type of human being. The overwhelming eternal advantages of Euclidean space as against these abstract arts ought not to be forgotten.

The reason for the glorification of "mechanistic" physics by the advocates of organicism is that for their argument they need the application of a kind of physics that is as narrow as possible and therefore most unsuited for the more involved events. Says Hillebrand:

> It is evident from what has been said above that according to our way of thinking mechanism is far superior to positivistic empiricism—so long as it does not attempt to explain living matter. Besides, since Science has abdicated in this respect, there is nothing lost; . . . the value therefore of exact scientific research is not attacked, in so far as it is restricted to "dead" matter nature. The human mind possesses two sufficient types of knowledge: the explanatory and the understanding. *"Anschauung"* in the explanatory sense is the mechanistic explanation of nature, the representation of bodily form in a Euclidean space-time relation going far beyond positivistic sense perception and yet conceivable or pictorial in a narrower sense of sight and taste sensation. The understanding type of knowledge is *"Anschauung"* in a wider sense, perception not as sensation, but rather as a palpable human event that need not be "sensible."

The German word *Anschauung* has two meanings, both of which are used in this quotation. It means, first, "optical perception" or "pictural representation"; second, however, it means "mental intuition" or "emphathic understanding." This ambiguity makes the word *Anschauung* a favorite term in idealistic metaphysics. It provides a philosophic basis for the "intuition" of the totalitarian leader.

The tendency is very clearly seen to allow mechanistic science to pass as the only "explanatory" type of knowledge that is useful for exact science, so that it might be easier if necessary to introduce the so-called "understanding" type of knowledge (intuition) in the sciences of human conduct.

Logical empiricism, as opposed to this, stresses the unitary character of science. It is not interested in splitting human knowledge into "mechanistic-explanatory" and "understanding-intuitive" types. Our modern logic of science depicts the factual process of successful knowledge and scientific representation. Mechanistic explanation and intuitive understanding both are popular and rather superficial types of scientific representation, but by no means particularly profound types of knowledge.

Chapter 11

Logical Empiricism and the Philosophy of the Soviet Union

WHEN I SPEAK of philosophy in the Soviet Union, I mean only the system that is officially taught in all schools as philosophy—"dialectical materialism," abbreviated to *diamat*. Of course, in the writings of physicists, mathematicians, and biologists one can find many remarks associated with the logic of science. These are mostly only echoes of the views predominant in European and American science. Besides the official diamat, no other consistent conception of science has developed in the U.S.S.R. If one wishes to discuss the features that are characteristic of the intellectual life of Soviet Russia, one must speak only about diamat, concerning which there are prevalent in European science very unclear and often greatly distorted views.

At first sight, it appears that diamat is extremely hostile to the various forms of logical empiricism. This attitude is shown especially by the following examples:

Empiricism is styled in a stereotyped way "crawling empiricism," because it can never rise to the formation of a scientific system. The various forms of neopositivism and logical empiricism are all branded with the label "Machism," and, as such, are sharply condemned. It was perhaps an ominous event for the history of philosophy in the U.S.S.R. that Lenin set forth his philosophic views in a book directed against the Russian followers of Mach and Avenarius—the book *Materialism and Empiriocriticism*.[1] In 1935 the twenty-fifth anniversary of the appearance of this book was celebrated by all philosophical societies and journals of the U.S.S.R. Because in it the doctrines of diamat were elucidated by being contrasted with the conceptions of Mach, the opinion was established in the official philosophy of the U.S.S.R. that Machism was a movement especially hostile to diamat, and hence to be attacked vigorously. In reality, Lenin took issue with Machism because it is in many respects related to diamat, and he considered it especially suitable for him to bring out his

[1] English translation by David Kvitko (London, 1927).

own teachings very sharply by means of a polemic against it.

Because in the teachings of Mach everything is built on the perceptions as elements, Lenin saw in them a degenerate form of the subjective idealism of Berkeley, who had denied the reality of the world of experiences and thus had made room for the acceptance of a supernatural world. On the other hand, because of the connection of Machism with the enlightenment philosophy of the eighteenth century, its predilection for contact with the physical sciences and its aversion to the introduction of any anthropomorphic factors or "psychic" tendencies into science, Machism was reproached with having a "mechanistic narrowness" which rendered it particularly incapable of encompassing social and historical events.

If we ask what is the attitude of diamat toward the movements which have arisen from the synthesis of Mach's positivism and Russell's logic, we need only open the latest textbook of diamat in the U.S.S.R. for information.[2] There we find it asserted, in effect, that the newest Machists want to deepen Machism by the use of symbolistic methods. They regard science as a game with empty symbols and thus make it incapable of embracing the colorful fullness of the real multiform world. Idealism, mechanism, and logicism are only three ways of leading people to a fictitious supersensual world and of restraining them from occupation with the practical questions of the real world. These three doctrines therefore, like religion, are opium for the people, putting them into a narcotic sleep which shows them a faded picture of the real world. Philosophers who teach idealism, mechanism, and logicism are in the service of the bourgeoisie, just like the clergy, and make their disciples unfit to work for the social reorganization of the world.

While one gets from these statements the impression of a fundamental antipathy, yet scientific and sociologic considerations indicate that this attitude of diamat is rather of a polemical and tactical nature, and that it must also contain many elements which are closely related to the ideas that we represent.

Logical empiricism developed primarily in the struggle against the idealistic metaphysics of the school philosophy, which with its odd mixture of faded theology and obsolete science has fulfilled a very definite social function. The main

[2] M. Mitin, *Dialekticheskii Materializm* (Moscow, 1934).

struggle of diamat is also against this metaphysics and this function. In a German textbook of diamat we find "metaphysics" described as "an examination of the pseudo-real surface, without penetrating into the essential." Since this description is in fair agreement with logical empiricism, we must expect to encounter still other similarities.

The main points of a scientific doctrine related to logical empiricism which we find in diamat are perhaps the following: (1) Science should be "materialistic," but not "mechanistic"; (2) the criterion for the truth of a proposition should be only its confirmation in actual life, the doctrine of "concrete truth"; (3) the propositions of science are to be understood not only from their logical connection with the propositions of the previous stages of science, but also from the causal connection of scientific pursuits with other social processes. The investigation of this causal connection is carried on by a special factual science, the sociology of science.

Here we wish to consider only the first two of these points.

(1) First of all, we must be quite clear as to what diamat means by the word "materialism." What we generally understand by this word as used in popular and even in scientific writings is the conception of all natural phenomena, including human evolution, as analogous to a machine. This view would be called by diamat "mechanistic materialism" or "mechanism," and is very strongly opposed. If we look up the definition of the word "materialism" in the official textbooks of diamat, we find, roughly, the following: "By 'materialism' is meant the conception that science speaks of a world that is completely independent of any arbitrariness, a world that is neither the creation of a world spirit, as the objective idealism of Hegel holds, nor the creation of the individual consciousness, as the subjective idealism of Berkeley assumes."

From this form of the definition of materialism, which simply establishes the objective character of scientific principles, we shall not be able to draw any very specific conclusions of the materialistic conception. If, however, we observe how this definition is applied in practice, we find that all scientific propositions are to contain only terms that occur in statements about observable facts. The description of a process is of use to science only if all of the observable aspects of the process are embraced. In particular, the part played by the so-called psychic processes is not to be emphasized one-sidedly; that would lead to "idealism." If, to take an example given by a textbook on diamat, it is asserted that the great power station on the Dnieper, the Dnieprostroy, is the product of the engineering plans, the matter is being described idealistically and one-sidedly. The materialist will say: "Besides the plans of the engineers, a decisive part is also played by the new social organization introduced by the communist revolution, the new conditions of the workers, etc." Everything in the world that is describable through intersubjective expressions is called "matter" by diamat.

This is not to say that matter actually has the properties which Newtonian mechanics or even the newer physics attributes to matter. Such an opinion would be "mechanical materialism." According to diamat, every investigation of the world that makes use of intersubjective expressions is an investigation of matter. The properties of matter reveal themselves to us only in the course of the development of science. They will never be completely known to us as long as there are new laws to be discovered.

This conception comes very close to the viewpoint that science is based on an intersubjective language, which Neurath and Carnap have designated more precisely as the physicalistic language. Just as, for physicalism, the biologic or psychologic propositions are "physical in the broadest sense," so for diamat the propositions about the development of life and even about human history are propositions about matter. However, just as physicalism does not claim that psychology can be reduced to actual physics, so diamat does not say that the social development of mankind can be reduced to those laws of matter that have been discovered by physics. According to diamat, sociology itself discloses new laws of matter.

Diamat seeks, however, to set up quite general laws for matter, laws which are to hold for physics as well as for biology and sociology. For this purpose it takes the three laws which Hegel formulated for the processes of thought, and from which he also made laws for living and inanimate nature because he believed that the whole world is the product of thought. Marx and Engels turned Hegel's teachings upside down and began by setting up his three dialectical laws of thought as the laws for matter. In this way they founded diamat, "dialectical materialism." The three laws are "the unity of opposites, the transition from quantity to quality, and the negation of the negation." We see that they still wear their idealistic eggshells. Their application to reality is often very much forced, and from their consequences there results what L. Rougier [3] once called "Soviet mysticism." With these three laws of dialectics, originating in idealism, diamat often strays from the path of establishing the properties of matter through the methods of exact research. Today a determined struggle is being carried on within diamat against the "trivialization" of dialectics.

Such rather indefinite principles can often serve to order to some extent the empirical material in fields that are still only slightly developed, like sociology. If, however, they are applied to sciences where we possess better ordering principles, they at once reveal their imperfections.

Because of these dialectical laws, diamat bears within itself the germ of idealism. Even in the U.S.S.R. it must perpetually struggle against "idealistic deviations," which in recent years have received the name "menshevizing idealism" after the political party of the Mensheviks. Diamat wages continually a "war of two fronts" against idealism and mechanism without being able to mark out unequivocally the boundaries separating it from these two deviations.

If it carried on this war of two fronts consistently, it would have to discard the idealistic eggshell of Hegelianism, the exaggerated opinion of the significance of the three dialectical laws. On the other hand it would have to avoid the description of matter as something existing objectively—which is also, in the last analysis, an idealistic conception—and instead would speak of intersubjective propositions. Then it would approach more and more closely the conception represented by logical empiricism, especially by the Vienna Circle. For these groups carry on the same two-front war, against the idealistic school philosophy and against the belief that Newtonian mechanics in its original form is a basis of all science.

Though, therefore, in our opinion, the dialectical laws do not have the importance for a modern conception of science ascribed to them by diamat, we must nevertheless admit that something in what it calls "dialectical thinking" is quite in line with our ideas.

This "dialectical thinking" is characterized by Lenin in his remarks on Hegel's works simply as thinking which has the necessary elasticity not to stick to a definite scheme, but which builds itself a new scheme corresponding to the given stage

[3] L. Rougier, *Les Mystiques politiques contemporaines* (Paris, 1935).

of development of science. This kind of dialectical thinking is demanded also by logical empiricism.

(2) The second point essential for the understanding of diamat is the "doctrine of concrete truth." According to this doctrine, the truth of a proposition can never be judged by its abstract formulation, but only by examining the practical conclusions that can be drawn from it. Whether the idealists or the materialists are right can be judged only by seeing what consequences the two doctrines have for practical life. This conception is related to American pragmatism. The textbooks of diamat try to distinguish it from pragmatism by saying that pragmatism always means a "bourgeois," that is, an individualistic practice, a test in the life of the individual—in "business life," as they often add derisively. Diamat understands by test, above all, the test of a principle in social life—in revolutionary practice, as they put it.

From this doctrine of "concrete truth" one can understand the much-discussed attitude of diamat toward religion. By religion is never to be understood an abstract system of principles of faith. A thing of that sort cannot be tested for truth. By "religion" is always meant a concrete institution, as, for instance, the institution of the church. This can be investigated to determine whether it has socially desirable influences or the opposite. Definitions of religion like "a feeling of oneness with the universe," "devotion to a higher duty towards humanity," are rejected by diamat. One textbook remarks scornfully that European philosophers, on the basis of such definitions, call even communism itself a religion. By religion should be understood a concrete organization which seeks to propagate the belief in a supernatural being among men and thus to deter them from the struggle against their oppressors. From this point of view one must judge the struggle against idealistic philosophy and against Machism and logicism. To this "doctrine of concrete truth" Lenin attributed a great importance for the practical political struggle. One must never hold fast to abstract formulas such as: *for* the defense of the fatherland or *against* the defense of the fatherland, *for* parliamentarianism or *against* it. One must rather examine in every individual case the practical consequences arising from such a demand and see whether they are favorable to the goal pursued—hence, for Lenin, to the rise of the working class to power.

Lenin, however, applied this doctrine not only to political but also to scientific principles. He insisted that propositions such as "Matter is infinitely divisible," or "Matter is composed of indivisible atoms," are never to be labeled as true or false; they are to be judged by their practical consequences, which can also change in the course of the development of science.

The doctrine of concrete truth, if it is formulated conceptually, and wherever it is applied exactly, is nothing else than the view that the truth of a proposition can only be judged if the methods of testing it are given. If somebody states a proposition and fails to state the conditions, observable in practice, under which he would be ready to accept it as true, then it is a proposition that is not scientifically applicable—it is meaningless for science. With the doctrine of concrete truth, diamat is therefore defending a standpoint which is very closely related to that of positivism and pragmatism.

The conception held by many representatives of diamat, that logistics is only a formalistic game which avoids having to do with reality, is perhaps correct in the case of many metaphysically inclined logicians. It is certainly not correct for the Vienna Circle, which uses logistics only as an aid to a radical empiricism and positivism.

In any case, the doctrine of concrete truth will some day be applied in the U.S.S.R. also to the teachings of science. Then it will be said: In our time it is no longer appropriate to embrace the new empirical and positivistic groups with the idealistic school philosophy in *one* concept, "the bourgeois conception of science." The patterns that Lenin set up for a concrete situation of struggle should not be regarded as general patterns, suitable for the representation of scientific development. It will then turn out that there are very fundamental ties between diamat and logical empiricism.

An analysis of the present situation leads to the conclusion that to designate the logical empiricism of today, or logistic neopositivism, as "idealistic" or "mechanistic" Machism would be the same sort of abstractly schematic conception as if one were to label diamat "Hegelian idealism" because of the historical connection with Hegel, and for that reason to reject it.

The creative scientific work, particularly in chemistry, physics, and biology, that enjoys favorable conditions for development in the U.S.S.R. and is in a state of rapid growth, still has very little practical effect on diamat. In this situation lies the danger for diamat, which may develop in isolation from science like the European school philosophy, which also claims to give direction to science but succeeds only in becoming more and more estranged from science, and consequently languishes.

If, in the U.S.S.R., diamat will strive to coöperate with concrete science, those tendencies in it that point toward logical empiricism will be strengthened. It will be obvious that the two-front war against idealism and mechanism can really be carried on consistently only from the standpoint of critical positivism; otherwise one will surely slide again into metaphysics to the left or to the right.

Chapter 12

Why Do Scientists and Philosophers So Often Disagree About the Merits of a New Theory?

IF, IN SEEKING an answer to the question that heads this chapter, we put the preliminary question, "Do they really disagree?" my answer is: At the beginning they do, mostly, but by and by the disagreement weakens and finally the philosophers come to agree too completely. Frequently just at this moment the physical theory in question turns out to be doubtful to the physicist. He advances a new theory and the whole cycle of disagreement and agreement begins again. If we succeed in understanding this periodically recurrent cycle we have performed a great step toward the understanding of the interaction between science and philosophy.

The divergences between physicists and philosophers have become very clear recently. We have only to glance at the discussions about space, time, and causality connected with relativity and the quantum theory to see this. There are a great many people who believe that these divergencies are characteristics of our twentieth-century physics. In order to counteract this erroneous impression I shall start by discussing the attitude of scientists and philosophers toward the Copernican world system at a time when it was news. My point is that the dispute of that time was of the same character as the dispute of today.

Copernicus published his system in the middle of the sixteenth century. A century afterwards this system was condemned by the Roman Inquisition as "philosophically false." During this century the Copernican system was taught in the universities and presented in the official textbooks as a remarkable achievement in science which was—unfortunately—"philosophically false." This attitude is illustrated by some sentences from a textbook of astronomy of 1581 written by the Jesuit C. Clavius:

One may doubt whether it would be preferable to follow Ptolemy or Copernicus. For both are in agreement with the observed phenomena. But Copernicus' principles contain a great many assertions that are absurd. He assumes, for instance, that the earth is moving with a triple motion which I cannot understand. For according to the philosophers a simple body like the earth can have only a simple motion.

After setting forth a number of arguments of the same type the author concludes:

Therefore it seems to me that Ptolemy's geocentric doctrine must be preferred to Copernicus' doctrine.

In spite of the agreement with the observed facts the Copernican system had to be rejected because it was in contradiction with certain principles which were regarded as firmly established. For instance, a simple body like the earth can have only a simple motion, such as a rectilinear or circular one. Or, to quote a second principle of the same type: We see that every piece of earth falls downwards along a straight line; therefore the earth as a whole cannot possess a circular motion. For it was an established principle that to every particular kind of matter there corresponds a particular type of motion.

All these principles were part of Aristotelian physics. They originated from generalizations of observation, just like any physical theorems. They belonged, however, to an earlier state of physical science. At the time of Copernicus they were already in a state of "fossilization"; they were believed to be eternal truths which could be derived from pure reason. Every statement of science that was in disagreement with these principles of Aristotelian physics was called "philosophically false." In this sense the Copernican system could be declared "mathematically true" but "philosophically false." This meant only that it was in agreement with the observed facts but in disagreement with the principles of Aristotelian philosophy or physics—physics being a part of philosophy.

It may be objected that this was the opinion of a Jesuit and orthodox believer in scholastic philosophy. I shall quote, therefore, the statement of a very progressive man of that time. Francis Bacon has been called in the textbooks of philosophy the very father of empirical science. He says, in 1622:

In the system of Copernicus there are found many and great inconveniences; for both the loading of the earth with a triple motion is very incommodious and the separation of the sun from the company of the planets with which it has so many passions in common is likewise a difficulty and the introduction of so much immobility into nature by representing the sun and the stars as immovable . . . all these are the speculations of one, who cares not what fictions he introduces into nature, provided his calculations answer.

If we compare this judgment of an empirical philosopher with that of the follower of Aristotle we perceive this difference: the self-confident statements of Aristotelian physics now have faded into rather vague statements of so-called common sense. We no longer derive from profound metaphysical principles the conclusion that the sun must possess the same type of motion as the planets, since it is of the same nature. It is just a "difficulty" to separate the sun from the company of the stars, since they look so similar.

The philosopher's attitude toward physical science had, however, remained essentially unchanged: physical theorems that are in contradiction with certain established general principles have to be rejected, even if these physical theorems are in agreement with all observed facts. The scholastic philosopher just as well as the advocate of empiricism upheld the distinction between "scientific truth" and "philosophic truth." The truth of a physical theorem in the first sense has to be checked by experiments. The truth in the second (the philosophic) sense depends upon whether the theorem is compatible with certain established principles.

In this sense the Copernican system was declared to be "mathematically true" but "philosophically false." And this severe judgment has been passed again and again by philosophers upon new physical theories. Let us direct our attention to Bacon's characterization of Copernicus' personality:

> Copernicus was a man who did not care what fictions he introduced into nature provided his calculations answer.

We cannot help remembering how many philosophic reviewers have charged the authors of recent physical theories (particularly relativity and quantum theory), with the same thing. We can perhaps understand this divergence in the attitude of philosophers and physicists most clearly if we examine the example of Newton's physics. For in this case we are able to pursue the fate of a great theory from its birth to its death.

As a starting point I quote a judgment on Newton by a great philosopher who was Newton's contemporary—Bishop Berkeley. The point he makes is again the difference between two ways of judging a physical theory: either by its agreement with general principles (the philosophic criterion) or by the agreement of its consequences with observations (the scientific criterion). In his book *The Analyst*, which is devoted mostly to a criticism of Newton's doctrine, Berkeley puts the rhetorical question:

Whether there can be science of the conclusion when there is no evidence of the principle? And whether a man can have evidence of the principles without understanding them? And therefore whether the mathematicians of the present age act like men of science in taking so much more pains to apply their principles than to understand them?

This sounds like a twentieth-century philosopher criticizing Einstein. It may perhaps be objected that Berkeley was not competent to pass judgment on a scientist like Newton. However, a man like Leibniz, equally competent as scientist and philosopher, considered both Newton's law of inertia and his law of gravitation philosophically false and even absurd.

Two traits in these laws seemed to be incompatible with the established principles of philosophy. According to Newton a moving body keeps its direction with respect to the empty space. This was regarded as absurd. How could the empty space exert any action? Moreover, the law of gravitation assumed that material bodies attracted each other at any distance and instantaneously. This action at a distance was incompatible with Aristotelian philosophy as well as with the "mechanistic" and "geometric" philosophy of Democritus or Descartes. For a material body could only be set in motion by contact with a second body, by push or pull.

Newton himself did not believe that his force of attraction was a causal explanation of the motion of planets. He expected always to find a derivation of these laws from general principles which were connected with a medium exerting an impact upon the planets. He compared himself to a man who could explain the operation of a piece of clockwork. Such a man can describe the mechanism by which the fall of a weight is transformed into the motion of the hands. But if you ask such a man how the weight manages to fall he would be at a loss. Nonetheless, you are forced to admit that he has given you a better understanding of the clockwork than you had before.

This attitude is defined in Newton's famous dictum, *"Hypothesis non fingo—*I don't set up hypotheses." This word has been frequently misinterpreted. For from our present viewpoint Newton's law of gravitation is a hypothesis too. Newton disappointed his most ardent followers in the question of the action at a distance as well as in the question of the corpuscular theory of light. He was always convinced that this theory was not the negation of the undulatory theory but would have to incorporate some elements of the latter. In short, Newton was not a faithful Newtonian.

The great success of Newton's physics was based upon the wide range of observable facts embraced and by the simplicity and elegance of the mathematical methods employed. It was justified by its consequences, or, to speak in the language of the Middle Ages, by its mathematical truth. But the "philosophic truth" of Newton's principles was regarded as very doubtful by his contemporaries. Not only "pure" philosophers but scientists also passed the judgments that these principles were obscure or even absurd.

But presently the confirmation of these principles by the increasing range of physical facts that could be derived from them changed the attitude of the philosophers too. If we examine the general opinion toward the end of the eighteenth century we notice a complete revolution. The law of inertia and the law of gravitation were no longer regarded as absurd; on the contrary, they were declared more and more to be self-evident, derivable from pure reason, the only way in which the human mind can understand nature.

As an example of this changed attitude we can point to Immanuel Kant's "Metaphysical Elements of Natural Science," which was published in 1786. We find in this book all the theorems of Newton's *Mathematical Principles of Natural Philosophy*, but they are transformed, so to speak, into a petrified state. Newton had invented bold generalizations in order to cover a large range of facts that had formerly defied all attempts at rational approach. All of these general statements, which seemed to Newton's contemporaries so new, so amazing, so absurd, are now quoted as self-evident. Kant claimed to have demonstrated that the law of inertia can be derived from pure reason; he claimed that the recognition of that law is the only assumption under which nature is conceivable to human reason.

One may say that this was merely the opinion of a philosopher who was a product of the German inclination toward a foggy metaphysics. But when we look at the great advocates of empirical philosophy in the nineteenth century we find almost the same opinion. We may choose as an example the British champion of empirical and mechanistic philosophy in the middle of the nineteenth century, Herbert Spencer. In his standard work, *Synthetic Philosophy,* he expresses himself about the law of inertia. He says:

This law means that motion like matter is indestructible. This indestructibility is not inductively inferred, but is a necessity of thought. For destructibility cannot be conceived at all . . . it is a pseudo-idea. To say that something can become nothing would establish a relation between two terms of which one (nothing) is absent from consciousness, which is impossible.

This was written in 1860.

But we may leave the philosophers and examine the attitude of the scientists of that period. We soon notice that their attitude is strongly influenced by the success claimed by the philosophers. The scientists would not exactly say that Newton's principles of mechanics could be derived from pure reason, but they would fervently proclaim that no physical theory is satisfactory which fails to prove that the observed phenomena are derivable from Newton's laws. Without this proof no theory could be regarded as a real step toward the understanding of nature. I quote two striking examples. About the middle of the nineteenth century, in 1847, Helmholtz published his famous paper, "On the Conservation of Energy." [1] He was a great physicist who was also a great physiologist and psychologist. He said:

The task of physical science is finally to reduce all phenomena of nature to forces of attraction and repulsion the intensity of which is dependent only upon the mutual distance of material bodies. Only if this problem is solved are we sure that nature is conceivable.

Perhaps still more impressive are the statements of the well-known physiologist Du Bois-Reymond. He gave, in 1872,

[1] H. von Helmholtz, *Über die Erhaltung der Kraft* (Berlin, 1847).

an address "On the Limitations of Natural Science." This speech was widely discussed in the last quarter of the nineteenth century. Du Bois-Reymond said:

The cognition of nature is the reduction of changes in the material world to the motions of atoms, acted upon by central forces, independent of time . . . It is a psychological fact of experience that wherever such a reduction is successfully carried through our need for causality feels satisfied *for the time being.*

Is this not an amazing fact in the history of human mind? As Newton set up his theory the introduction of the central forces of attraction was regarded as a particularly weak point of his theory. It was accused of requiring the introduction of an element that is philosophically absurd. But what happened about a hundred years later? It was claimed as a "psychologic fact" that just the same thing—the reduction of a group of phenomena to the action of central forces—satisfies our need for causal understanding. And the derivation of physical theorems from the action of these forces, which were formerly condemned as unconceivable, was now the guarantee that nature is conceivable.

What is the point of all these considerations? By examining the changes in the appreciation of Newton's laws we are able to find out and to understand the origin and the formation of established philosophic principles. Both the law of inertia and the law of gravitation originated as physical hypotheses that enabled the physicist to describe and predict a large group of observable phenomena in a very convenient way. These laws were justified by the success of this enterprise—that is to say, by their effects—but they could not be recognized as compatible with established philosophic principles. They were, if we apply the language of the Church in its struggle against Copernicus, "philosophically false" and merely "mathematically true."

But what was the situation in the middle of the nineteenth century? Now, the same laws, the law of inertia as well as the law of gravitation, became themselves established philosophic principles, with which all physical theorems had to be in agreement. A physical theorem was now by definition "philosophically true" if it could be derived from Newton's laws. We understand now very well that these "established philosophic principles" are nothing else than physical hypotheses in a state of petrifaction.

It may be asked why we should call it "petrifaction." A physical theory can be changed when new facts are discovered that are not embraced by this theory in a convenient way. But a philosophic principle which is derived from pure reason can never be changed or even modified. If Kant and Spencer are right, that the principle of inertia can be demonstrated by purely mental operations, no future discovery of new physical phenomena can bring about any modification of this principle. The transformation of a physical hypothesis into a philosophic principle is therefore a petrifaction of that hypothesis.

And now it seems very plausible that the philosophic principles of earlier periods are of the same origin. Aristotle's principles of physics were originally also generalizations that covered in a convenent way a certain group of observed facts. When Copernicus and Galileo advanced their new physical theories they were declared to be "philosophically false." This meant only that they were in contradiction with the petrifactions of Aristotelian physics.

In the same way we can now understand the widespread claim that the theory of relativity and the quantum theory are valuable descriptions of observed facts but give us neither a causal understanding nor a description of physical reality. To put it briefly, they are taxed with being only mathematically true but philosophically false or even absurd. This means in this case only that they are in contradiction with the petrifactions of Newton's physics. Or in other words, in twentieth-century physics we are confronted with new experimental facts and have to change the hypotheses of Newton's physics. This is possible as long as these hypotheses are not petrified. But once Newton's laws are regarded as philosophic principles which can be deduced from pure reason they can no longer be changed. Now every modification of Newton's law will be "philosophically false."

But knowing the origin of philosophic principles we need not be terrorized by the verdict "philosophically false." It means only that the new physical laws are in contradiction with the old physical laws which appear now disguised as philosophic principles with pretensions of eternal validity. The old physical theory was a good description of a restricted group of facts. But to cover the new facts the old theory became inconvenient. It is natural to drop it, if an obsolete physical theory does not pretend to be an "eternal philosophy."

This very simple state of affairs has often been described by the pretentious term "crisis of physics," or even "crisis of science."

And now we can answer with a few words the question put in the title of this chapter. Why do philosophers and scientists so often disagree about the merit of a new theory? They mostly disagree because the new theory seems to be in contradiction to established philosophic principles. Moreover —and this is my chief point—this disagreement arises from necessity, for the established philosophic principles are mostly petrifactions of physical theories that are no longer appropriate to embrace the facts of our actual physical experience.

Chapter 13

The Philosophic Meaning of the Copernican Revolution

IN 1543, four hundred years ago, Copernicus died. This year was in a certain sense also the year of the birth of the Copernican system. His great book, "The Revolutions of the Celestian Bodies," [1] was published in the same year. When this book was published, nearly fifty years had passed since Columbus discovered America. This event was one of Copernicus' starting points. He refers in one of the first pages of his book to this discovery as the final proof of the spherical shape of the earth. (Incidentally, he does not mention Columbus and says, as a matter of course, that "America is named after her discoverer.") The earth was now definitely a globe, and, to speak in terms of today, "global thinking" could begin.

To understand a phenomenon means to interpret our present experience as the repetition of a similar phenomenon of the past. This is true in science, but it is true as well in history. Today, we understand the French Revolution better than our parents did because we are contemporaries of the Russian revolution, and we understand the Copernican revolution better than did nineteenth-century scientists did because we are contemporaries of the Einsteinian revolution.

Let us formulate the central problem of all philosophy of science in the simplest possible terms. We have to face two worlds: on one hand, that of our sense observations, such as, in astronomy, the observed positions of the stars in the sky; on the other hand, that of the general principles of science, such as the law of gravitation and the principle of relativity. To what extent are these general principles justified by those sense observations?

This sounds simple enough, but to appreciate the immense gap between these two worlds means to start grasping the central problem of all philosophy of science. Unfortunately, the pedagogic effort of science teachers has been often directed towards camouflaging this gap. If, however, the very goal of science teaching is to help the students in the understanding of

[1] *De Revolutionibus Orbium Celestium.*

nature, the actual depth and width of that gap must be emphasized over and over again. The state of mind acquired by the average student of science as the result of inadequate training has been largely responsible for the failure to appreciate exactly the philosophic meaning of the Copernican revolution.

Only recently, under the violent impact of twentieth-century physics, particularly the theory of relativity, have the eyes of science students been opened and has the meaning of the Copernican revolution become clear.

If we look into a typical textbook or listen to an average teacher, we learn that before Copernicus, men believed in the testimony of their senses, which told them that our earth is at rest, that the planet Jupiter traverses in twelve years a closed orbit on the celestial sphere and that this curve contains twelve loops. Finally, Copernicus recognized the fallacy of this testimony and proved that "in reality" our earth is in motion and that the planet Jupiter traverses "in reality" a smooth circle around the sun as center. Copernicus exposed the illusions of our senses. Human reason thus scored a clear victory in its struggle against naïve sense experience.

This description of Copernicus' achievement seems to me, conservatively speaking, inadequate. The loops traced by the planets are by no means a sort of optical illusion and neither is the immobility of the earth. As a matter of fact, the planet Jupiter actually traverses every year a loop with respect to a system of reference that participates in the annual revolution of the earth. But the same Jupiter traverses just as truly every twelve years a smooth circle with respect to the system of fixed stars. Neither the loops nor the smooth circle are results of our naïve sense experience. They are two different diagrams representing one and the same set of sense observations. Therefore, the interpretation of Copernicus' achievement as a victory of abstract reason over naïve sense experience is hardly justifiable.

However, we meet occasionally a second interpretation which says almost the opposite of the first one. The hard facts of our sense experience become more and more incompatible with medieval philosophy, which had its roots in speculative reasoning rather than in sense observation. Copernicus finally decided to overthrow the obsolete doctrines of Aristotle and Ptolemy and scored a victory for experience in its struggle against pure speculation. As a matter of fact, Copernicus was not particularly "tough minded," if we may use the famous phrase of William James to describe the empirical scientist as distinct from the "tender-minded" believer in pure reasoning. No new facts had been discovered by Copernicus, which had forced him to abandon the geocentric doctrine. The astronomical tables calculated from the Copernican system were in no better agreement with the observed positions of the stars than the previous tables.

Therefore we have to start from the fact that the Copernican revolution meant neither a victory of reason over the illusion of our senses nor a victory of hard facts over pure speculation. To be sure, Copernicus invented a new pattern of description for our observations. His genius manifests itself in the beautiful simplicity of this pattern: he replaced loops by concentric circles.

Copernicus died in 1543. The Roman Holy Office did not utter an official judgment on the Copernican system until 1616, seventy-three years after Copernicus' death. This Roman verdict will give us the best hint about the philosophic meaning of the Copernican revolution. For the verdict considered specifically the philosophic merit of the new system. The Copernican theory was called "philosophically foolish and absurd."

But not even Copernicus' greatest opponents ever doubted that his system meant a great advance in astronomy. The general opinion in these quarters was that the heliocentric system is "astronomically true," or as it was sometimes phrased, "mathematically true," but in any case "philosophically false" or even "absurd."

We have to do here with a conflict between two conceptions of truth. This conflict has existed through the ages and has created quite often a great confusion of mind. This double meaning of truth has never been dramatized so clearly as by the Copernican revolution and its repercussions. To understand and to evaluate this conflict is the great lesson we can learn from the history of the Copernican ideas.

The medieval philosopher St. Thomas Aquinas described very distinctly two different criteria of truth:

There are two ways to prove the truth of an assertion. The first way consists in proving the truth of a principle from which this assertion follows logically. In this way, one proves in physics the uniformity of the motion of the celestial spheres. The second way consists not in proving a principle from which our assertion can be derived but in assuming our assertion tentatively and in deriving results from it which can be compared with our observations. In this way one derives, in astrology, the consequences of the hypothesis of eccentrics or epicycles concerning the motion of celestial bodies. However, we cannot conclude in this way that the same assumptions cannot be derived, perhaps, from a different hypothesis also.[2]

If a statement of astronomy met only the second criterion, the agreement with observed facts, it was termed "mathematically true." Only if it met also the first criterion, that is, if it could be derived from an evident principle, was it recognized to be "philosophically true." Since Aristotle's physics was supposed to be derived from evident principles, to be philosophically true meant practically to be in agreement with Aristotelian physics.

As Copernicus had been anxious lest his system might not be philosophically true in this sense, he feared some hostility on the part of theologians who were strict believers in Aristotelian philosophy. He looked for advice on how to behave in this situation, and strange as it may seem to us, the Catholic churchman Copernicus asked a Lutheran theologian from Nuremberg how to avoid trouble. The Nuremberg scholar, Osiander, answered him in a letter of 1541:

As for my part, I have always felt about hypotheses that they are not articles of faith but bases of calculation. Even if they are false, it does not matter much provided that they describe the observed phenomena correctly . . . It would, therefore, be an excellent thing for you to play up a little this point in your preface. For you would appease in this way Aristotelians and theologians, the opposition of whom you fear.

This advice meant precisely that Copernicus should not claim "philosophic truth" for his system but should be satisfied with a claim for "mathematical truth."

But Copernicus did not like this compromise. He claimed his system to be at least as philosophically true as the Ptolemaic system, and perhaps even more so. In this way a conflict flared up, the issue of which was a very subtle distinction. Was the Copernican doctrine a true description of the universe or was it merely an hypothesis which served for calculating the positions of the stars? And how did Coper-

[2] *Summa Theologiae.*

nicus himself look upon this question? Most of the scientists of today are accustomed to regard every theory as a working hypothesis only, and would hardly be prepared to give serious thought to that subtle distinction which is rather an issue of the philosophy of science. But if we go a little deeper into the logical structure of science, we have to recognize that, as a matter of fact, every scientific theory, of whatever period, had to meet the two requirements of a "true theory" which were already familiar to Thomas Aquinas. In reality, no theory was accepted merely because it was a good working hypothesis. In every period of the history of science a theory had to be in agreement with the general principles of physics. The physicists of the nineteenth century would hardly have admitted a theory that was in disagreement with the principle of conservation of energy.

For that reason, practically every theory has been a compromise between these two requirements. This is particularly true of the Ptolemaic system. We read and hear frequently that the Ptolemaic system was in agreement with the Aristotelian philosophy and physics. But Copernicus, we are told, disturbed this harmony and advanced a theory that would contradict explicitly the laws of medieval physics. This was certainly not the opinion of the medieval philosophers themselves. One of the basic principles of medieval physics was the law that terrestrial bodies move in rectilinear paths toward or away from the earth while celestial bodies move in circular orbits with the earth as center, but the Ptolemaic system assumes that sun and planets traverse eccentric circles or epicycles the center of which is not the earth. Therefore, the Ptolemaic system could not be regarded as philosophically true, but at most as a hypothesis that might serve as a basis of calculation.

Thomas Aquinas judged the Ptolemaic system as follows:

The assumptions made by the astronomers are not necessarily true. Although these hypotheses seem to be in agreement with the observed phenomena we must not claim that they are true. Perhaps one could explain the observed motion of the celestial bodies in a different way which has not been discovered up to this time.

The twelfth-century Arabian philosopher Averroes and his school emphasized very strictly the philosophical criterion of truth and declined to ascribe any truth value to the Ptolemaic system. Says Averroes:

The astronomers start from the assumption that these [eccentric or epicylic] orbits exist. From this assumption they derive results that are in agreement with our sense observations. But they have not proved by any means that the presuppositions from which they started are, in turn, necessary causes of these observations. In this case, only the observed results are known but the principles themselves are unknown, for the principles cannot be logically derived from the results. Therefore new research work is necessary in order to find the "true" astronomy, which can be derived from the true principles of physics. As a matter of fact, today there is no astronomy at all, and what we call astronomy is in agreement with our computations but not with the physical reality.

The common opinion among philosophers was rather that the true picture of the universe cannot be discovered by the astronomer, who is restricted to finding out what hypotheses are in agreement with observed facts. If different hypotheses meet this requirement, science cannot decide which is true and, as the Jewish medieval philosopher Moses Maimonides puts it:

Man knows only these poor mathematical theories about the heavens, and only God knows the real motions of the heavens and their causes.

It is certain, therefore, that before the Copernican revolution no theory of the motions of the celestial bodies existed that would meet both criteria of truth. There was in every theory a discrepancy between mathematical and philosophic truth. Against this background we have to interpret the famous dedication letter which Copernicus published as a preface to his great book and in which he recommended his work to the good will of Pope Paul III.

Copernicus affirms that he did not advance his new theory of the motions of the heavens in a spirit of opposition against the established doctrine. His only motive was his conviction that there was no established doctrine. The hypothesis of a circular motion of planets around the earth as center did not account for the observed facts, and the hypotheses of eccentrics or epicycles were not in agreement with the general principles of physics which required uniform circular motions around the earth as center. Since no doctrine existed which could be regarded as "true" from the philosophic as well as from the mathematical angle, Copernicus felt free to suggest a new hypothesis assuming the mobility of the earth.

This hypothesis accounted for the observed motions nearly as well as the Ptolemaic theory of epicycles, but removed some of the epicycles. The motions of the planets became now circular orbits around the sun as center, except for the epicycles which were necessary to account for the inequalities in the motion of planets. In any case there were fewer epicycles and more homocentric orbits in the Copernican, than in the Ptolemaic, system. Therefore Copernicus claimed that his theory was in some sense nearer to the requirements of Aristotelian physics than was the geocentric system. The Ptolemaic system was a compromise between the two criteria of truth. Copernicus claimed that his system was in the same sense a compromise and, as he believed, a better one.

In any case, Copernicus claimed to give in his theory a true picture of the universe, true in every sense of the word. By a strange coincidence, Copernicus' book was edited by the same Osiander of Nuremberg whose advice Copernicus did not like to follow. We understand now the famous words of the editor's preface, which had been originally ascribed to the author himself but which reflect only the editor's opinion:

The hypotheses of this book are not necessarily true or even probable. Only one thing matters. They must lead by computation to results that are in agreement with the observed phenomena.

While Copernicus tried to achieve the compromise by arguing that his theory is to a large extent in agreement with the principles of Aristotelian physics, Galileo Galilei, in his famous *Dialogue on the Copernican and Ptolemaic Systems of the World,* went a good deal further in the overthrow of medieval science. He no longer attempted to reach the compromise by adjusting his working hypotheses to the requirements of the established principles of physics. On the contrary, he ventured to adjust the principles of physics to the best suitable working hypotheses. This meant dropping the bulk of Aristotelian physics and starting a movement in science that led in time to the philosophy of science which we would call today positivism or pragmatism. The two criteria of truth which were for medieval thinkers like St. Thomas Aquinas two distinct requirements, have fused more and more into one single requirement: to derive the best description of the observed phenomena from the simplest possible principles, while these principles are justified solely by the fact that they permit this derivation.

Galileo's ideas were not brought into a coherent system of propositions until Isaac Newton advanced his celebrated laws of motion in his *Mathematical Principles of Natural Philosophy*. This book appeared in 1687, approximately 150 years after the Copernican revolution. From the Newtonian principles the Copernican doctrines could be logically derived. Therefore, to the believer in these principles, the Copernican system was now true in the full sense of the word, philosophically and mathematically true.

Let us now ask, What did the Copernican hypothesis look like when it was derived from the Newtonian principles? It said that the earth is rotating with respect to absolute space and that the planet Jupiter traverses smooth circular orbits with respect to absolute space. But Newton himself was very well aware that "motion relative to absolute space" has, to use P. W. Bridgman's term, no *operational* meaning, this is, that by no physical experiment can the speed of a body in rectilinear motion with respect to absolute space be measured.

Therefore, the Newtonian system of principles is not a logically coherent system within the domain of physics. Newton himself restored logical coherence by enlarging his system of physical statements by the addition of some theologic propositions. As we read in Burtt's book on the *Metaphysical Foundations of Modern Physical Science*:

Certainly, at least God must know whether any given motion is absolute or relative. The divine consciousness furnishes the ultimate center of reference for absolute motion. Moreover the animism in Newton's conception of force plays a part in the premises of the position. God is the ultimate originator of motion. Thus real or absolute motion in the last analysis is the expenditure of divine energy. Whenever the divine intelligence is cognizant of such an expenditure the motion so added to the system of the world must be absolute.

Under the influence of the spirit of the eighteenth century the mixing of theology into science began to be regarded as illegitimate. Strange as it may seem, by the abandonment of theologic argument the Newtonian physics lost logical coherence, Burtt says very correctly:

When in the twentieth century Newton's conception of the world was gradually shorn of its religious relations, the ultimate justification for absolute space and time as he had portrayed them disappeared and the entities were left empty.

Therefore the new principles of physics from which the Copernican theory could be derived were far from being satisfactory. The "philosophic truth" of the Copernican system was still a doubtful thing.

Toward the end of the nineteenth century, Ernst Mach exposed very specifically the logical incoherency of the Newtonian mechanics as a purely physical system. He claimed on good grounds that the principles from which the Copernican system was derived are essentially theologic or metaphysical principles. Mach claimed in the nineteenth century, as Averroes had done in the period of the Ptolemean system, that we have no true astronomy, if "true" means "derived from a coherent system of principles of physics."

Mach asked for the removal of the concept of absolute space from physics and for a new physics which contains only terms which have within physics, to speak again with Bridgman, operational meaning.

This program, however, was not carried out until Einstein created his general theory of relativity and gravitation between 1911 and 1915. This theory, as a matter of fact, was the first system of purely physical principles from which the Copernican system of planetary motions could be derived. But the description of these motions looked now very different from the way it had looked as derived from Newton's principles. The concept of absolute space was no longer present. Therefore the statement of the rotation of the earth and of the smooth circular orbits of the planets had now to be formulated quite differently.

From Einstein's principles one could derive the description of the motions of celestial bodies relative to any system of reference. One could demonstrate that the description of the motion of planets becomes particularly simple if one uses the system of fixed stars as a system of reference, but there was still no objection to using the earth as system of reference. In this case, one obtains a description in which the earth is at rest and the fixed stars are in a rotational motion. What appears to be in the Copernican heliocentric system the centrifugal force of the rotating earth becomes in the geocentric system a gravitational effect of the rotating stars upon the earth.

The Copernican system became for the first time in its history not only mathematically but also philosophically true. But at the same moment the geocentric system became philosophically true, also. The system of reference had lost all philosophic meaning. For each astronomical problem, one had to pick the system of reference that rendered the simplest description of the motions of the celestial bodies involved.

The reception of the Einsteinian revolution by the scientists of the twentieth century reminds us in many respects of the reception of the Copernican revolution by the scientists of the sixteenth century. This comparison might help us to understand the philosophical meaning of both.

We may take as an example the way in which Einstein deals with the contraction of moving bodies in the direction of their motion. The verdict of quite a few twentieth-century physicists was: the theory of relativity permits us to derive the observed phenomena from hypothetical principles but it does not give a physical explanation of the contraction. This was an exact repetition of the Roman verdict against the Copernican system. For the meaning was: the theory of relativity may be "mathematically true" but it is certainly "philosophically false." Now "philosophically false" meant not to be in agreement with Newton's principles of physics, while in the sixteenth century the same expression meant not to be in agreement with Aristotle's physics and Scholastic philosophy.

But what are the facts affirmed by the Copernican doctrine which are still accepted today as true? Copernicus enthusiastically proclaimed the sun as the center of the universe and said:

In the center of the Universe the sun has its residence. Who could locate this lamp in this beautiful temple in a different or better place than in the center wherefrom it can illuminate the whole of it simultaneously?

Even if we restrict the meaning of the word "universe" to our galactic system, the Milky Way, this universe is not spherical and the sun is not located in the center. It has been known for a long time that our galactic system has the shape of a lens. Before the distance of very remote stars could be estimated, it was plausible to believe that our sun, with our earth as attendant, is located in the center of this lens. However, in the twentieth century new methods were developed for estimating the great distances of remote stars, in large part by Harlow Shapley and his collaborators of the Harvard Observatory. In particular, Shapley found that our sun is not located near the center of that lens, but approximately 30,000 light years away from it. This means that the sun with our planetary system is near the edge of the lens. According to Copernicus, we inhabitants of the earth have no longer the great satisfaction of being the center of the universe, but we have at least the small satisfaction of being the attendant of a master who has his residence at this center. But according to Shapley, man has lost all reasons for complacency. He is not even the attendant of a master who occupies the central stage of the universe.

Copernicus probably believed that the orbits of celestial bodies can be described in the best and simplest way by taking the sun as a body of reference. In our twentieth century, we know that this cannot be true universally. According to Einstein's theory of gravitation, there is no "all-purpose system of reference." Copernicus' suggestion of using the sun is practical only if we restrict ourselves to the motions in our planetary system. For every particular purpose a particular system may be the most suitable.

Copernicus did not discover any new fact that could be regarded as established for all eternity. But he denied to the earth its former role as the only legitimate body of reference, he demonstrated that the sun is the most suitable system for a particular purpose, and he cleared the way for the great new truth that we have complete freedom in our choice of a system of reference.

The Copernican revolution did not end by replacing the earth as master of the Universe by the sun or by absolute space, but it was only the first step in a series of revolutions that culminated, so far as we know today, in depicting a democratic order of the universe in which all celestial bodies play an equal part.

Chapter 14

The Place of the Philosophy of Science in the Curriculum of the Physics Student

IF WE WISH to exercise sound judgment about the success or failure of science teaching in the general scheme of our educational system, it may be a good idea to arrange a hearing. We may then listen to people who were compelled to submit to this teaching and later achieved such a great reputation in our cultural life that we cannot ignore their opinions about the contribution of science teaching to general education.

Ralph Waldo Emerson, who complained that science had become abstract and remote from human life, says in his essay on Beauty in "The Conduct of Life":

> The formulas of science are like the papers in your pocketbook, of no value to any but the owner . . . There's a revenge for this inhumanity. What manner of man does science make? The boy is not attracted. He says, I do not wish to be such a kind of man as my professor is.

If the goal of a teacher is to stimulate, by his own example, enthusiasm for his subject, Emerson's teachers of science seem not to have come very near this goal. It may be that Emerson was not a science-minded type. We may quote, therefore, a recent writer, who, besides his wide interests in all domains of human life, had a particular leaning toward science— H. G. Wells. He describes his reaction to his physics teachers in the Normal School of Science in London. He realizes exactly that what is wrong is not the ability of a particular teacher. "No man," says Wells, "can be a good teacher when his subject becomes inexplicable." He amplifies this statement:

> To a certain point it had all been plain sailing, a pretty science, with pretty subdivisions: optics, acoustics, electricity and magnetism, and so on. Up to that point, the time-honored terms which have been crystallized out in language about space, speed, force, and so forth sufficed to carry what I was learning. All went well in the customary space-time framework. Then things became

difficult. I realize now that it wasn't simply that neither Guthrie nor Boys was a good teacher . . . The truth, of which I had no inkling then, was that beyond what were (and are) the empirical practical truths of the conservation of energy, the indestructibility of matter and force, and so forth, hung an enigmatic fog. A material and experimental meta-physics was reached . . .[1]

H. G. Wells indeed laid a finger on a very sore spot in our science teaching. The "subject has become inexplicable" because the teachers themselves did not have training that put the emphasis on logical consistency and satisfactory coherence between abstract law and sensory observation. Their upbringing was a purely technical one, with little regard for the role of science within our culture as a whole. Where physics teaching reached a domain beyond mechanical and electrical engineering, the subject was not satisfactorily explained because it was "inexplicable."

There is no doubt that the current interest in science has its origin not only in its technical application, but also in its bearing on our general world picture. Our generation is witness to the "relativity boom." At the peak of this boom, Einstein's theory was of hardly any use to the engineer. But, to express it perfunctorily, it changed our view about the "nature of time and space." The statement that concurrently with a given event here a certain event is occurring on the planet Mars, was formerly taken to have a definite meaning. We know now that such a statement can only be asserted "relative to a certain system of reference." This new doctrine appeared to add credit to the doctrine of the "relativity of truth" and seemed therefore to some people a "social danger," since it might contribute to a disbelief in the "absolute values" of ethics.

These problems have been haunting our generation for decades. But if we ask a trained physicist (not to speak of a graduate engineer) what his opinion is on these questions, we notice immediately that his training in physics has not provided him with any balanced judgment. The scientist will, as a matter of fact, often be more helpless than an intelligent reader of popular science magazines. We face the same situation if we ask our graduate in physics whether the theory of quanta has justified the belief in the freedom of will or

[1] H. G. Wells, *Experiment in Autobiography* (New York: Macmillan, 1934), pp. 175 ff.

whether it has made a contribution toward the reconciliation between science and religion, as has been maintained frequently, even by scientists and philosophers of high reputation.

The great majority of these trained physicists—and by "majority" I mean more than 90 percent—will be unable to give any but the most superficial answer. And even this superficial answer will not be the result of their professional training, but the profit they have made from reading some articles in newspapers or periodicals. As a matter of fact, most of them will not even be able to give a superficial answer, but will just say, "This is not my field, and that's all there is to it."

The result of conventional science teaching has not been a critically minded type of scientist, but just the opposite. The longing for the integration of knowledge is very deeply rooted in the human mind. If it is not cultivated by the science teacher, it will look for other outlets. The thirsty student takes his spiritual drink where it is offered to him. If he is lucky, he gets his information from popular magazines or science columns in newspapers. But it can be worse, and he may become a victim of people who interpret recent physics in the service of some pet ideology which has been, in quite a few cases, an anti-scientific ideology. The physical theories of the twentieth century have been interpreted, indeed, as having "abandoned rational thinking" in favor of—I don't know exactly what, as I cannot imagine what alternative exists to rational thinking in the field of science.

It is a fact which one may regret, but which is established empirically with no less certainty than the law of gravitation, that the science student who has received the traditional purely technical instruction in his field is extremely gullible when he is faced with pseudophilosophic and pseudoreligious interpretations that fill somehow the gap left by his science courses. I would even venture the statement that this gullibility increases in inverse proportion to the familiarity of the student with the conceptual analysis of science. I think that, statistically, the experimental physicist is more gullible than the theoretical physicist, and the graduate of an engineering school still more so.

For our purpose, it is sufficient to realize that the present type of science instruction does not enable the student to form even the faintest judgment about the interpretation of recent physics as a part of a new world picture. This failure prevents the science graduate from playing in our cultural and public life the great part that is assigned to him by the ever-mounting technical importance of science to human society. It is obvious that the necessity of teaching twentieth-century physics has made conspicuous the shortcomings in our methods of science teaching. It would be erroneous, however, to think that the teaching of earlier, so-called classical, physics is not handicapped by the same kind of shortcomings. But, certainly, these deficiencies become the more conspicuous the more rapid the changes in physics that have to be presented in class.

If we look, for example, at the treatment of the Copernican conflict in an average textbook of science, we notice immediately that the presentation is far from satisfactory. In almost every case, we are told that according to the testimony of our senses the sun seems to move around the earth. Then we are instructed that Copernicus has taught us to distrust this testimony and to look for truth in our reasoning rather than in our immediate sense experience. This presentation is, to say the least, very misleading. Actually, our sense observation shows only that in the morning the distance between horizon and sun is increasing, but it does not tell us whether the sun is ascending or the horizon is descending. Starting from this fundamental mistake, the average textbook does not provide the student with an adequate picture of the historic fight of the Roman Church against the Copernican system. The student does not learn the way in which a powerful organization can oppose a doctrine established by science, and how this opposition can muster the support of reasonable and bright persons like the father of British empirical philosophy, Francis Bacon, who denounced the Copernican system as violating our common sense.

By its failure to give an adequate presentation of this historic dispute our traditional physics teaching misses an opportunity to foster in the student an understanding of the relations between science, religion and government which is so helpful for his adjustment in our modern social life. With a good understanding of the Copernican and similar conflicts, the student of science would have even an inside track in the understanding of social and political problems. He would be put at least on an equal level with the student of the humanities.

Let us now proceed with our hearing: having listened to Emerson and Wells, let us question an intelligent college student who is not a concentrator in science but who has taken, say, a beginning course in chemistry or biology to round out his general education. We shall hear often of a deep dissatisfaction with these science courses as a contribution to general education. While such a student may carry away from his courses in history or literature the impression that they have guided him into a wide-open field of human interest with an outlook in a great many new directions, he has had a very different reaction to his science courses.

We may take our example from the chemistry classes, where, according to an old tradition, the general outlook is more neglected than in the other sciences. In such courses, where science teaching is at its worst from the educational angle, formulas like H_2SO_4 are thrown upon the head of the student, and he will really feel, as Emerson did, that these formulas are "notes in a pocketbook, which are valuable only to the owner"—who is, in this case, the professional chemist —but without any broad human interest. The general student will get the impression that he sits in a show where formulas are tossed around in a kind of juggling game. This is, of course, a very inadequate impression, but one to which the student will inevitably be led by the purely technical approach in the teaching. He will probably not be much impressed if he is told that this juggling leads eventually to interesting results, perhaps in the field of solid and liquid fuels. For "fuel" is, after all, no broad human interest either, but obviously a concern for some specialists.

If, however, chemistry should be taught in a more human way, it would be clear that a formula like H_2SO_4 contains the history of mankind, the evolution of the human mind in a much more impressive and certainly more condensed way than does all the history of the British kings. What a good teaching of science has to achieve on behalf of general education is to bring out the heroic mental efforts of mankind, which are packed in the formula H_2SO_4 as in a nutshell, and to let the student live through the exciting historical and psychological experience that eventually found its abridged expression in such a formula. Then the "note in a pocketbook" will become a flaming manifesto to mankind.

The foregoing discussion raises serious doubts as to the ability of the traditional method of science teaching in fitting science into the broader framework of human knowledge. For the scientist himself this state of affairs may be satisfactory or at least tolerable, provided that the student gets a good understanding of his own field, say physics. But I am afraid that the same shortcomings that have in the past been obstacles to fitting physics into a broader frame of reference may also be obstacles in the path leading to a satisfactory understanding of physics itself.

In order to check this apprehension, we have only to put to a student of science the following simple question, which is, in a certain way, a key question: What does it mean when you say that a geometric theorem—for example, the sum of the angles in a plane triangle is equal to two right angles—is "true"? The significance of this question was emphasized with the advent of non-Euclidean geometry. Even in a perfunctory treatment of non-Euclidean geometry the question will arise: What does it mean to say that our actual space is Euclidean or non-Euclidean? This question was regarded as very natural and pertinent by the founders of non-Euclidean geometry. It was, actually, a very common question when this new geometry was a novelty. But if, today, you examine a graduate in mathematics or physics, the majority will never have heard of such a question, and if you put it to them they will not understand its meaning without a very thorough interpretation. If we look into any current textbook of non-Euclidean geometry, which may have several hundred pages, hardly half a page will be devoted to the question of "truth," and these few lines are mostly an attempt to dodge the question. In most cases, the student will not even learn such a simple thing as that mathematics can prove only statements of the type: if theorem A is true, then theorem B is also true; but it can never prove whether A is true or not.

This failure of science teaching in the foundations of geometry has a devastating effect on the mind of the student. For if he does not grasp the exact relationship between mathematics and physics in this simplest example offered by geometry, later he will certainly be unable to understand precisely the relation between experimental confirmation and mathematical proof in the more involved domains of physics or, for that matter, in any exact science. This means that he is bound to misunderstand altogether the role of mathematical theory in physics. The failure of a satisfactory elucidation in such a fundamental matter has made it possible to find in a well-known textbook of college physics statements like this: Einstein proved "mathematically" that a material body cannot move with the speed of light. The student of physics is not even trained to get the instinctive feeling that no statement of physics can be proved mathematically, but that every "proof" in physics consists only in deriving mathematically one physical fact from other statements about physical facts.

By the failure to give a good account of the exact relation between mathematical proof and experimental confirmation, our traditional science teaching again misses an opportunity to teach the student a reasonable and scientific approach to all problems of human interest. For in all these fields the central problem is the relationship between sensory experience (often called fact finding), and the logical conclusions that can be drawn from it. The failure to grasp exactly the nature of this relationship accounts for the confused attitude of many people toward the complex problems by which they are faced in private and public life.

The role of mathematics and physics in the understanding of geometry is perhaps the simplest example by which the student can learn how to discern the role of facts and logical conclusions in the involved problems of human relations. As a matter of fact, every problem of physics where mathematics is applied gives us such an example. A simple and typical example is provided by Newton's laws of motion. The first law (law of inertia) and the second law look very simple, but they are a crucial issue for every instructor who teaches physics to beginners. Their apparent simplicity makes it easy to discover every confusion in the presentation, whereas in the treatment of an advanced subject of mechanics, such as the problem of three bodies in celestial mechanics, a little confusion can pass unnoticed.

It is not an exaggeration to say that 90 percent of the textbooks of physics on the college level present the law of inertia in such a way that its meaning is obscure; it is formulated in words that are not applicable to any actual situation in the physical world. We learn mostly that a body upon which no force is acting is "moving along a straight line." But obviously the expression "moving along a straight line" has a physical meaning only if a system of reference is physically given, in which a straight line is fixed that serves as the model by which we judge whether a certain motion is rectilinear or not. But in the current textbooks of college physics one finds hardly even the perfunctory statements that the system of reference needed in the first law is the system of the so-called fixed stars. Hence, the statement of the law as it occurs in the textbooks has not even a vague meaning, for no method is described by which the validity of the law can be tested in a concrete case.

Since the method of testing remains obscure, one finds all imaginable opinions regarding the possibility and method of testing the validity of the law of inertia. In some books one reads that the law is self-evident and does not need any empirical proof; other authors, however, say that it is confirmed by the most familiar experience of our daily life; for example, a book lies quietly on a table if it is not taken off. This, again, is in contradiction to the assertion of some textbooks that the law of inertia is a hypothesis that cannot be proved by any experiment.

If one seeks an evaluation of this law of inertia as an achievement of the human mind, one finds not infrequently such statements as: it is amazing that it took so many centuries to discover such a simple and trivial law. It does not occur to these authors that this law may, after all, not be so "simple" as they believe, if so many great scientists were unable to discover it earlier. Obviously, to call it "simple and self-evident" means not to understand its real significance and not to give to the students a correct presentation.

While in the elementary textbooks the law of inertia is formulated in an elaborate but mostly meaningless way, many advanced textbooks take pride in minimizing the law. I even found a book in this category in which the law of inertia is called "self-explanatory." The author himself fails to explain it, relying evidently on the ability of the law to explain itself. In these advanced books the law of inertia is treated as a special case of the second law: acceleration is proportional to force. If the force is zero, the acceleration obviously is zero too, and the body moves with constant velocity. But the only distinction between this and what the elementary books say is very often that in the advanced book not the first, but the second law is formulated in a meaningless way. The result can be easily checked, if we ask any graduate student in physics what the word "acceleration" in the second law means. He will certainly know that the acceleration is the second derivative of the coördinates with respect to time; but when we ask him what is meant exactly by "coördinates," he will say that they refer to a Cartesian coördinate system. But a motion of a physical body is described only if we specify its coördinates with respect to a coördinate system that consists of physical bodies at which we can point. Therefore, to give an "operational" definition of what is meant by "acceleration" in the second law, we have to describe a particular physical Cartesian system. This certainly must not be in fixed connection with our earth. In the first approximation, we can take the body of fixed stars, our Milky Way, as such a Cartesian system. Then acceleration is, approximately, "acceleration with respect to our Milky Way." Most students of physics will be at a loss if asked a simple question like this. Even a candidate in the Ph.D. examination will sometimes answer that "acceleration" in the second law means "acceleration with respect to a Cartesian system the axes of which are fixed in space." Many will not even have a vague apprehension that the expression "fixed in space" may be meaningless in physics. But if one asks them a little more insistently, they will become confused and will guess that there is something rotten in their knowledge of the simplest laws of physics.

This failure to describe the physical system of reference to which Newton's laws refer does not do any harm to the student who takes mechanics for its use in mechanical engineering. For in this restricted domain he can work on the assumption that our own earth is the system of reference that is meant in the definition of "acceleration." In the extreme case, he will have to resort only to the system of fixed stars, as in computing the influence of the rotation of the earth on the orbit of a launched projectile. The engineer who has never heard of the difficult problem involved in the expression "acceleration" in Newton's law will by this failure not imperil the lives of people who use a bridge that was built according to his computations.

Obviously this state of happy innocence becomes obnoxious if it is preserved in the treatment of cosmological problems. The fixed stars, of course, are not at rest with respect to one another and do not exactly form a rigid Cartesian system. Therefore, they cannot be substituted in the Newtonian laws for the abstract term "Cartesian system." Rather, we must say that the positions and velocities of the fixed stars, and even of the remote nebulas, determine in some way the system of reference that the Newtonians mean when they use the term "acceleration" without any specifications. This means that the motion of a rolling billiard ball on earth is physically influenced by the positions and velocities of our Milky Way, and even by the galaxies that are millions of light years away from the earth. They determine the motion that we call "motion under no force." By ignoring the influence of the large but remote masses of the universe, the mysterious concept of "absolute space" was introduced into science. It remained there as a heritage of an ancient state of science which later was interpreted as metaphysics.

Obviously, as in the case of geometry, by the failure to give a satisfactory presentation of Newton's laws the teaching of metaphysics misses a valuable opportunity. It could give to the student an example of the elimination of concepts that are leftovers from an earlier state of science and have survived in the disguise of metaphysical concepts. The "absolute space" and the "Cartesian system without physical background" can be proved to be superfluous for any logical derivation of observable fact. The student understands easily that they have no legitimate status in science, and are only the source of an odd verbiage about "real motions" in contrast to "apparent motions."

In the sciences that deal with human behavior the situation is essentially the same. One makes use of expressions like "real freedom" in contrast to "pseudofreedom," but the muddle around these expressions is very hard to disentangle. To learn how "real motion" was eliminated from science is a very good example of how to proceed in other fields. Hence, it has an educational value that can hardly be overestimated. It paves the way for a correct analysis in the social sciences. But we are not to restate this issue of value for general education in this section. Rather, we shall stress the point that the same shortcomings which make the traditional presentation of Newton's laws unfit for general education, bar also its use for the understanding of physics itself, particularly of recent physics.

It is a fact which can hardly be overlooked that in the average college curriculum little attention has been paid to the theory of relativity compared with the great interest which this theory has met among the general public, and compared with the bearing of this doctrine on atomic and nuclear physics, not to speak of its key role in the logic of science. When, for example, the theory of the electromagnetic field is treated in the regular college curriculum, there are many teachers who skip the relation to the theory of relativity or treat it perfunctorily. They will tell the student that "relativity" is an obscure theory which the student would hardly understand. By treating the subject in this perfunctory way they certainly contribute to the obscurity that may prevail in the mind of the student. He becomes convinced that the theory of relativity is fundamentally different from "sound" physics, such as Newtonian mechanics or Maxwell's electromagnetic field. He is likely to believe that modern theories are less logical and less closely related to the observed facts. The origin of this attitude must be found, certainly, in the insufficient training of teachers in the field of relativity. As a matter of fact, there is even a shortage of appropriate textbooks. There are good textbooks on relativity for advanced students and there are fairly good books for laymen, but a book on this subject for the undergraduate hardly exists.

It is easy to put the finger on the gap in the training of college teachers which produces their antipathy to a thorough treatment of relativity theory in the regular physics courses. The lack of precision in the foundations of geometry and mechanics at which we pointed does no harm in mechanical engineering, but becomes a major danger when we have to teach relativity. To the mechanical engineer the whole problem of the system of reference is trivial. He can get along splendidly with our good old earth as such a system. But when we go in for more general problems, such as motion with great speed, propagation of light, and so forth, we have to keep in mind constantly that these phenomena can be described with respect to different systems of reference. For some particular changes of the system of reference the laws of motion remain unaltered. This fact turns out to be the most important property of these laws, and is the very basis of the theory of relativity.

If the teacher fails to stress the role of the system of reference in ordinary mechanics, the student will later fail to grasp the gist of the theory of relativity. Moreover, if words like "absolute space" or "absolute rest in space" are not eliminated by adequate teaching of mechanics, the student will have trouble eliminating the concepts of "absolute length" or "absolute time" in relativity. Frequently, the teaching of traditional college mechanics has not been used to give to the student a correct understanding of the relation between mathematics and observation in science, but instead the metaphysical formulation of Newton's laws is hammered into the student's brain, as is done in most textbooks. Then the study of the theory of relativity will be a hard job for instructors and students. They will easily wind up in the pitfalls of metaphysical prejudices which are mostly covered by a thin stratum of common sense. They will believe that expressions like "absolute simultaneity" or "absolute length of a time interval" are immediately understandable to common sense. The result is, of course, that these students, on becoming instructors in physics, will never be able to get rid of the opinion that the theory of relativity is somehow contrary to common sense, or, at least, not as agreeable to it as traditional physics has been.

This situation is still worse in the approach to the quantum theory. As this theory is badly needed to organize experimental results in atomic physics, it would be hard to eliminate the quantum theory from the regular physics curriculum. But the teachers who do not feel on firm ground in the foundations of geometry and mechanics will teach the quantum theory as a collection of useful recipes, "quantization laws," which often take the form of "prohibitions." They will dodge as much as possible the new general laws that have replaced the Newtonian science. The student will get little of Heisenberg's principle of indeterminacy or Bohr's principle of complementarity, which are the most relevant points in quantum theory for our general world picture. And if these points are touched, the same thing will happen as in the ordinary treatment of relativity. The student will be left with the impression that the new physics is somehow obscure and even "irrational." This perfunctory presentation of the new principles is, in some respects, even worse than the practice of restricting the teaching precisely to the formulas that describe actual observations. For the feeling that science has to be satisfied with an obscure theory makes the student an easy victim of quacks who exploit modern science in their endeavor to prove that we have to surrender our reason to a kind of blind instinct. This means in practice that we have to surrender our good judgment to the control of people who are bold enough to pretend that they are in possession of that intuitive instinct.

To summarize these remarks: if the teacher of science takes it easy in the presentation of the foundations of geometry and mechanics, the consequences of this carelessness will leave imprints on the minds of the student that will make it very hard to train him later as a teacher of modern physics.

H. G. Wells, in his criticism of the science teaching he went through, says very correctly:

> The science of physics is even more tantalizing today above the level of elementary introduction (optics, acoustics, etc.). Brilliant investigators rocket off into mathematical pyrotechnics and return to common sense with statements that are, according to the legitimate meanings of words, non-sensical. Ordinary language ought not to be misused in this way.

This statement gives a good diagnosis of the disease by describing it as basically a "semantic maladjustment," as the school of general semantics would call it today. "Clearly," Wells continues, "these mathematical physicists have not made the real words yet, the necessary words that they can transmit a meaning with and make the basis of fresh advances." As we shall see in the next section, these words even hint at the remedy of the illness.

We have shown that our traditional way of teaching science is responsible for two deficiencies in the education of our students. First, not all instructors in science are up to the role that science, particularly physics, has to play in our general cultural life. Second, the twentieth-century theories (relativity and quantum theory) are still an obscure domain outside the well-illuminated field of common-sense physics. Uneasiness has not been removed by our usual teaching of physics.

If we now put the question of how to improve this situation, we know from the preceding discussion the sources from which the failure of our traditional teaching has originated. We know how it has happened that our science instruction is not successful in fitting science into our cultural life, and the modern theories into the frame of common-sense physics.

We discovered the main source in the failure to teach the students a clear distinction between the observation of facts and the drawing of logical conclusions. David Hume, the father of empiricist philosophy, has urged us to "surrender to the flames" all books that contain neither observed facts nor mathematical conclusions. This recommendation has become the basis of all attempts to make science a coherent and empirically confirmed system of knowledge. Accordingly, we have to teach our students how to eliminate all statements that are neither propositions describing the result of an observation, nor propositions that are part of a logical conclusion.

Therefore, we have to insist, above all, that the student learn to analyze the statements of his science in such a way that it becomes obvious what is a statement of observation and what is a logical conclusion. Many statements made in the traditional presentations of physics, particularly of recent theories, do not belong to either of the two types.

If we have carried out this analysis, it is convenient to present the result in such a way that from the wording of every statement it immediately becomes clear what its logical status is. For, in the traditional presentation of science, we are often unable to recognize whether a given statement is meant to be a statement about observed facts, or a hypothesis about facts that will be observed, or a statement that merely introduces new words or rules for construction of propositions. This distinction, however, is necessary.

If we try to single out the purely logical statements, we find them in every science. In geometry, for instance, a great part of scientific work consists in deriving conclusions from a given set of propositions called axioms. In drawing these conclusions, we do not need to know what the words in the axioms mean in the physical world. If the "points" and "straight lines" and "triangles" have the properties that are ascribed to them in the axioms, they also have the properties that are ascribed to them in the theorems, which we obtain by logical conclusions from the axioms. In the same way, in mechanics, if we start from Newton's equations, $ma = f$ and $a = \mathrm{d}^2x/\mathrm{d}t^2$, we can derive, by logical conclusion, a great many theorems. We find that if the force is zero, the coördinate x is a linear function of time, and if the force is constant, the coördinate x is a quadratic function of time, and so on. These statements are true whatever the meaning of "force f" or "coördinate x" or "time t" may be in the physical world.

We obtain in this way purely logical statements. One occasionally calls them "tautological statements" because they tell us only that one and the same assertion can be expressed in different ways. If $ma = f$ and $f = 0$, it follows that x is a linear function of t. But from this conclusion we do not learn anything about the physical world; we learn only to say one thing in different ways. By this perfunctory hint we learn already that more than a few failures in our customary science teaching have originated in the failure to recognize clearly the tautological character of these statements.

The world of physical experiments—briefly, the "physical world"—is described by statements about the procedure and results of physical measurements. They boil down, eventually, to statements like "a certain colored spot covers a second colored spot," or statements about a "pointer reading," as Eddington calls it. They consist only of words that are familiar to everybody. The description of physical experiments does not contain any element that is not used in describing our breakfast, and is therefore understandable to everybody who is trained to use the English language in his daily life. These statements have, obviously, a certain vagueness, and they are never completely unambiguous.

These "observational statements" are the second type of statement that we can single out in any science. In geometry, for example, we show how to measure the angles of a triangle and can find that the sum of the results is approximately 180°. In mechanics we measure the distance of a body from the floor of a room, and can find that in the case of a launched ball the distance from the floor is approximately a quadratic function of the angle traversed by the hand of a clock.

These two types of statements, the logical and the observational, contain different types of words. In the first one, we have symbols like "points" or "forces" or "coördinates," which have no meaning at all in the physical world, while the second type contains words of our "kitchen language," which denote familiar things of our environment.

Customarily, the student learns in science classes that by observational statements it is possible to confirm or refute the axioms of geometry or laws of mechanics. But, obviously, this way of speaking is somewhat superficial and logically incorrect. For the "observational statements" contain words of everyday life like "green," "hard," "overlapping spots," and so forth, while the "axioms of geometry and mechanics" contain symbols like "point," "circle," "acceleration," "force." A statement of the second type can never be confirmed or refuted by a statement of the first type, because it does not contain the same terms.

If science consisted only of principles and observations, its validity could not be tested by scientific methods. It is, therefore, of the utmost importance to teach the student that, besides these two types of statement, science has to make use of a third type by which the language of the abstract principle can be translated into the language of observation. If the principles contain, for example, the word "length," one has to describe the physical operations by which the length can be measured. As these operations can be formulated in the language of everyday life, of observational statements, the description of the operation translates the abstract term "length" into terms of observational language.

These translating sentences have been studied with particular emphasis and care by P. W. Bridgman, and are called, according to his suggestion, "operational definitions." By this definition, an abstract term like "length" acquires "operational meaning." When these "operational definitions" are introduced into the abstract principles, the latter become "observational statements." Then we can check by actual experiments whether these observational statements, derived from the principle, check with the observational statements that describe our direct physical experiments. It is necessary to understand that only in this indirect way can the principles of science be checked by experience.

Nowadays, the term "semantics" is often used to denote the study of the relation between words and meaning. Hence, the sentences by which symbols are coördinated with observable things are called "semantic rules." They occur in the writings on the logic of science under different names. F. S. C. Northrop uses them as "epistemological correlations," H. Reichenbach as "rules of coördination," and so on.

This "logico-empirical analysis," or "semantic analysis," is a general method of "making our ideas clear." It is an efficient method for communication of thoughts and for influencing people. This analysis is the chief subject that we have to teach to science students, in order to fill all the gaps left by traditional science teaching.

If the student were taught this method effectively, he would be able to present and to understand recent physical theories —like relativity and the quantum theory—as precisely as classical physics, if—and this is the great "if"—if he understands ordinary geometry and mechanics precisely. Therefore, as charity should start at home, so semantic analysis should start in our own scientific back yard, at the foundations of our familiar geometry and mechanics. The application of logico-empirical analysis was never presented so clearly and concisely as in Einstein's paper, "Geometry and Experience." He summarizes the results by saying: As far as geometry is certain, it does not tell us anything about the physical world, and as far as it makes statements that can be tested by experience it is not certain—that is to say, not more certain than any statement of physical science. By operational definitions "straight lines" can be translated into "light rays" or "edges of rigid bodies." Then the theorems of geometry become statements of optics or mechanics. Without these definitions, all theorems of geometry are tautological propositions about symbols.

Moreover, if we apply this type of analysis to mechanics, we shall naturally ask: what is the operational meaning of "acceleration"? If we want to translate this symbol into an expression consisting of observational terms, we have to describe the physical system of reference to which the coördinate x refers.

If we apply the same method to the theory of relativity, this doctrine will lose its isolated and obscure character. It will be obvious that "length" or "simultaneity" have to be defined by the description of physical operations by which these quantities can actually be measured. If yardsticks and clocks are affected by motion, it is equally obvious that the operational definitions of spatial or temporal "length" have to contain the velocity of the yardstick or clock relative to a physical system of reference. This means that only "relative length" has an operational meaning, not "absolute length."

The reason why the theory of relativity has appeared so obscure to the physicists will then be very clearly understood by the student. Every alteration of the laws of physics seems understandable to common sense, if the semantic rules are unaltered. This would be the case if we replaced the wave theory of light by the corpuscular theory, provided both theories remain within the frame of Newtonian mechanics. But the experiments on bodies moving with great speed suggest the introduction of new semantic rules. Such a change is much more fundamental and will appear obscure to the student of physics, if he is not, from the start, taught the role of these semantic rules in every domain of science, beginning with his high school plane geometry.

Bridgman rightly stresses the point that for a student who has studied relativity successfully, there is no need for a subsequent introduction to logico-empirical analysis. He could not understand relativity without it. The instruction in the two theories is inseparable.

In a similar way, if we apply this analysis to the quantum theory, no student would fall for the talk that there is some "irrational" or "organismic" aspect in the quantum theory. He would understand that the very meaning of Bohr's principle of complementarity can be defined as the introduction of new semantic rules into the language of physics. As the alterations required by these rules are much more radical than those required by the relativity theory, the confusion of language has been tremendous. As our traditional teaching fails often to apply a correct logico-empirical analysis, a great many authors —scientists and philosophers alike—have failed to recognize that we have to do with a radical alteration of semantic rules. Many of them have even been caught by a widespread propaganda by which the new physics of the twentieth century has been exploited in the service of a campaign against the spirit of science, in favor of a confused "organicism," "spiritualism" or "irrationalism."

Clearly, by learning the application of semantic analysis, the student will not only profit from a better understanding of his own science, but also gain a more correct appreciation of the role his science plays in the frame of human culture in general. The close relationship of semantic analysis to modern physical theories on the one hand, and to the understanding of our general social and cultural life on the other hand, has perhaps nowhere been stressed so bluntly and sharply as by Bridgman, in a paper published in 1945.[1] He discerns the technical and the semantic significance of twentieth-century science, when he says:

The second aspect of the modern epoch in science is, I believe, of incomparably greater significance . . . He [the physicist] has come out with what amounts to a new technique of analysis, of great power and unexpectedly wide range of applicability. The new technique is applicable to all questions of meaning . . . The potentialities of the new technique, when applied to domains outside the present application of science, may be glimpsed by contemplating the confusion which now reigns . . . It is becoming evident to an increasing number of people that an important part of our difficulties in analyzing and conveying meaning is of verbal origin . . . There are popular discussions of semantics.

To appreciate this popular trend toward semantics, we need

[1] P. W. Bridgman, *Yale Review* 34, 444 (1945).

only look at such books as Hayakawa's *Language in Action*,[2] which was a best seller. In *ETC: A Review of General Semantics*, edited by Hayakawa, semantics is applied to the problem of race relations, to labor problems, to the psychology of fear, and so forth.

Our point has been that an important step toward improvement of our science teaching could be taken by consistent application of semantics or logico-empirical analysis. I do not believe, however, that this step would be sufficient. Even if such an analysis is carried out in a careful and competent way, there still remains much to be done if we want to bring out all the educational value that is inherent in science.

Once when I explained to a class the second law of Newton by the method of logico-empirical analysis, stating precisely the operational meaning of the symbols m, a and f, a student asked: Is this really everything contained in the law? Has the intuitive conception of a "force acting upon a body," which has played such a decisive role in the history of our thought, completely evaporated into the thin air of logical rules and physical measurements? As another example, everybody who has ever participated in discussions about the principles of physics occasionally encounters the person who becomes excited when the question is raised whether the concept of force can be eliminated from physics. At this point an emotional element enters the debate. The heat of the argument had its origin certainly not in science itself, but in the stretch of history of the human mind, which is now packed into the word "force." In the time when the Nazi party and its philosophy flourished, we could frequently find in German writing the view that the concept of "force" is somehow connected with the Nordic race. All people who wanted to eliminate it from physics were branded as enemies of the Nordic race. On the other hand, those who plead for the elimination of the concept of "force" regard it as a remainder of an animistic and anthropomorphic world picture, which even has a touch of spiritualism and superstition.

We learn from this example that, in order to understand the role that the concepts and principles of science have played in our cultural life, we need, in addition to the semantic, an analysis of a different type. We have to learn not only the

[2] S. I. Hayakawa (Harcourt, Brace, 1941); also see W. Johnson, *People in Quandaries* (Harper, 1946).

operational meaning of symbols like "force" and "mass," but also how it has come about that just these symbols were chosen. Obviously the choice has not been unambiguously determined by their ability to form a basis for the derivation of observable facts. The symbols also have a life of their own. If we go in for this kind of research, we find that extrascientific reasons have been largely responsible for the predilection in favor of or the aversion to some symbols. We learned it from the example of "force." A careful and thorough investigation has shown that psychologic reasons have played their part, as have habits carried since childhood, and even wishes emerging from the subconscious.

Besides these factors of individual psychology, the religious, social and political trends of the period have been responsible for the predilections and aversions of which we spoke. What we need, therefore, for an all-round understanding of science is an analysis of the psychologic and sociologic factors that went into the determination of our scientific symbolism. We may speak, briefly, of a "socio-psychologic" analysis. We can summarize and say that this second type of analysis has to be added to the semantic analysis.[3]

Both types of analysis are parts of what one calls in more or less popular discourse "philosophy of science." Thus we may say that the remedy for the afore-described shortcomings in our traditional way of teaching science is to give more attention to the philosophy of science. More precisely, we mean by it logico-empirical and socio-psychologic analysis, or, in the terminology of the school of thought known as logical empiricism: we need semantic analysis and "pragmatic analysis."

We have now to attack the more practical question of how the desirable instruction in the philosophy of science should and could be given to the students of science.

In my opinion, the best solution is that the elementary science courses themselves should contain a good deal of the philosophy of science. This solution presupposes, of course, that there are a sufficient number of science teachers available who have adequate training in the philosophy of science. Speaking now in terms of what should be, rather than in terms of what is, I believe that no teacher should give an introduc-

[3] Jean Piaget, *Les Trois Conditions d'une épistèmologie scientifique. Analysis* (Milan, 1946), Vol. 1, No. 3, p. 25.

tory course in science if he lacks training in semantics and the history of science. I realize that this solution is not feasible today. Hence, my second choice is to introduce courses in the philosophy of science which are to be obligatory for the students of science, at least for those who are later to become teachers of science. In a certain way every scientist is a teacher of science in his environment, whether he works as an engineer, a physician, or even a pharmacist.

Courses in the philosophy of science for the benefit of science students have been given rarely; hence there is no coherent tradition. We are faced with the problem of building up such a tradition. There are two reefs that have to be avoided. The greatest weakness of the attempts which have been made occasionally to give such courses has been the lack of any definite conviction on the part of the professor. We must never forget that the word "professor" is derived from "profess," and this holds true, particularly, for a teacher of philosophy. His work with the students should be a "profession" in both meanings of this word. Scientists who have been teaching the philosophy of science have mostly offered a kind of incoherent digest of philosophic opinions. The choice has been mostly determined by the chance acquaintances of the teacher. The students have remained unimpressed by such courses or books. We meet this eclectic attitude even in the writings of such excellent scientists as Jeans or Planck. I remember the lectures of a great physicist, Boltzmann, on the philosophy of physics, which I attended as a student. Despite the personal greatness of the lecturer, the effect of the course was slight, because of a lack of a coherent approach. We can notice, on the other hand, that scientists who built their books around a central idea have shaped the minds of science students for decades. I mention, just as examples, Mach, Poincaré and Bridgman.

Although a coherent approach is the first requisite for successful instruction, the second reef on which our course could be wrecked is a narrow-minded indoctrination. I remember that an intelligent girl student told me once: "It is a very unpleasant feeling to have a certain doctrine drilled into your brain without being provided with an outlook into the open field of widely divergent opinions." These two requirements of a coherent approach and of an open field seem to exclude each other. But this is true only superficially. If the socio-psychologic approach is added, it becomes clear that every opinion which has been advocated in history has its legitimate place within a coherent presentation of science, based on logico-empirical and socio-psychological analysis.

Our problem now is, practically, to build a course in which the student gets training in both types of analysis—a course that not only fills the gap left by the traditional science teaching, but also leads into the wide field of controversial ideas for bridging this gap.

For six years I have given a course at Harvard with this goal in mind. I have tried to improve it from year to year according to my increasing experience with students. I will describe the content of this particular course because of my familiarity with it, and not because I believe that it necessarily represents the best possible course. The course takes two terms. Actually, I give two half-courses which are designed for students of different backgrounds. But in this description I am going to integrate both half-courses into one coherent presentation.

My starting point has been the traditional distinction between "scientific truth" and "philosophic truth." Specifically, I have referred to the formulation that the great medieval philosopher, Thomas Aquinas, gave to this distinction. According to him, there are two criteria of truth: the first requires that a proposition can be logically derived from "evident principles" (philosophic truth); the second requires that the logical sequences of the proposition in question can be confirmed by experience (scientific truth). Obviously, if the truth of the principles themselves can be tested only by comparing their logical consequences with experience, the two criteria merge and we have only one criterion, namely, the scientific one. Then the traditional distinction disappears. This is the view that is called "empiricism," or "positivism." To assume the distinction obviously means to believe in principles the truth of which can be checked by extrascientific methods. In modern science this distinction is no longer upheld as an absolute distinction, but it has always played a certain role in a weakened and "relativized" form. We still say that there are propositions of physics which can be "proved" if we use the traditional language of physics textbooks. This means that they can be derived from general principles (like conservation of energy) which we hold to be true with a high degree of plausibility. Distinguished from these are propositions that are records of direct observation and cannot be "proved."

After these introductory remarks, a historical survey is given of the principles that have actually been used by the scientists as the basis from which the propositions of physics have been logically derived. There is one period in history that we can study from the origin to the end. This is the period of mechanistic physics, which lasted approximately from 1600 to 1900. Its basic principles were Newton's laws of motion. A proposition of physics was regarded as "explained," or "understood," or "proved to be true," if it could be logically derived from Newton's laws of motion. But the question arose, of course, whether Newton's laws, themselves, were "evident principles." The belief that they are arises very often among students of physics as a result of the perfunctory way in which these laws are presented in the traditional textbooks. The only effective way to destroy this belief is to give a thorough presentation of the period before 1600, which preceded the era of mechanistic physics. In my course, medieval and Aristotelian physics is presented and analyzed carefully. I call it "organismic physics," because the basic principle is the analogy between physical phenomena and the behavior of organisms.

If the student has become aware that there was a time when reasonable people did not believe in Newton's mechanics, it will not contravene his "common sense" to learn that after 1900 a period could start in which these classical laws of motion were modified radically. Having become familiar with a conception of physics that prevailed before the period of mechanics, the student will look at the disintegration of mechanistic physics around 1900 as a phenomenon analogous to the disintegration of organismic physics around 1600. In both cases, before the actual revolution took place under the impact of new discoveries of facts, the belief in the certainty of the ruling principles was shaken from within by logically minded critics. In medieval physics this role was played by the school of nominalism (Occam's razor), while the criticism of mechanistic physics came from the "positivists" of the last quarter of the nineteenth century, men like Stallo in America and Mach in central Europe.

The rise of twentieth-century physics, of relativity and the quantum theory, was closely connected with a new view of the basic principles. It was no longer taken for granted that the principles from which the facts had to be derived should contain a specific analogy, either to an organism or to a mechanism. Nothing was required except that the observed phenomena could be derived from the principles in a consistent way and as simply as possible. The words and symbols that occurred in the principles, and the way these were connected, could be invented according to their fitness as bases for deriving the phenomena discovered by the experimental physicist.

This means that the symbols used in the principles had in themselves no meaning beyond their value for the derivation of facts. From this introduction of abstract symbols arose the obvious need for including in the theory prescriptions for relating these symbols to sense observations. The necessity and the importance of these sentences were particularly emphasized and elaborated by Bridgman in his requirement of "operational definitions." This new aspect of physics, which dismissed any traditional analogy and stressed only the criterion of empirical confirmation and logical coherence, may be called "logico-empirical physics."

Under this name I refer in the course to the physics of the twentieth century, and dismiss by this terminology all misleading metaphysical interpretations of relativity and quantum theory which we owe to philosophers, sociologists, theologians and—I am sorry to say—also to some physicists.

After this historical framework has been established, I proceed to the application of logico-empirical analysis to the most relevant parts of physics. The start is made with geometry, where the situation is easier to explain than in any other field. I believe that the logico-empirical analysis of geometry provides the student of science with the best introduction to the philosophy of science. I would even venture to say that, if there is little time available, the familiarity of the science student with the analysis of geometry would suffice to fill, in a fairly satisfactory way, the gap left by traditional mathematics and physics teaching. By this analysis the student will learn that mathematics cannot prove any facts, but can only derive facts from other known facts. He will learn that there are two fields of science that we call "geometry." "Mathematical geometry" has the previously described tautological character and cannot teach us anything about the "nature of space." He will learn that only by the introduction of operational definitions —for example, "a straight line is a light ray"—can theorems of geometry become statements about facts and be confirmed experimentally like any law of physics. He will learn that no geometric theorem by itself can be confirmed by experience, but only a geometric theorem—such as the one about the sum of angles in a triangle—plus the operational definitions, of straight lines, and so on. He will learn that statements like "the axioms are self-evident," or even "they are true," are meaningless if no operational meaning is given them.

I would even venture to say that a thorough semantic analysis of geometry contributes more to the intellectual outlook of the student than a superficial philosophic interpretation of the whole field of physics. By this analysis of geometry the student will be introduced to the new logical techniques in modern physics. Bridgman says of these techniques that their impact on the pattern of our culture will eventually be greater than that of the technical consequences of modern physics, including atomic energy. The logico-empirical analysis of geometry will, moreover, enable the student to form a sound judgment about the "truth" of non-Euclidean geometry, and in this way fill a gap that yawns in most textbooks. The problem of "truth" is usually dodged in the presentation of non-Euclidean geometry, so that this part of mathematics has remained obscure to most students.

Then the course passes to the analysis of Newtonian mechanics. From the beginning, the operational meaning of terms is stressed. This means, above all, that the role of the system of reference emerges clearly. Newton's laws are presented not as self-evident, but as paradoxical, for so they appeared to Newton's contemporaries.

We proceed then to the mechanical theory of light. When inter-action of light propagation with the motion of large material bodies occurs, and both phenomena are assumed to follow Newton's laws of motion, one can predict phenomena that are in contradiction to observed facts, as in Michelson's experiment.

This contradiction is the origin of the restricted theory of relativity, which is analyzed thoroughly with the emphasis on the logico-empirical aspect and on the place of operational definitions. Then all those misunderstandings disappear that have made this theory "obscure" and "contradictory" to common sense. It becomes obvious that the role of the observer is not different from his role in Newton's physics. No subjective element occurs in physics and, hence, there is no argument in favor of idealistic philosophy. The revolutionary changes brought about by relativity consist, first, of new observational facts, such as the change of the rate of clocks by motion, and second, in the suggestion which Einstein made to alter the language in such a way that these new phenomena can be described in a simple and practical way. The relativity of time, for example, is no advance in metaphysics, but it is in physics and semantics.

In the same way the quantum theory is analyzed. The famous relation of indeterminacy has nothing whatever to do with the introduction of a subjective or spiritual factor into physics. It is actually a suggestion for introducing a language that best fits the facts. Since there is no law of physics that incorporates the expression, "the position and velocity of a small particle at one and the same instant," there is no reason to introduce such an expression into the language of physics. Bohr's principle of complementarity suggests that our physical world be described in a complementary language.

The course then proceeds to a logico-empirical analysis of the concepts of causality, determinism, indeterminism, and chance along the same lines. Eventually the concepts of mass and energy are analyzed.

After this description of the way in which semantic analysis is actually applied to physics, the course turns to problems of what has traditionally been called "philosophy." The first, historical part was a survey of the way in which principles of science have developed from the organismic to the mechanistic physics, and further to the logico-empirical stage. In this stage there was no demand for a specific type of principle or a specific form of words in the principles. The wording of the principles became irrelevant from the viewpoint of science itself. But there have been extrascientific reasons for insisting on principles of a certain type. These reasons include mere sluggishness in changing old principles or, very often, theological, ethical, or political factors. It has been argued that the principles of science have to be in agreement with the prevailing principles in those extrascientific fields. We remember the Thomistic distinction between philosophic and scientific truth. This distinction is based on the belief that one can assume some principles for reasons which are not in agreement with their consequences as experienced. This means that one assumes these principles for extrascientific reasons. Every system of thought that has this belief as its basis is a metaphysical system. Since in these systems the principles are closely connected with the religious, moral and political predilections of a certain period, the study of the metaphysical foundations of science is important for the understanding of the position of science in our cultural life. Therefore, the next part of the course is devoted to the metaphysical and antimetaphysical interpretation of science.

The most important point, as it seems to me, is to get the student to understand the extremes. I take pains to present an adequate conception of "straight metaphysics" and, at the other extreme, "straight positivism," which bluntly says that there is *no* principle except those which can be confirmed by the agreement of their consequences with experience.

As the example of straight metaphysics, the Thomistic philosophy is presented at length as far as it serves as a basis of science. The students are encouraged to read a textbook of "cosmology" that is currently used in Catholic colleges and contains the Thomistic foundations of physics. Once I asked a teacher at a Jesuit college, who was taking my course, to explain to the students the authentic teaching of Thomistic philosophy.

Then I proceed to the other extreme, which denies the distinction between the two kinds of truth and recognizes only scientific truth. I give a short historical survey starting with David Hume, followed by a short account of A. Comte's "positive philosophy" and a more elaborate discussion of positivism at the end of the nineteenth century; of the Americans, Stallo and C. S. Pierce; of the Europeans, Mach and Poincaré. Passing to the twentieth century, we discuss the "operationism" of Bridgman and its relation to the pragmatism of William James and Dewey. Bridgman's emphasis on the role of language leads us to the last phase of positivism, the logical positivism of Wittgenstein, Carnap, and others.

After the presentation of straight metaphysics and positivism, we discuss some attempts to produce a reconciliation between the two views. There are scientists and philosophers who present science generally in the positivistic manner, but reserve a separate compartment for metaphysics. Among them are Spencer, Fiske and P. Duhem. Systematic attempts at reconciliation have been made on the basis of idealism and materialism. The most powerful idealistic attempt is the school of thought founded by the German philosopher, Kant. Proponents of this school claim that there are self-evident principles, but that they are actually statements about our own minds. By making statements about geometry, we actually make statements about our own way of describing nature. Therefore, these statements are, in a certain sense, checked by experience, but not by external experience. We observe ourselves and believe that we observe the external world. An outstanding representative among the scientists of recent days of this Kantian compromise is the British astronomer, Eddington, whose views are discussed elaborately in the course. There are a great many varieties of Kantian idealism. They fill the whole spectrum of opinions between positivism and metaphysics.

The other important scheme of reconciliation is materialism. In its original form it was a generalization of mechanistic physics, with no metaphysics in it. Later it became obvious that the phenomena of life and of human behavior could not be interpreted easily in terms of Newton's mechanics. But a great many people felt the relevance of keeping to the mechanistic scheme. In contrast to mechanistic materialism, Marx and Engels developed the system of dialectical materialism, in which "matter" no longer means the matter of mechanics, but a substance which possesses all the qualities that are needed to account for the evolution of human life, individual and social. The importance ascribed to the principles of this system often went beyond their value for the description of observable phenomena, and the possibility of any change in these principles was minimized. This attitude brought a bit of metaphysics into dialectical materialism. After it had become the official philosophy of the Soviet Union, the relevance of the principles themselves was bolstered by extrascientific reasons. Dialectical materialism is discussed in the course in its application to the foundations of science. As in Kantian idealism, we find in dialectical materialism all varieties from almost pure positivism to almost pure Hegelian metaphysics.

These discussions of the philosophic interpretations of science are of great importance to the general education of future scientists. The interpretations should not be neglected in the teaching of the philosophy of science, for they are the link connecting science with the humanities. They provide the instrument that is used by religious, ethical, and political creeds to muster the support of science. F. S. C. Northrop emphasized in his recent book, *The Meeting of East and West*,[4] the great importance of the philosophy of science for any ethical or political creed. To understand this connection, we have to understand the philosophic interpretations of science and the link of metaphysical creeds with religious and political creeds.

The last part of the course is devoted to the description of these ties. It has become almost a commonplace that the com-

4 Macmillan, 1946.

munist and other left-wing creeds have their philosophic basis in materialism, while the right-wing groups look for their foundation mostly to some kind of organismic metaphysics, for example, to Thomism. It is, therefore, very important that the student have a good training in these philosophic interpretations which have become the bases of political creeds. The combination of philosophic and political creeds is often referred to as "ideology." The student of science does not need to be ignorant of this important field. He can take science and its interpretations as his door of entrance. For this reason, in the course in philosophy of science much attention should be paid to these philosophic interpretations of science that have been the basis of ideologies. The most elaborate of these interpretations are Thomism and dialectical materialism. Prominent cardinals of the Roman Church, as well as prominent political leaders like Lenin, who were able to look under the surface of things, have taken pains to introduce into the teaching of science an interpretation that is favorable to their creed. Hence, the future scientist should be taught to take advantage of these ties and get a real insight into historical and contemporary ideologies.

The discussion of these ties helps to make the course in the philosophy of science relevant and attractive to the student. Moreover, this way of presenting world problems makes it possible to include a discussion of the relations between science and religion—a subject often regarded as too delicate for a sincere presentation, and so either omitted or presented in a conventional way. On the other hand, I have noticed that students are extremely interested in this topic, and ask embarrassing questions if it is treated evasively. If religion is discussed among the ideologies, the treatment can become sincere, precise and inoffensive. It will become clear that in this question also the best way of approach is from science through its philosophic interpretation.

This is one possible outline of a course on the philosophy of science. The choice which I made among a great many possibilities is, of course, determined by my own background, scientific and personal. A great many paths can lead to the same goal. But all possible courses must, in my opinion, be based on logico-empirical and socio-psychological analysis of science. Only by this method can we steer our ship between the two reefs of overspecialization and superficiality.

Chapter 15

Science Teaching and the Humanities

1. Special Field and General Education

THERE IS a widespread belief that the rising contempt for tolerance and peace is somehow related to the rising influence of scientific thought and the declining influence of ethics, religion and art as guides of human actions. This contention is, of course, debatable. There is hardly a doubt that the causes of war can be traced back quite frequently to religious or quasi-religious creeds and very rarely to the doctrines of science. The humanities, including religion and ethics, have been for centuries the basis of education and the result has been, conservatively speaking, no decline in the ferocity of men. The scientists have never had a chance to shape the minds of several generations. Therefore, it would be more just to attribute the failure of our institutions to educate a peace-loving generation to the failure of ethical and religious leaders than to impute the responsibility to the scientists.

I do not think, however, that it makes much sense to discuss the share of responsibility. For I agree wholeheartedly with the critics of science in the belief that the training of generations of scientists in mere science, without making them familiar with the world of human behavior, would be harmful to the cause of civilization. Whether we like it or not, scientists will participate more and more in the leadership of society in the future. Also there is hardly a doubt by now that the contribution of the scientists to our political life has been more on the side of peace and tolerance than have the contributions of the students of law or government, or, for that matter, of philosophy proper.

In order to make this attitude of our leading scientists a habit among the rank and file, it is important to imbue the future worker in science with an interest in human problems during his training period. Since for this purpose it is futile to argue for the supremacy of humanistic education over science education, the debate "science *versus* humanities" or *vice versa* is, of course, without point here. But it is also of little avail to compel the student of science to take some courses in the

253

departments of humanities. According to the record of all the people I know, the mentality of the average science student is such that he will not sufficiently appreciate these courses, and therefore will not assimilate them well. What we actually need is to bridge the gap between science and the humanities which has opened and widened more and more during the nineteenth and twentieth centuries. According to my opinion, this can be done only by starting from *the human values which are intrinsic in science itself.* The instruction in science must emphasize these values and convince the science students that *interest in humanities is the natural result of a thorough interest in science.*

In this way the science teacher will be giving his support to the whole cause of general education as well as to his specialized teaching of science.

Everyone who has ever tried to raise his voice for the cause of general education among the faculty members of a university has been running almost regularly against one very definite objection: whatever of their time the students have to spend in classes on general education they have to subtract from the time they devote to specialized work in their own scientific field. As this field is, in any case, so vast that it cannot be covered during their stay in college, it would be almost a crime to curtail this short and valuable time. This attitude is particularly strong among the teachers of science proper.

I am going to discuss the issue "special field *versus* general education" mainly from the viewpoint of science students. However, I am sure that the general picture will be about the same in any other field of study, in languages, in history, and so on.

Even the departments of philosophy have kept to a policy of isolationism. Instead of working toward a synthesis of human knowledge, they have proposed a kind of truce between science and philosophy. In my opinion, this gap is greatly responsible for the rift in our general education, or, exactly speaking, the gap between science and philosophy is the most conspicuous part of the gap between science and the humanities—and hence the gap between science and the realm of human behavior in general.

This gap is perhaps nowhere so clear-cut and conspicuous as in the domain of physical science. Therefore, the battle for the renewal of liberal education will not be won without a willing and intensive coöperation of workers in the physical sciences. On the other hand, if we want the students of the humanities to go in gladly for general education which requires them to take in quite a few helpings of science, we must convince them that by learning science they will also advance toward a better understanding of human behavior.

I am going, first, to describe the harm that the rift between science and philosophy has done to both of these fields and to the cause of liberal education in general. Second, I am going to make some suggestions as to how this rift can be repaired by removing the causes through which philosophy and science have been estranged.

2. Philosophic Interest in Physics

There is no doubt that the public interest in the physical sciences is primarily due to their technical applications: television, radar, the atomic bomb. When Copernicus suggested that the motion of the celestial bodies be described with respect to the sun rather than with respect to the earth, this suggestion was quite irrelevant for any technical purpose. Yet the public interest and the heat of the debates were certainly greater in this than in the case of any new technical device. But we need not go back several centuries for examples, since we ourselves have been witnesses of the "relativity boom" which arose when Einstein advanced his new theory of motion and light. Although this theory seemed at that time very far from any technical application, the public interest was in some cases rather hysterical, and there are examples of people who were almost killed in an attempt to get into an overcrowded lecture room where Einstein in person tried to put over relativity to his audience. There is also no doubt that the philosophic and even religious implications of such general physical doctrines account for the fact that quite a few clergymen have been eager to make use of relativity in their sermons. In order to appreciate this situation correctly, we must not forget that Newton, during and after his lifetime, was a popular topic of parlor conversation and that many books popularizing Newton were published, some of them especially designed for "the use of the ladies."

Nowadays we find, not infrequently, books and magazine articles written by clergymen, philosophers, or, for that matter, by scientists, in which the theories of modern physics (relativity and quantum theory) are recommended for their philosophic or religious benefits. We learn from these papers that twentieth-century physics has restored the place of mind in the universe, that it has reconciled science with religion, and that the tide of materialism characteristic of eighteenth- and nineteenth-century science has definitely been broken in the twentieth century. As "materialism" has always been connected with some political and social systems, these authors conclude that the new physics means also a defeat of all political systems based on materialism, by which they mean, according to their personal bias, Communism or, occasionally, Nazism (racism).

There is no doubt that the correlation between physics and philosophy has been largely responsible for the great interest in twentieth-century physics of wide sections of the general public. The intelligent reader who follows the trend of contemporary thought in books and magazines, who listens to popular lectures of scientists, preachers, philosophers and global politicians, would often have a greater interest in the general ideas of twentieth-century physics than an average student of physics who specializes, say, in radar. Even after graduation, a student of physics usually knows very little about the relation between physics and philosophy, let alone between physics and human behavior. He is generally less trained than the educated layman in forming a well-balanced judgment on such problems as are daily discussed in magazines and lectures about the influence of modern physics on human affairs. If a student in high school or, for that matter, in most colleges, asks his physics teacher for information about problems of this kind, he will hardly get a satisfactory answer. The information, if any, will mostly be perfunctory and evasive. Therefore, the graduates in physics will rarely be able to advise the general public on questions which this public regards as relevant for their general outlook on man and the universe.

This failure of the learned physicist will not stifle the public interest. The thirst for knowledge which is not quenched by the scientists will be assuaged by people who are ignorant in science but know how to give answers that flatter the wishes of the majority of people. Thus the longing for knowledge of large sections of the public will become grist for the mills of some organized propaganda groups.

The textbooks of physics mostly claim to stick to the facts and to exclude "idle philosophic talk." But actually, they formulate the general laws of nature often in such a way that no physical facts whatsoever can be logically derived from these laws. This means that they really formulate not physical but purely metaphysical laws.

Thus, the physical sciences provide very good examples from which students can learn that the expression "sticking to the facts only" is frequently used as a pretext for avoiding all logical analysis, and therefore for favoring all kinds of obsolete prejudices. What one should reasonably mean by "sticking to the facts only" is to make only statements that can be checked by experience, that is, by observable facts. This habit is certainly of great use in debunking empty slogans and bigotry in politics or religion.

As "sticking to the facts" is the slogan of traditional physics teaching, "ignoring the facts" is a slogan cultivated in the traditional teaching of mathematics. Both these slogans are logically legitimate within a restricted domain of thought. However, on occasion, the students have to learn the limitations of these slogans; otherwise, the meaning of the most important laws of nature cannot be made clear to them, and the very goal of general education on the basis of science would be frustrated.

3. Chance Philosophies

Without an understanding of the tie-in between mathematics and physics, the student misses the best opportunity of grasping the most important trait of human knowledge: the relation between sense observation and logical thinking. If this bridge between the fields is not built by a thorough analysis of the empirical and logical procedure in science, that is, by a systematic philosophy of science, the necessity for it is so overwhelming that it will be built anyway. This will be done mainly by some obsolete but popular philosophy which will replace the thoroughly logical analysis of science. It is noteworthy that, in practice, crude empiricism in science, without critical analysis, has often made possible the flourishing of crude metaphysical systems.

Quite a few great thinkers who belonged to very divergent schools of thought have been unanimous on one point: if a scientist believes that he has no philosophy and keeps tightly to his special field he will really become an adherent of some "chance philosophy," as A. N. Whitehead puts it. This great contemporary metaphysician with a solid scientific background assures us that for a scientist deliberately to neglect philosophy

is to assume the correctness of the chance philosophic prejudices inbibed from a nurse or a schoolmaster or current modes of expression.

We find complete agreement with this opinion in a statement of Ernst Mach, a philosopher and eminent scientist who was the most radical enemy of all kinds of metaphysics. He says, about obsolete doctrines of philosophers, that they "have survived, occasionally, much longer within science where they did not meet such an attentive criticism. As a species of animals which has been badly adjusted to the struggle of life has survived sometimes on a remote island where there have been no enemies, obsolete philosophy has survived within the borders of science."

As a third and again very different type of thinker we may quote Friedrich Engels, the lifelong collaborator of Karl Marx, who was particularly interested in the consequences of obsolete philosophy in social and political life. He says:

Natural scientists may adopt whatever attitude they please, they will still be under the domination of philosophy. It is only a question whether they want to be dominated by a bad fashionable philosophy or by a form of theoretical thought which rests on acquaintance with the history of thought and its achievements.[1]

One thing seems to be certain: if we try to eliminate from, say, physics, all teaching of the philosophy of science, the result will be not a crop of scientifically minded physicists, but a flock of believers in some fashionable or obsolete chance philosophy.

Among science students, the students of engineering are those who get traditionally the worst training in philosophic analysis. They often absorb science, stripped of its logical structure, as a mere collection of useful recipes. Is it only a coincidence that the students of engineering have on the whole been more impresssed by empty political slogans (like Fascism) than the students of "pure" science? There is no doubt that general slogans play a role in politics similar to the role that general principles play in science. If someone is trained to

[1] F. Engels, *Dialectics of Nature*, English translation by C. Dutt (New York: International Publishers, 1940), p. 243.

understand to what degree general principles like conservation of energy or relativity are based on confirmable facts and how far on arbitrariness and imagination, he is more immune to the political slogans of demagogues than a student who has been trained only to record his immediate experience and to regard the general laws as gifts dropped from heaven for helping him to bring some order into his record sheet.

Practically, the separation between science and philosophy can be kept up strictly only during a period in which no essential changes in the principles of science take place. In a period of revolutionary changes the walls of separation break down. In Whitehead's statement quoted above, he makes particularly the point that the lack of philosophy of physics among the physicists may be harmless in a time of stability, but during a period of reformation of ideas this lack will lead unavoidably to the chance philosophy of which we spoke. Our own age, with the rise of relativity theory and quantum theory, is an obvious example. These new fields have actually become, not only for the layman but also for the physicist of average training, a kind of mystery.

Different methods have been used by physics teachers to dodge the issue of giving to their students a coherent picture of the laws of nature. The simplest thing to do is to stick as closely as possible to the description of physical devices and the presentation of mathematical computations. This way of teaching has given the nonphysicist the impression that the science of physics, which has been, historically, the spearhead of enlightenment, has become in some cases a source of obscurantism. Quite frequently physics has actually been used to attack belief in human reason and to bolster belief in irrational sources of truth. This misuse had its basis certainly in the failure of many books and instructors to give a logically consistent interpretation of the physical meaning of the formulas that express the most general laws.

4. "Professional Philosophy"

Besides the departments of the special sciences there is in most colleges a department of philosophy, which is to counteract the extreme specialization. It is devoted to the task of investigating the foundations that are common to all the special sciences. According to our previous argument, the average instruction in the special sciences has not achieved the goal of giving to the student an understanding of the place of his science in the whole of human knowledge and human life. Let us now inquire how the average instruction in philosophy has done the job which has been ignored by the instruction in the special sciences. As a matter of fact, philosophy (as taught in most departments of philosophy) has become a special science itself which is more separated from mathematics, physics, or biology, than these branches are separated among themselves. The width of the gap that has separated science from philosophy became noticeable when the rise of completely new theories like the theory of relativity produced a confused situation among the scientists. The contribution of the philosophers trained in their special field toward a clarification of the new concepts and their integration into the whole system of our knowledge has been all but negligible. The students of philosophy trained in the traditional way have mostly studied the theory of relativity and quantum theory from superficial popularizations which were written by "physicists" who, in turn, had no training whatsoever in the logical analysis and philosophy of science. Therefore, their popular writing is imbued with their "chance philosophy" which they have picked up somehow. Concepts like space, time, causality are used according to these "chance philosophies." In this way, again, their own traditional and sometimes obsolete philosophy has been returned to the philosophers in the disguise of the gospel of "science."

To form an estimate of the width and the depth of the abyss which we have mentioned again and again, we have only to make an attempt to locate a philosopher who has a "clear and distinct idea" of, say, the real issue in the old conflict between Copernicus and the Roman Church, let alone of the conflict between the Newtonians and Einstein. We would find very few. But it seems obvious that nobody can grasp the philosophic meaning of an issue in the history of human thought if he does not understand the issue itself—and by "understand," I mean "thoroughly understand."

Among philosophers the apology is current that it is just impossible for them to have an exact insight into a scientific issue because the sciences have become, in our time, so highly specialized that only the specialist can have a thorough understanding. But if this is so, how again can one have a philosophic judgment about an issue that one understands only superficially because the matter is too complicated? In this situation a great many philosophers have chosen to establish as their redoubt a special field of philosophy outside the field of science. To master this field one supposedly needs only an acquaintance with the prescientific knowledge that is familiar to the man in the street. According to this program of action, the philosopher investigates the concepts and beliefs that are the logical basis from which the experience of our everyday life can be derived. On this level we make free use of words like "time," "space," "existence of external objects," in the sense in which the man in the street uses these expresssions. The special sciences like mathematics, physics, biology, as isolated branches of knowledge, are taken for granted and the policy of nonintervention is upheld. These recognized special sciences have been born somehow. They thrive happily without bothering about philosophic analysis. The philosopher wants them to be happy in their innocence and not to intrude into his "living space," which is located between and above and below the domain of these isolated special sciences.

Actually, these autonomous sciences exist only in the oversimplified scheme set up by a large group of philosophers. The domain between mathematics, physics, biology, history, is exactly of the same stuff and has exactly the same logical structure as the domain within physics or within mathematics. The borderlines between the special sciences are drawn only for the sake of the division of labor and not for any profound philosophical reasons. The special fields of physics and chemistry were regarded for centuries as being of an essentially different nature, since physics has to do only with quantitative changes while chemistry inquires into qualitative or even substantial changes. Today we have between physics and chemistry two new special fields—physical chemistry and chemical physics—which replace the mysterious something that was supposed to be the philosophic link between physics and chemistry.

The schools of thought that have advocated the separation of philosophy from science have certainly tended to coöperate in the integration of the sciences, but they perform this job by using as binding material some prescientific stuff, while we learn from our last example that the binding material between the special sciences is itself a full-fledged science. But another school of thought, which claims to be very up-to-date, takes an attitude that we may call an attitude of defeatism. It leaves the special sciences untouched and autonomous. But according to this school, philosophy does not even attempt to fill the gaps between these special sciences but plans to build up a completely separated stratum of knowledge "beyond science." This "knowledge" is claimed to be completely independent of any advance of science proper, for it is based only on the prescientific experience of mankind.

We may distinguish two groups within this school. Both insist that when the scientist has done his job as thoroughly as he can, the philosopher's job begins. When, for example, the physical laws of motion are established by the scientist, the philosopher, says the first group, steps in and puts his particular questions. The scientist has formulated by his laws *how* motion takes place, what it is like, and so on. But the philosopher wants to know what motion *is*, with the emphasis on the "is." While the scientist explores the observable attitude of motion, the philosopher wants to find out the "being," the "essence," of motion. This essence of motion can be discovered on the basis of our prescientific knowledge about motion and cannot be affected by any further advance in our science of mechanics. To this group belongs the present-day neo-Thomist.

The second group starts also from the special sciences as having accomplished their job. But instead of looking for the "being" of things this group claims that these special sciences take some "presuppositions" for granted without investigation, such as the existence of material bodies, the law of causality, the law of induction. Then, they say, the philosopher has to step in and investigate whether these presuppositions are correct. When I hear this claim, I have sometimes the feeling that the shoe may be on the other foot. For quite frequently scientists investigate the presuppositions that philosophers have taken for granted without investigation. The founders of non-Euclidean geometry, Gauss, Lobatchevski, and Bolyai, doubted the axioms of Euclidean geometry. Einstein doubted the axioms of Newtonian mechanics, while a great many philosophers believed in these axioms as eternal truths. Moreover, it is quite debatable whether "presuppositions" like the existence of material bodies really play any role in science and whether presuppositions that do play a substantial role can be investigated by any method which is not scientific itself. Whatever may be our final judgment about this investigation of presuppositions, the practical effect of this philosophic school is again the establishment of philosophy as a special science besides mathematics, physics, economics—and the perpetuation of a wide gap between science and the humanities in our educational system.

The role of philosophy as an integration of human knowledge is ignored, or, at least, neglected; consequently, the educational values intrinsic in mathematics or physics are not exploited. These special sciences are reduced to the status of useful knowledge without truth value while, on the other hand, "philosophy" becomes a type of discourse without contact with the advance of science and, therefore, without contact with the evolution of human intellect.

From these considerations, it seems obvious that the traditional teaching of philosophy may have contributed considerably toward sharpening the thinking of students and giving them a certain touch of sophistication, but has certainly made little contribution toward the synthesis of human knowledge which should be the chief goal of liberal education.

5. Neo-Thomism and Dialectical Materialism

There is a suggestion which has been widely discussed during recent years—the idea of Robert M. Hutchins, Chancellor of the University of Chicago. The essential point of his thesis is that we have to base the integration of knowledge taught in our colleges on the last available synthesis in the history of thought, on a kind of "standard tradition." According to this group, the spokesman of which has been the philosopher Mortimer J. Adler, the last system in history that has really achieved a synthesis of science, ethics, politics, and religion is the philosophy of St. Thomas Aquinas. His *Summa Theologiae* and his *Summa Catholicae Fidei contra Gentiles* present a coherent system in which, from the same set of principles, not only astronomy, psychology, ethics, and politics are derived logically, but also the behavior of the angels—for example, whether the speed of their flight is finite or infinite.

It seems, of course, debatable whether actually Thomism is the last coherent system that has attempted or achieved such a sweeping synthesis. Some people would, certainly, claim that the philosophy of dialectical materialism, which is the official basis of education in the Soviet Union, is also a set of principles from which are derived not only physical science but also the laws of history and sociology. Just as well as Thomism this more recent system claims to give guidance not only in scientific research, but also in the question of what is a "good life."

The basic contention of Hutchins and his group is that a synthesis which may not be perfect is preferable to no coherent synthesis at all. There is no doubt that it is the chief asset of Thomism that such disparate subjects as astronomy and theology can be regarded as conclusions from one and the same set of principles. But disregarding theology, hardly anyone would claim that Thomism is a good system from which to derive an answer to the question whether the Newtonian or the Einsteinian mechanics is preferable.

In the same way, the chief asset of dialectical materialism is the fact that the laws of physics are derived from the same principles as the laws of human societies. We learn from the textbooks of dialectical materialism, for instance, the law of the transition of a capitalistic society into a communistic one follows from the same principle as the transaction of water into steam. Both are conclusions drawn from the dialectical principle that quantitative changes eventually become qualitative changes. But if we are not interested in the synthesis of physics and sociology into one set of principles, hardly anyone would claim that dialectical materialism is the best foundation of physical science—for example, the most helpful interpretation of the evaporation of liquids.

Dialectical materialism has, as a matter of fact, nowhere been chosen as a basis of education except in countries where the government has been committed to Marxist economic and political principles. In this case, there is clear advantage in having these principles linked up with the laws of physical science by a common set of principles. With the same right we can assume that Thomism is not commendable as a basis of education except where the government is committed to the political and religious doctrine of the Catholic Church. For it will enlist science by regarding science, politics and religion as derived from common principles.

There is, on the other hand, no doubt that in an education which emphasizes the integration of human knowledge, much more attention than usual should be given to the systems that historically have performed such an integration, however we may judge the actual political and religious way of life which is coherent with this system. The student should get a good and unbiased presentation of both Thomism and dialectical materialism as synthesis of human knowledge. But to make either of these systems the main or exclusive basis of education in the philosophy of science can be justified only if a particular political and religious indoctrination is intended.

6. Integration of Science and Philosophy

Before we can set up a constructive plan for bridging the gap between science and philosophy and, as a result, between science and the humanities, we have to remove the chief obstacles blocking the way toward this goal. As we have learned, the two principal obstacles are, first, the exaggerated belief of scientists in specialization which sometimes leads even to a prejudice against general ideas and, second, the recent tendency of the schools of philosophy to establish "philosophy" as a new special science, instead of working on the synthesis of knowledge.

The negative attitude of many scientists is based on their conviction that any trespassing beyond the limits of one's own field would lead to unavoidable superficiality. Therefore, the genuine scientist has to mind his own business and keep within the fences of his own department. There is, of course, a grain of truth in this argument of avoiding superficiality. However, it does give only one side of the picture, for the advance of science has revealed not only more and more complexities in science, but also more and more cross-connections between the "isolated" special branches. By this fact it has become much easier than formerly for one man to grasp the findings of several special fields. We have only to consider the example of physics and chemistry.

If we want to get a sound judgment of how, despite the abundance of factual material, to acquire a thorough knowledge across departmental lines, we have to ask, for example, how some people have managed to become experts in a field like biophysics. They certainly did not do it by a thorough study of the whole of physics plus the whole of biology, for this cannot be achieved in one lifetime. Instead, they acquired a balanced survey knowledge in both fields, physics and biology, and tried to acquire a really thorough knowledge in those parts of physics and biology which are relevant for the interaction of the phenomena of life with physical phenomena. As a matter of fact, the behavior of the scientists who have worked within a traditional field like physics has not been different. An average physicist will survey first general physics and then obtain a detailed acquaintance with his special field within physics. If he wants to become a biophysicist his survey information has to be broader, but his field of special interest need not be larger than the special field of an ordinary physicist. Moreover, to be quite truthful, the average physicist learns some part of physics outside his special field only through popular generalizations. This is frequently true for the theory of relativity. The individual physicist is, of course, not to blame for this situation, for without using popularizations he would not be able to get any information about important fields of science.

From these remarks it becomes obvious what must be the training of the "philosopher of science" if his goal is a synthesis of human knowledge. He has to acquire a survey knowledge of several sciences and a thorough and precise knowledge of those parts of each special field that are relevant for the relations across the borderlines and for the relation between science and human behavior.

Some people may object that a survey knowledge would not be sufficient, for one cannot know what part of science will be relevant for the purpose of philosophy before the integration has been actually achieved. There may be some truth in this argument, but it proves too much. For according to this argument, every physicist must have a thorough knowledge of the whole of physics; otherwise he cannot know what knowledge may be relevant for his special field of physics. Nothing can be done about it and he just has to take the risk in his training as a physicist. He will learn by and by to smell what is relevant and what is not. No greater effort is, in principle, required of the philosopher who wants to acquire a training in the philosophy of science. There is no doubt, however, that even a survey knowledge in the sciences will take so much of his time that he will not be able to get the training that a philosopher has to get if he goes into "philosophy as a special science."

But it may be sufficient for a student who specializes in the philosophy of science and wants to take his Ph.D. in philosophy to get along with a survey knowledge in the history of philosophy, without learning the details of all the opinions that have been uttered through two or three thousand years. Every philosopher of science should, of course, be familiar with the ideas of the great thinkers like Plato, Aristotle, Thomas Aquinas, Leibnitz, Descartes, Kant, Nietzsche. But it is perhaps sufficient if this special candidate becomes familiar with the language of these men and knows how to locate their ideas within the great stream of the evolution of scientific thought. This would leave him time and, more important, the leisure to acquire a good survey of the physical and biological sciences. He would concentrate his effort on those parts of these sciences which are the most relevant for judging the borderline problems arising between the special sciences and between science and traditional philosophy. He would concentrate, for instance, in mathematics on problems like the "truth of non-Euclidean geometry"; in mechanics on the role of "absolute motion"; and, in particular, on the ties between mathematics and physics, such as the distinction between mathematical and physical truth of geometric axioms. He would, of course, try to acquire a thorough understanding of Einstein's theory of relativity, of Heisenberg's principle of uncertainty, of Bohr's complementary concept of nature, and so on. In traditional philosophy he would try to understand the approaches of different schools to the question of what is the precise borderline between physics and philosophy. He would try to learn the answers of the great philosophers to questions like: What is the logical status of the general laws of nature? Are they a result of experience or of reason or of what? What are the roles of chance and of casualty in the general laws of nature and in their application to observed phenomena?

Teachers of philosophy with a similar type of training could give to the students reliable information about the problems of the "philosophy of science" and of the "integration of sciences."

But then we are confronted by a further task. If we know even the problems, do we know also the solutions? What should we present to the student as the result of the integration of science? One should give him reliable guidance without providing him with a "chance philosophy" which may be either the result of an old and now obsolete tradition or just the fashion of a year and a certain social group.

There is no doubt that the integration of knowledge on the college level can be promoted among the students only by the use of philosophical and historical argument. However, the starting point has to be living science itself. Philosophical and historical discourse must emanate from this source. There are quite a few good reasons for this, but it may be sufficient to consider the practical reason that in no other way can philosophy and history be made palatable to the student of science, and he will fail to appreciate this unusual food if he has no appetite for philosophical and historical ideas. It would be, of course, a poor teaching method just to add to the traditional presentation of science some philosophic spice or sauce. We have rather to give to the presentation of science itself a philosophic touch.

The teacher of the special sciences will perhaps be afraid lest time would be wasted by such a treatment. The student would pay for this philosophical and historical touch by a deficiency of information in science proper. But it seems to me that this new approach will rather save time. For by this method a great many laws of physics, for example, could be much more attractively presented to the students than by traditional methods. However, I do not mean that the approach should be made by one of the numerous metaphysical systems that have been invented during the ages for the purpose of an integration of human knowledge. Every attempt of this kind would introduce very questionable doctrines into the teaching of science and would lead to disaster. We have to make use of the philosophic argument that has grown up on the soil of science and has been fed with the blood of science. We must never forget that metaphysics divides people and science unites them.

If we try to build the bridge between science and philosophy, our first step will be to present to the students their own special science as a chapter in the book of human knowledge. Every scientist is confronted with the amazing fact that it is possible to derive from a few simple principles by means of logical argument a wide range of facts which can be checked by actual observations. The existence of these principles allows us to put the phenomena of nature into our service, for they enable us to construct methods by which the outcomes of physical processes can be predicted from the start.

Philosophy of science is concerned with the nature of this method or device which man has invented in order to bring about the prediction of physical phenomena. To have a certain understanding of this device is a basic requirement for everyone who wants to understand the history and the behavior of mankind in past centuries, and in our own.

An understanding of the logical structure of science is a long step toward the understanding of the meaning of statements in any domain outside science proper and, indeed, toward judging truth of any kind. In fields like ethics, politics or religion, we have also to distinguish clearly between the factual content of a certain doctrine and the symbolic language in which the statement of this doctrine is couched. The example of physical science is a guide in a more difficult world and will help us to disentangle statements of religious or political principles with respect to whether they are really statements about observable phenomena or only attempts to use a certain type of symbol.

In physics this analysis is comparatively simple and not so loaded with emotional and egotistic elements. If someone asks people in the strongest language to "follow the voice of their conscience" or to "follow the will of God," this bid will be empty if he is not able to describe the criteria by which we can know whether a "voice" is actually the voice of our conscience or how actually to find out the will of God. The student of science who has been trained in the "understanding" of science will immediately turn his attention not so much to the strength of the language, but to the question of who is authorized to interpret the will of God.

7. Role of the Human Mind

By logical and empirical analysis the student will learn that the principles of science are neither "proved by reason" nor "inferred by induction from sense observation." They are a structure of symbols accompanied by operational definitions. This structure is a product of the creative ability of the human mind and consists of symbols which are products of our imagination. But the truth of this structure can be checked by observations that can be described in everyday language. By logico-empirical analysis the creativity of the human mind emerges as the primary factor in science. Thus the student will learn that the role of this creativity in science is by no means inferior to its role in the humanities and even in art or religion. And we now can understand that the emphasis on science teaching will no longer interfere with interest in the humanities but will rather support it.

However, the role ascribed to the human mind by logico-empirical analysis does not exhaust the contribution of science teaching to the understanding of the human aspect in our picture of the world. For by logico-empirical analysis the role of the human mind is only hinted at in a rather abstract way. But our imagination and inventiveness are much too limited to enumerate and discuss all possible principles that the creative ability of the scientists may set up in order to derive the wide range of phenomena of our experience. For this we have to study the principles that have been actually set up in history. We have to complement our logico-empirical analysis—where "empirical" implies individual experiences— by "historical analysis," which is empirical not for the individual but for the human race. The history of science is the workshop of the philosophy of science. We have to teach the student all the relevant principles that have been set up in the course of history. And we mean by history extension in time as well as in space, the development of structures of science through the ages and over the surface of our globe.

In this way the logico-empirical analysis gains life and color and becomes a living link between science and the evolution of the human race. The average textbook of physics tells us very little about the evolution of the principles of this science, except some dates of anniversaries. Very often these books speak about ancient and medieval science in a derogatory way; they claim not to understand why for ages people were not able to discover such a simple law as the law of inertia, which today every schoolboy knows is an obvious result of our everyday experience or is even self-evident. But despite these smug remarks the same textbooks are not able to formulate this law of inertia in a satisfactory way. They even block the understanding of this and similar principles. For it is clear that a principle which intelligent men have not found through centuries cannot be as obvious as the statement presented by these books as the law of inertia. This complacent attitude imperils even the understanding of the evolution of thought and helps to spread the spirit of intolerance and bigotry among the students, while an attitude of adequate logico-historic analysis would contribute toward good will between people of different backgrounds and different creeds.

The best way to help the student to understand the steps in the evolution of human thought is to present to him in elaborate detail the chief turning points in the evolution of science, with the emphasis not so much on the discovery of new facts as on the evolution of new principles of change in the symbolic structure. It would be, for example, of the greatest importance to discuss thoroughly the conflict between Copernicus and the Roman Church (or, for that matter, the Lutheran Church). I think that every student of science and the humanities should have a clear understanding of this issue, which was one of the greatest and most interesting in history. If this subject were discussed thoroughly and completely, the student could get a good understanding of the eternal conflict between established patterns of presenting the facts and attempts radically to alter the symbolic structure of science. He would learn that the tendency to preserve the old pattern of presentation is often disguised under the name of "common sense," and how the appeal to common sense has been used in the history of mankind to cloak the interest of established governments and churches. For, as he would learn in particular, the role that the interaction among science, philosophy and religion has played in the justification of political aims is very great.

Equally, students of science and philosophy should learn exactly what were the issues between Descartes and Newton and between Newton and Leibnitz. From these disputes has arisen what we now call the classical physics of the nineteenth century, which until today has been the basis of the training in science that our students get in colleges of engineering or liberal arts. To grasp these issues would help them to understand our present science as a dynamic living being. This would not happen if they were confronted only with the desiccated and artificially stuffed skin of science that is presented in most of the current textbooks.

8. Science and Political Ideologies

If the students get an understanding of the earlier turning points in science, it will be much easier for them to grasp exactly the meaning of the turning point around 1900, when our twentieth-century science was born.

This last turn has been dramatized by the phrases "crisis of classical physics" or "decline of mechanistic physics" or "refutation of materialism." If one has been trained to analyze the nature of a "turning point in the history of science," one will be less inclined to believe that the "crisis of classical physics" is a "crisis of rational thinking" or even a justification of an irrational approach to science.

As we have already mentioned, it is not sufficient to approach these turning points of human thought by logico-empirical analysis only, for the human mind is not strong enough to carry out an exact analysis of such a complex structure. One has to study classical physics as an extinct organism, which grew up against immense obstacles, defeated its opponents, and then turned out to be no longer fit for survival. With this training one would have a clear understanding of, say, the broad analogy between the fight of medieval philosophy against Copernicus and the fight of modern Newtonian philosophy against Einstein.

Students who have this kind of logical and historical training will easily see through attempts to exploit the "breakdown of Newtonian physics" and the "defeat of materialism" in order to justify a return to ancient "organismic science." They will be, moreover, on their guard against attempts to exploit this "crisis of thought" in a fight against liberalism and democracy, or, for that matter, against all progressive trends which have been historically labelled "materialistic" or "atomistic" or "mechanistic."

By this approach the student of science would be led in a natural way to an understanding of the struggle among rival ideologies. It will be a great attraction for him to approach these problems starting from the role that has been played by his own special field. *The student of science will get the habit of looking at social and religious problems from the interior of his own field and entering the domain of the humanities by a wide-open door and not by the rear door of some isolated humanity course which he may take for "distribution."* He will need neither a spoon feeding of trivial information nor a stuffing with technical material that is of no real profit for his general education.

There is no better way to understand the philosophic basis of political and religious creeds than by their connection with science. The student who understands the relation of his science to these creeds has an access from an inside track. He will easily and confidently cross the bridge between science and the humanities.

The attentive student of science will notice soon that the traditional symbols of science have a life of their own. They persist in a changing world where the scope of science is continually growing. This point is made particularly clear by focusing the attention of the students on the turning points in the evolution of scientific thought.

The student will learn, for example, in what sense materialism has been encouraged by the physics of the nineteenth century and how this in turn was anticipated to a certain degree by the Epicurean School in old Greece. He will learn how the transition from medieval physics—which was based, in its turn, on the Aristotelian school of Greece—to the physics of Galileo and Newton found its continuation in the school of Laplace at the end of the eighteenth century at the time of the great French Revolution. He will appreciate, then, how the fight of Newtonian (mechanistic) physics against Aristotelian (organismic) physics became connected with the fight of liberalism and tolerance against feudalism and bigotry.

He would thus understand that what scientific and corresponding political (ideologic) issues have in common is the use of the same symbols, with their wide range of connotations. In this way the student of science would learn to appreciate the great value of symbols in the history of human thought and, for that matter, in the history of human behavior.

Whoever has understood these historic issues correctly will attain a sound judgment regarding the last great transition, around 1900, when mechanistic physics had to give way to a more general approach. The transition from the nineteenth-century to the twentieth-century physics culminated in the relativity and quantum theories which, in turn, have led to new philosophic slogans describing this transition as an "overthrow of the concept of absolute time and space" and an "overthrow of physical determinism." The student who has been through the training in logico-empirical and historical analysis will assess the attempts that have been made to exploit the new physical theories for the benefit of particular religious and political ideologies. He will see through the argument by which the "overthrow of eighteenth- and nineteenth-century deterministic physics" has been used in the fight against liberalism and tolerance, since these creeds had grown up in a period of mechanistic and deterministic science. He will understand that the breakdown of mechanistic physics did not actually imply a return to organismic physics, which was, historically, connected with the political and religious doctrines of the Middle Ages. He will understand why twentieth-century Fascism has gladly interpreted the "crisis of physics" as a return to organismic physics which could provide a "scientific" support for a return to some political ideas of feudalism.

But, above all, the well-trained student will understand the paramount fact that, actually, mechanistic physics was replaced not by any organismic physics, but by an entirely new approach to science by logico-empirical analysis, which has been in the twentieth century the starting point of all the new physical theories.

If science is taught in this way, the emphasis on science and technology will no longer be an obstacle to a liberal education of the student. The deplorable gap between science and the humanities will not arise, let alone widen. On the other hand, the intensive study of science as a living being will give to the student of it a profound understanding of the role of the human mind in human action, which is the very goal of instruction in the humanities.

9. Science and the Historical Systems of Philosophy

By emphasizing the historical evolution of scientific thought the student will learn, moreover, that the human mind has not always been satisfied with the logico-empirical analysis of science, since this presentation of science is only satisfactory for the "purely scientific" purpose of predicting and mastering the observable phenomena of nature. But the phenomena are derived from principles that are couched in symbols and, as we have already hinted, these symbols have their own life, which is to a certain degree independent of the evolution of science proper. These symbols which are created by the scientists may even become occasionally a Frankenstein's monster. However, as these symbols are not unambiguously determined by the scientifically observed facts, they are strongly influenced by extrascientific factors. The choice of symbols is, as a matter of fact, very dependent on the impact of current social and religious movements. These influences are largely responsible for the decision whether one prefers rigid pieces of matter as fundamental symbols (materialism) or whether one builds up all concepts from mental elements (idealism), whether one picks as the ultimate building stone a nondescript reality (realism), or whether one starts from elements that coöperate toward a certain goal (organicism). Every satisfactory instruction in the philosophy of science has to discuss these choices of symbols on the basis of logical and historical analysis. The influence of political and religious trends on the choice of these symbols should by no means be minimized, as is often done in the presentation of the philosophy of science. On the other hand, if "metaphysical integrations of science" are discussed, particular attention should be given to those integrations that have played a role as bases of ideologies. For this reason, doctrines like Thomism or dialectical materialism should be carefully and correctly presented to the student and more time should be devoted to them than is devoted to some sophisticated systems that have played only a small role in human life and human actions.

If the foregoing plan is followed, we shall have no more graduates in science who have no clear idea of the teaching of men like Aristotle, St. Thomas, and William of Occam or, for that matter, of Hegel, Marx, and Lenin. The type of science graduate who is without humanistic training will disappear just like those who have not even a clear picture of what the contribution of Copernicus was to our world.

The educational value of this type of instruction for science students seems to me beyond doubt. However, there is still the question of where to find a place for it in the curriculum. The most natural plan probably would be to teach the science courses of broader scope according to this method. This would hold, for example, for the elementary courses in college physics, chemistry and biology. Such a start would certainly be very stimulating and helpful for the beginning students. However, since these students have not the background necessary for the study of subtle problems, these "survey courses for beginning students" should be complemented by "survey courses for advanced students." These would be appropriately given just before graduation. They should answer the questions that were prompted by the elementary courses and treat them on a higher level. These new courses should not be "superficial surveys" as this term is often understood, but should give a bird's-eye view of the results of science, with emphasis on special unsolved problems. These courses could be given according to the suggestions of this paper.

If there are not a sufficient number of science teachers in a college who are interested and trained in this plan of instruction, one or two "special" courses outside the usual science curriculum should be established, to be given by the few available teachers who have the necessary training and inspiration for this task. One may give these courses under the title of "philosophy of science" or "foundations of science" or "science and the humanities."

The present trend toward general education has, in some colleges, led to the establishment of science courses for non-science students. The program of these courses emphasizes the bridge between science and philosophy or science and the humanities somewhat along the lines discussed in this paper.

In these plans, however, only the nonscience student will be presented with the educational value of science, while the concentrator in science will not be able to give information about the role of science in human society to his future pupils or to his community in general. The questions regarding science that are most interesting to the general public should be answered by a competent and responsible man; and this obviously can be only the science teacher in the high school or college.

Chapter 16

The Place of Logic and Metaphysics in the Advancement of Modern Science

ONE OF THE most brilliant writers on intellectual history, Carl Becker, claims that the most important event in this field in modern times was the shift in the place of logic in science. According to Becker, the high esteem in which logic had been held by the scientist in the time of St. Thomas Aquinas and through all the Middle Ages declined in the period of Galileo and Newton. But at that time this decline was not yet fully understood. "The marriage of fact and reason," as Becker puts it, "proved to be somewhat irksome in the nineteenth century and was altogether dissolved in the twentieth century." The modern, twentieth-century, physicist lives in an "atmosphere which is so saturated with the actual that we can easily do with a minimum of theoretical. . . . We have long since learned not to bother much with reason and logic." To describe the spirit of twentieth-century physics, which emphasizes facts and minimizes reason, Becker says:

Experiments seem to show that an electron may, for reasons best known to itself, be moving in two orbits at the same time. To this point Galileo's common-sense method of noting the behavior of things, of sticking close to the observable facts, has brought us. It has at least presented us with a fact that common sense repudiates.

I do not think that Galileo was actually less concerned with logical consistency than Aristotle, nor do I think that Einstein's theory of gravitation is more factual and less rational than Newton's. I shall not enter here into historical arguments; I shall restrict myself to investigating the nature and the bearing of that "most important event in the intellectual history of modern times" which Becker stresses so strongly.

The pre-Galilean period, say until about 1600 A.D., adhered to a kind of organismic world view founded largely upon the philosophy of Aristotle and the medieval schoolmen. The "mechanistic" conception of nature began with Galileo and Newton. Its peak, however, was reached in the first half of the nineteenth century. According to Becker, this whole period including the Middle Ages, the Renaissance, and the eighteenth-century enlightenment, was characterized by the belief that there is a rational picture of the world, there is a way by which man can comprehend nature by reason. But in the twentieth century this belief faded more and more. An acute observer would have already noticed this fading in the Galilean period when the confidence in the scholastic type of philosophy declined. More and more, the "climate of opinion," as Becker calls it, became less logical and rational and more factual and in some ways irrational.

We shall probably not seriously believe that science has ceased to be logical. If we use this word in its technical sense, everyone will agree that a science that repudiates logic has never existed and can never exist. Now, what did Becker really mean by his "decline of reason and logic" in the twentieth century and even in the approaches to this century? Why did he believe that the organismic medieval world picture was rational as well as the Newtonian and Laplacian mechanistic picture, while the twentieth-century picture of physics, characterized by relativity and quantum theory, is no longer concerned with reason?

We shall understand this point better if we direct our attention to the fact that, according to Becker, this decline of the rational world view had already started in the Galilean period and is, therefore, somehow connected with the decline of scholastic philosophy. The common feature of medieval and of mechanistic physics seems to me to be that their principles seemed to have a certain plausibility by themselves. Medieval science derived all observable phenomena from the principle that they are somehow analogous to the well-known phenomena in a living organism. Seventeenth- and eighteenth-century science, in turn, preferred the analogy to simple mechanisms which are familiar to us from our everyday life experiences. Not only were the principles confirmed by demonstrating that the conclusions drawn from them were in agreement with observed facts, but also the principles themselves used to be directly confirmed by a kind of short cut. If a law of physics was in agreement with the organismic or mechanistic analogy, this agreement accounted for a certain degree of confirmation. A more careful analysis would probably lead to the result that the organismic as well as the mechanistic principles of science drew their plausibility from the fact that they seemed to reflect faithful pictures of our everyday experience. In scientific theories a long chain of intellectual and experimental work connects the principles of a theory with the protocols of observation. The organismic or mechanistic principles, however, could, it was believed, be confirmed directly by a very obvious type of experience. Everybody knew that a piece of earth that is dropped falls to the ground. It therefore seemed obvious that the earth as a whole could not remain suspended in space and circulate around the sun. It was to fall to the center of the universe like a small piece of earth. This tendency toward the center as the natural place of the heavy element earth seems to be a principle of physics with firm roots in everyday experience. In the same way, a mechanistic principle like the law of inertia seemed to be directly confirmed by the most familiar facts of our daily experience.

In this sense we can say that the organismic as well as the mechanistic physics were based on principles that could be interpreted directly in terms of everyday experience. The validity of the principles did not need any further confirmation by the development of more refined methods of observation and theoretical argument. Science, in those days, was based on principles to which an eternal validity was ascribed. They appeared to be "rational" or "reasonable" or, expressed in a loose way, "logical." The philosophers of the eighteenth-century enlightenment still felt that theirs was a world view, provided completely by reason. The age of enlightenment shared this belief in reason with the "dark" Middle Ages. This is the historical point that Carl Becker wanted to make in his book. In the nineteenth century, according to Becker, a drive was initiated to tell reason that it had to know its place, which was considerably lower than previously; but in the twentieth century, science emancipated itself from reason altogether.

After these few remarks about the place of reason in the science of past centuries, it is obvious what the characteristic of twentieth-century science is. With the rise of non-Euclidean geometry, the physics of relativity and the mechanics based upon the de Broglie waves, the basic principles of physical science were no longer a direct formulation of our everyday experience; they were no longer obvious and plausible to common sense. Their only justification consisted now in their property of yielding observable facts by means of a chain of logical conclusions. The illusion disappeared that the principles of science were of eternal validity or could at least be interpreted as conclusions from such principles. Therefore, one ought not to say that twentieth-century science has no use for logic but rather that it has no use for metaphysics. To interpret the principles of science as results of our common sense leads to the opinion that they are self-evident and cannot be refuted by further empirical checking. This belief is the very core of the metaphysical interpretation of science.

One should rather reformulate Becker's argument as follows: In the period of Galileo and Newton the firm belief in the metaphysical foundation of science faded a little. Mechanistic physics was less imbued with metaphysical argument than was medieval, organismic science. But the belief in Newton's laws as results of the simple experience of everyday life had been bolstered up during the eighteenth and a great part of the nineteenth centuries, although it was by no means a common opinion among Newton's contemporaries. With the new physical theories of the twentieth century—non-Euclidean geometry, relativity and the quantum theory—the belief practically disappeared that the basic principles of physics ought to be plausible according to the criteria of common sense. The metaphysical conception of science lost ground and the logico-empirical interpretation of the scientific method became the method that was actually used. We can see in the evolution of science from the seventeenth century to the twentieth century the gradual decline of metaphysics in favor of a positive conception, if we want to use the terminology of August Comte.

I am using the term metaphysics here with a positive and precise meaning: direct interpretation of the basic principles of science in terms of common sense or everyday experience. I think that it is not sufficient to characterize metaphysical statements as "meaningless." There are a lot of meaningless statements that are not at all "metaphysical." By using the term in the way I suggested we can probably cover all the statements which have been made with the claim to be metaphysical. Metaphysics, according to our way of speaking, is certainly meaningless from the scientific viewpoint because the terms "true" or "false" cannot be applied to these statements. Charles Morris speaks, however, of a "metaphysical discourse." I agree with him in the sense that I regard metaphysics as a direct interpretation of scientific principles in terms of the language of everyday life experience. "Interpretation" means translation. Metaphysics attempts a translation of the basic principles of science, but not according to a strictly fixed dictionary; the univocal relation between a term and its translation has been replaced by an analogical relation. But we cannot tell by any exact criterion what is a "correct" analogy. We shall elaborate this conception of metaphysics more exactly toward the end of this paper.

If one even agreed that the place of logic and reason in science had not lost in importance in our time, a great many people, including even scientists and philosophers, would claim that the actual advance of science had been promoted not by logic and reason, but rather by intuition and metaphysics. Logic, so this argument goes, is useful only for systematizing scientific knowledge and statements that are already known; it can never be of any help in finding new statements and, still less, fundamentally new theories. This assertion has been repeated again and again, but it cannot stand a critical test. If we include in logic not only syntax of language but also the theory of meaning, semantics, one could easily make a good case for the assertion that the "experimental" theory of meaning, which has been advocated by pragmatists and logical empiricists, is the very basis of twentieth-century physics. Not only does it provide the method of presenting this physics systematically, but one can also point out that the authors of this new physics made explicit use of this theory of meaning. This theory was one of the historical roots of the new physical theories.

It is hardly necessary to stress the fact that this theory of meaning guided Einstein in his "restricted" theory of relativity as well as in his general theory. When Einstein in 1905 introduced his interpretation of the Lorentz transformation which was the essence of the special theory of relativity, he pointed out that the statement "two events at a spatial distance take place at one and the same time" cannot be used to derive any observable fact. Therefore, this statement cannot be a part of any physical theory. Einstein clearly understood that this statement needs in addition a semantic rule or operational definition. In the development of the general theory we again have statements of the type "the rotation of this body is responsible for a centrifugal force." This statement is regarded as a legitimate statement in Newton's mechanics.

But Mach pointed out that such a statement cannot be used to derive observable facts because it does not contain any rule by which one can check by observations whether a body is rotating. This remark was one root of the general theory and the theory of gravitation. This correlation between the theory of meaning and Einstein's relativity was fully appreciated by Bridgman.[1]

It is perhaps less generally known that the development of quantum mechanics also has its historical root in the empirical theory of meaning. The decisive turning point in the history of quantum mechanics was Heisenberg's paper [2] of 1925. Until this date the state of the quantum theory was characterized by Bohr's theory of the hydrogen atom, by the Keplerean orbits of the electrons around the nucleus which obeyed the Newtonian laws with certain restrictions. Bohr's theory superimposed upon Newton's laws the quantum laws, according to which only some specific orbits could be performed without giving rise to a radiation which according to classical physics would destroy the orbit. This pre-1925 state of quantum theory can be described as a "Newtonian mechanics patched up by quantum laws." Heisenberg, in the paper mentioned, was the first to replace Newtonian mechanics, in his application to the movement of electrons, by a completely new physical theory which became known under the name "quantum mechanics." His starting point was exactly the experimental theory of meaning. He says:

In this paper I am going to attempt to find foundations for a mechanics of quantum theory. This mechanics is based exclusively on relations between quantities that are observable in principle. . . . As it is well known, a very relevant objection can be raised against the formal rules that are used in quantum theory for the computation of observable quantities (e.g., the energy of the hydrogen atom). These rules of computation contain as an essential part relations between quantities that are unobservable in principle (e.g., the position and the period of an electron). Therefore, those rules are without any intuitive foundation if one does not expect that those quantities which are at present unobservable will eventually be accessible to experimental observations. . . . Under these circumstances it seems advisable to make the attempt to build up a quantum mechanics

[1] P. W. Bridgman, *The Logic of Modern Physics* (New York: Macmillan, 1927).
[2] W. Heisenberg, *Zeitschrift für Physik* 33, 879 (1925).

that is analogous to the classical mechanics but in which only relations between observable quantities occur.

Accordingly, Heisenberg introduced not the position of the electron but the Fourier coefficients of the radiation that is emitted by the atom as a result of the Keplerean motions of the electron. These Fourier coefficients developed later into Heisenberg's matrices and Schrödinger's wave function.

Hence, the heuristic value of the "experimental theory of meaning" is proved by the actual history of twentieth-century physics. It turned out later that the actual formulation of the principles of the new physics could not be achieved in this direct and simple way. It has not been sufficient to use only observable quantities as terms in these principles. One had to proceed in a more indirect and complex way. This has been the case in relativity as well as in quantum mechanics.

If we consider, as an example, Einstein's theory of gravitation, the principal part of this theory is the differential equations of the gravitational field. They contain mathematical symbols: the four general coördinates in the space-time continuum, the ten potentials of the general gravitational field, etc. One cannot lay down practical semantic rules for these symbols as they stand in the general field equations. But by mathematical conclusions we can derive results from these field equations which can be translated by means of feasible semantic rules into descriptions of actually observable facts. If, for example, we derive the bending of light rays in the gravitational field of the sun, we obtain statements in which the general coördinates in the space-time continuum can be connected in a clear-cut way with the spatial and temporal distances which are measured by our traditional ways of measuring length and time intervals. But such a connection cannot be laid down in full generality. If, for example, we consider the statement "*one and the same* factual event can be described by different sets of values of the general coördinates in the four-dimensional continuum," we can hardly lay down practical semantic rules by which the operational meaning of this statement can be defined in a simple way.

P. W. Bridgman maintained, therefore, that Einstein's general theory of relativity does not fulfill the requirements put forward by the experimental or operational theory of meaning. According to these requirements, one must give explicit operational definitions of all terms that occur in the general principles of a theory. While, according to Bridgman, the restricted theory of relativity was a brilliant example of the use of operational definitions, he thinks that the general theory has violated the requirement for such definitions.[3] There is no doubt that on the way from the restricted theory of relativity to the general theory the structure of a physical theory, as envisaged by Einstein, has changed in a noticeable degree.[4]

The restricted theory of relativity nearly fulfilled what has been called Mach's "positivistic" requirement, according to which all principles of physics should be formulated by using only observable quantities as terms. The general theory made use of this requirement only as a heuristic principle, as a hint of how to build up the system of fundamental principles. These principles themselves, however, fulfilled the "positivistic" requirement only in an indirect way. Einstein replaced it, consciously and deliberately, by a weaker requirement: it was merely required that from these principles mathematical conclusions could be drawn that were connected by semantic rules with statements about observable facts.

Albert Einstein, in his Herbert Spencer Lecture given at Oxford in 1933, speaks about this change in the way in which the abstract principles of physics are connected with the observable facts. This boils down to a change of the place where the semantic rules or operational definitions are attached to the abstract principles. Einstein speaks of "the ever-widening logical gap between the basic concepts and laws on the one side and the consequences to be correlated with our experiences on the other." He insists merely on the requirement that some results or propositions in the system be connected with observational statements by means of semantic rules. In his "Remarks on Bertrand Russell's Theory of Knowledge," [5] Einstein says:

In order that thinking might not degenerate into "metaphysics" or into empty talk, it is only necessary that enough propositions

[3] P. W. Bridgman, op. cit; The Nature of Physical Theory (Princeton University Press, 1936).
[4] Albert Einstein: Philosopher-Scientist (vol. 7 of The Library of Living Philosophers, P. A. Schilpp, ed.; Evanston and Chicago: Northwestern University, 1949).
[5] The Philosophy of Bertrand Russell (vol. 5 of The Library of Living Philosophers, P. A. Schilpp, ed.; Evanston and Chicago: Northwestern University, 1944), p. 289.

of the conceptual system be firmly enough connected with sensory experiences.

According to this new conception, the sentences that have to be connected with sense observations by semantic rules are no longer the general abstract principles (such as the law of conservation of energy) but some special conclusions drawn from these principles. The "positivistic requirement" now means that there must be some consequences of the general principles which can be translated into statements about sense observations. The general principles themselves are the product of mathematical and logical imagination which has to be checked by applying the "positivistic" or "operational" requirement.

The nature of a scientific theory in this sense can be understood even more precisely if we consider the new "unified field theories" proposed by Einstein and Schrödinger. A "unified field of force" is to be constructed which contains the gravitational, the electromagnetic and the nuclear field as special cases. Schrödinger, for example, introduces sixty-four symbols which are the components of this unified field. He does not lay down any semantic rules for these sixty-four quantities. But if this theory is to be of any scientific value, he has to assume, as a matter of course, that some special relations can be mathematically derived from the principles which can be connected with observable facts. He hoped, for example, that it could be derived that a rotating mass which obviously produces a rotating gravitational field would entail a magnetic field. One would be able to account in this way for terrestrial magnetism.

From a psychological viewpoint Einstein describes this way of producing theories by free imagination in a letter to the French mathematician Hadamard.[6] According to this new conception, it is true that physical theories are the product of free imagination, if we take the word "free" with a grain of salt. But it must not be concluded that these theories are products of metaphysics. For these theories are subjected to the operational or experimental criterion of meaning, though in a more indirect and complex way. The criterion of truth remains ultimately with the checking by sense observations, as the older "positivists" claimed. But we know now that this

[6] J. Hadamard, *An Essay on the Psychology of Invention in the Mathematical Field* (Princeton University Press, 1945).

checking is a more complex process than it was believed by men like Comte and Mach to be.

If we applied the name "metaphysics" to a system of statements the "truth" of which is judged according to the experimental criterion of meaning, there would be no distinction between science and metaphysics. We have, therefore, to reserve the word "metaphysics" as a characteristic of systems the truth of which is decided on other grounds. In metaphysics a statement or a system of statements is regarded as "true" if our common sense understands the validity of the principles immediately without having to draw long chains of conclusions from these principles and without checking some of these conclusions against our observations.

Such a metaphysical interpretation of twentieth-century physics was given, for instance, by Eddington.[7] He claimed that the validity of our physical theories can be demonstrated by what he called "epistemological arguments." This meant in his language that the principles of physics have to meet some requirements emerging from common sense. And these requirements are sufficient to determine our physics to such a degree that even the number of the electrons in the whole universe can be derived mathematically. Eddington's argument is actually "metaphysical." We could call it "epistemological" only if we regarded epistemology as a part of metaphysics. The point is that Eddington derives his system of physics from everyday experience and not from scientific experiments which are needed to check the results of a long chain of conclusions from the principles. The requirements of "common sense" actually are that these principles should be a convenient description of our everyday experience.

Certainly, men like Einstein and Schrödinger advanced their principles by following some requirements of simplicity or beauty which may also be regarded as requirements of common sense. But they would never claim that the validity of the principles could be proved without checking the conclusions drawn from these principles by physical experiments.

If we want to compare the respective places of logic and metaphysics in the actual advancement of science, we can point out two ways in which logic has been instrumental in the advance of twentieth-century science. We have already described the heuristic value of the experimental theory of

[7] A. S. Eddington, *The Philosophy of Physical Science* (New York: Macmillan, 1939).

meaning which played a decisive role in the rise of relativity as well as of quantum theory. But logic has also played in another way a guiding role in the advance of twentieth-century science. And this way is connected with formal logic, or what we may call "logical imagination." Einstein, in particular, has described repeatedly how the building of formal systems of symbols, the successive demolition, rebuilding and alteration of these symbolic structures, has had a great bearing upon the advance of new physical theories. In his letter to Hadamard, Einstein gives a psychological description of his creative work. He insists that the essential part in creative thinking is the free play with symbols. In his Herbert Spencer Lecture (1933), Einstein says:

> Experience, of course, remains the sole criterion for the serviceability of mathematical construction for physics, but the truly creative principle resides in mathematics.

This means, obviously, that the creative process in theoretical physics consists, in some important ways, in the creation of symbolic or formal systems by a kind of "logical imagination." Among the systems created in this way, experience is responsible for the natural selection that determines which system is the fittest for survival and which has to be dropped.

In order to appreciate the place of logic, we have to consider the shift in the conception of a physical theory that has developed from the times of Mach to the times of Einstein. The operational definitions or semantic rules are now no longer applied to the general principles themselves but to some conclusions drawn from them. However, this distinction should not be overstressed. It would be erroneous to believe that men like Ernst Mach actually believed that all principles of physics were direct descriptions of experimental facts. In his paper on the role of comparison in physics, Mach distinguished very precisely between "direct description" and "indirect description." The latter, he said, is also called "physical theory." He gives as an example the wave theory of light. In this theory there is certainly no explicit operational definition of the "light vector."

As for the heuristic value of *metaphysics*, we may quote one of the most prominent contemporary advocates of metaphysics, Jacques Maritain. He says bluntly:

It is true that metaphysics brings no harvest in the field of experimental science . . . Its heuristic value, as the phrase goes, is nil . . .

It cannot be of any help in promoting scientific research. He continues:

This universe in which metaphysics issues . . . is not intelligible by dianoetic or experimental means, it is not connatural to our powers of knowledge, it is only intelligible to us by analogy.

This means in the usual language of the scientist: In metaphysics we do not use either logical (dianoetic) or experimental argument, but we interpret the principles of science in a metaphoric language. Metaphysics attempts to interpret the general principles of science in a way that is plausible to our common sense. The principles then become analogous to the laws of everyday experience; they duplicate them, but on a higher level. The law of conservation of energy becomes metaphysically plausible because it is bolstered up by the well-known experience that objects of the physical world (stones, animals, etc.) cannot disappear. We transfer the conception of "disappearing" to an "object" called "energy" which is certainly not a physical object in the sense that a table is such an object. Therefore "disappearance of energy" can only be understood by "analogy" with the disappearance of a stone. According to Thomistic metaphysics, in an expression like "the being of God" or "the being of a spirit" the word "being" does not mean the same thing as it does in "the being of a stone." The meaning of "being" on these "higher levels" is only understandable by *analogy*, not by any direct operational definition or semantic rule.

I would not even go as far as Maritain in denying any heuristic value in metaphysics. The description by analogies can occasionally be of some psychologic value in setting up new principles. This was even recognized by so staunch an opponent of metaphysics as Ernst Mach in his paper on the role of comparison in physics.

But if we analyze a little further the nature of the actual metaphysical interpretations of physics, we soon notice one characteristic of them that can easily become prohibitive to any future advance of physics.

I shall not now go into an elaborate discussion of this

nature of metaphysics. I shall restrict myself to showing by some examples that philosophers who went in for both metaphysics and science frequently pointed out this characteristic of metaphysics. They stressed the point that metaphysics is an attempt to interpret the general principles of physics in terms of the language of our everyday life. In this way it is possible to muster the support of our everyday experience to make those principles plausible.

A very characteristic example is the French philosopher E. Le Roy. His goal was to prove on the basis of contemporary science that room is left for metaphysics and even for a metaphysical conception of religion. He especially liked to make use of the ideas that the famous French scientist, Henri Poincaré, had advanced about the logical status of science. Just at the turn of the century (1899) Le Roy published in the *Revue de Métaphysique et de Morale* a paper in which he says:

> Science departs from common sense and does not join it in its development as science proper. Thus science by itself does not close the cycle of knowledge and does not realize the unity of knowledge. Science needs therefore a prolongation and this will be philosophy . . . in one way science itself is a prolongation of common sense.
>
> Common sense, science, philosophy, common sense form a cycle.

The term "philosophy" refers here, of course, to the same thing as "metaphysics." In these words we see clearly the place assigned to metaphysics. Science departs from common sense by using a different conceptual scheme; words are used in a different way. Science even introduces expressions that have no meaning in the language of common sense. This becomes particularly clear if we consider the language of twentieth-century physics. The theory of relativity uses expressions like "one and the same object has different lengths relative to different systems of reference," and quantum mechanics uses expressions like "if the position of a particle is a definite one, its velocity is always indeterminate."

According to Le Roy's cycle, there are two ways of connecting science with common sense: the direct, which we may call the "scientific" one, and a second, which connects science with common sense by means of metaphysics. In the scientific way, the statements of science are interpreted by means of operational definitions as statements about observable facts, and every observable fact in physics can be expressed in the language of common-sense experience.

Einstein's statement that a rigid body has different lengths with respect to different systems of reference can be connected with common-sense statements in two ways. We can describe directly the way in which the length of one and the same rigid body can be measured by putting end to end yardsticks that have different velocities relative to the body. In contrast to this scientific connection, the metaphysical interpretation would be: the statement that "one and the same length is estimated differently by different observers" reminds us of the experience of everyday life that one and the same length is estimated differently by different observers. This "subjectivity" of every judgment about length seems analogous to Einstein's contention that the length depends on the system of reference. Therefore, Einstein's statement is interpreted as claiming the "subjectivity" of human statements about length. This is again in line with some statements of idealistic philosophy.

We also find similar views in writings of other philosophers of scientific background. I mention A. N. Whitehead, C. S. Peirce, and in particular, a Thomistic philosopher, H. V. Gill. He regards the metaphysical interpretation, as many people do, as a result of "intuition." But he realizes somehow that it is actually an application of common-sense judgment to the principles of science. He noticed that the scientists (he calls them "specialists") will not do well in finding these interpretations as the "man in the street" who relies on common sense only. Gill says: [8]

> The fact that a few "specialists" call in question some intuition generally accepted by men does not furnish a valid reason for doubting its truth. The specialist is indeed perhaps the one whose view on first principles should be taken most cautiously.

The metaphysical interpretation is actually a particular kind of semantic approach; it is a translation into common-sense language. We follow Charles Morris's excellent analysis of the "metaphysical discourse." [9] It is a "formative discourse" like the mathematical, logical, grammatical and rhetorical discourse. A criterion of truth (similar to the criterion of

[8] H. V. Gill, *Fact and Fiction in Modern Science* (Dublin: Gill, 1943), p. 21.
[9] C. Morris, *Signs, Language and Behavior* (New York: Prentice-Hall, 1946), pp. 175 ff.

"scientific truth") cannot be applied. The metaphysical discourse plays a role in organizing human behavior and has, therefore, "significance." The present paper means to be more specific and to describe the language used in metaphysics as the result of an attempt to interpret the general laws of science by using common-sense expressions. The "materialistic" and "idealistic" interpretations of science owe their appeal to the common-sense meaning of the words "matter" and "mind" and not to their scientific meaning, which can hardly be stated precisely.

From these considerations we can easily derive a sound judgment about the role of metaphysics in the actual advance of science. What we call in a vague way "common sense" is actually an older system of science which was dropped because new discoveries demanded a new conceptual scheme, a new language of science. Therefore the attempt to interpret scientific principles by "common sense" means actually an attempt to formulate our actual science by the conceptual scheme that was adequate to an older stage of science, now abandoned.

According to these considerations, one can easily estimate what the role of metaphysics in the advance of science has been. To believe that some "metaphysical interpretation" may tell us the "truth" about the "real world" means in practice to believe that the conceptual scheme of some older stage of science is necessarily the scheme to be used for all the future. This belief is, certainly, in a way stimulating: it encourages the scientists in their attempt to stick to a unified scheme into which every new discovery has to be fitted or perhaps even squeezed. To achieve a unified scheme in all fields of physics is certainly a goal that has been occasionally of great heuristic value. The most prominent example is, I think, the attempt to interpret all physical phenomena by Newton's laws of motion. This attempt has led to great successes in optics; we owe to it the corpuscular theory of light as well as the wave theory. We owe to it almost all atomistic theories in their first stages. But toward the end of the nineteenth century the physicists came more and more to recognize that there are phenomena which can be fitted into this "mechanistic" pattern only very artificially and incompletely. Hence the heuristic value of this "mechanistic" goal faded as time went on. Nevertheless the belief remained that only physical theories which can be derived from Newton's laws of motion satisfy human desire for "understanding" nature. In this stage this belief became a purely metaphysical creed. Some maintained, for example, that Einstein's modification of Newton's laws had to be rejected for metaphysical reasons. This actually means only that Einstein's mechanics cannot be derived from Newton's laws of motion. It is a historic fact that a great many physicists preferred to say that they rejected relativistic mechanics not for metaphysical reasons but for reasons of "common sense." Both types of reason for rejecting new physical theories, as the argument in this paper shows, are really one and the same thing expressed in two different ways.

The rationalistic metaphysician rejected new theories on the ground of "reason," the empiricist-metaphysician rejected them on the basis of "common sense." In my view, both types of rejection have a common origin: the belief in the interpretation of new theories by using the language of older theories.

Examples are abundant. I mention only cases in which "common sense" prevented the acceptance of new physical theories, because the scientists are more easily caught by "common sense" than by avowed metaphysics.

The father of empiristic philosophy, Francis Bacon, rejected the Copernican theory for not being in agreement with common sense; the leader of nineteenth-century British empiricism, Herbert Spencer, argued that the total mass of a system of material bodies cannot depend on their distribution in space. August Comte, the father of "positive philosophy," predicted that no mathematical theory of chemical phenomena will ever be advanced because our common sense tells us that the chemical processes are fundamentally different from physical processes. If we consider to what degree all these predictions have been refuted by the actual advance of science, we can learn two things: metaphysics has very often been an obstacle to the advance of science, and second, if we hear today that biology will never become a science in the sense that mathematical physics is, or that sociology can never use scientific methods, we shall hesitate in maintaining a smug belief in these assertions.

Bibliographical Note

The essays in this volume have appeared in the following journals:

1. "Kausalgesetz und Erfahrung," Ostwald's *Annalen der Naturphilosophie* **6**, 443 (Leipzig, 1907).

2. "Die Bedeutung der physikalischen Erkenntnistheorie Machs für das Geistesleben der Gegenwart," *Naturwissenschaften* **5**, 65 (Berlin, 1917).

3. "Ernst Mach—the centenary of his birth," *Erkenntnis* **7**, 247 (The Hague, 1938).

4. "Was bedeuten die gegenwärtigen physikalischen Theorien für die allgemeine Erkenntnislehre?" *Erkenntnis* **1**, 126 (Leipzig, 1930).

5. "La physique contemporaine manifeste-t-elle une tendence a réintégrer un élément psychique?" *Revue de synthèse* **8**, 133 (Paris, 1934).

6 and 10. "The mechanical versus the mathematical conception of nature," *Philosophy of Science* **4**, 41 (1937).

7. "Modern physics and common sense," *Scripta Mathematica* **6**, No. 1 (1939).

8. "Die philosophischen Missdeutungen der Quantentheorie," *Erkenntnis* (Leipzig, 1936),

9. "Bemerkungen zu E. Cassirer: Determinismus und Indeterminismus in der modernen Physik," *Theoria* **4**, 70 (Göteborg, 1938).

11. "Logisierender Empirismus in der Philosophie der U.S.S.R.," *Actes du Congrès International de Philosophie Scientifique* (Paris, 1936).

12. "Why do scientists and philosophers so often disagree about the merits of a new theory?" *Reviews of Modern Physics* **13**, 171 (1941).

13. "The philosophical meaning of the Copernican revolution," *Proceedings of the American Philosophical Society* **87**, 381 (1944).

14. "The place of the philosophy of science in the curriculum of the physics student," *American Journal of Physics* **15**, 202 (1947).

15. "Science teaching and the humanities," *Etc.: A Review of General Semantics* **4**, 3 (1946).

16. "The place of logic and metaphysics in the advancement of modern science," *Philosophy of Science* **15**, 275 (1947).

Chapters 1, 2, 3, 4, 5, 8, 9, and 11 also appeared in *Between Physics and Philosophy* (Harvard University Press, 1941).

INDEX

Index

297